OVER LAND AND SEA

A Biography of Glenn Hammond Curtiss

OVER LAND AND SEA

A Biography of Glenn Hammond Curtiss

by

ROBERT SCHARFF

and

WALTER S. TAYLOR

DAVID McKAY COMPANY, INC.

New York

OVER LAND AND SEA

A Biography of Glenn Hammond Curtiss

All photos in this book, unless otherwise noted, are
used with the permission of the Glenn H. Curtiss
Museum, Hammondsport, New York.

Library of Congress Catalog Card Number: 68-20776

MANUFACTURED IN THE UNITED STATES OF AMERICA

VAN REES PRESS • NEW YORK

ACKNOWLEDGMENTS

The story of Glenn H. Curtiss and his aviation career could not have been written without the help of many persons. It would be impossible to name all who have helped us, but we would like to single out Maurice G. Hoyt, Paul E. Garber, Robert Davis, Lee Pearson, Richard Sherer, Beckwith Havens, and G. Leonard Waters for special thanks. This is also true for Clara Studer, author of *Sky Storming Yankee,* who permitted us to use material from her book and aviation files. But, as we all know, behind every project of merit, there is a guiding light. In the case of this book, our guiding light was Otto P. Kohl, curator of The Glenn H. Curtiss Museum in Hammondsport, New York. Thanks again to all.

ROBERT SCHARFF
WALTER S. TAYLOR

CONTENTS

OVER LAND AND SEA

A Biography of Glenn Hammond Curtiss

A PROLOGUE TO GREATNESS

IT WAS July 4 of 1908, and just outside the village of Hammondsport, New York, the slopes of Pleasant Valley were crowded with people. They had not come for the usual Independence Day attractions—the games, races, flag-waving oratory, and fireworks. They had flocked to the Stony Brook Farm of Harry Champlin to see if "Glenn Curtiss could get that flying machine of his into the air."

They gazed curiously at the odd-looking contraption poised on one side of the Champlin's half-mile race track. Christened *June Bug,* the flying machine was a cratelike object held together by wire, spruce beams, and struts. No sensible aviator today would risk his neck in such a machine. But Curtiss wasn't always sensible when it came to speed and doing things out of the ordinary. Only the year before, he had driven one of his motorcycles at a speed of 136.3 miles an hour—faster than man had ever gone, on the earth's surface or above. Not until 1911, when Bob Burman drove a racing automobile 141.7 miles per hour, was his record broken on land; not until World War I neared its end was such speed attained in the air. And it was many years later—1930, to be exact—before anyone traveled faster on two wheels.

People in Hammondsport were proud of Glenn Hammond Curtiss. Many of them in the crowd that day remembered when he had been born in this little New York hamlet on May 21,

1

1878. The son of Frank and Lua Curtiss was named after a local landmark—a picturesque "glen" to the north of the village—and after the village's first settler—Lazarus Hammond. But this whimsey of naming her son after a local landmark was typical of Lua Curtiss. To her, a name like Glenn Hammond Curtiss had the rhythm and resonance that were so common in the poetry she wrote. At the time, of course, she could not have known she would someday petition the courts for permission to sign herself Mrs. Glenn H. Curtiss, Senior, so distinguished had the name become.

Glenn's paternal grandfather, Claudius, came to Hammondsport in 1865 with his wife, Ruth, to preach the gospel at the local Methodist church. The Reverend liked the grape-growing and wine-making community on the shores of Lake Keuka so well that he decided, after a few years, to retire from preaching and invest a portion of his savings in a house on the side of a hill and a little vineyard of his own. He soon became one of the most successful vineyardists in the area.

They had one child, Frank, who ran true to minister's-son traditions and was something of a trial to his parents. He was an amiable, indolent man whose personal charm offset his overfondness for wine. He had a small harness business, and after hours courted a local belle named Lua Andrews, whom he married.

When Glenn and Rutha, his sister, were five and four, their paternal grandfather died and Frank Curtiss moved his family up on the hill to live with his mother. The following year he, too, died. And to make matters worse, Rutha became totally deaf as a result of a severe attack of scarlet fever. Therefore, when Glenn reached the age of twelve, his mother, anxious about the children's education, took them to Rochester where there was a special school for the deaf that Rutha could attend.

While in Rochester, Glenn attended the public schools, and

earned money by working evenings and Saturdays as a Western Union messenger and an usher in one of the local theaters. In school, however, he was an average student. Mathematics seemed to be his strong point, but his scholastic achievements in spelling and grammar might better be left unmentioned. His leaning toward things mechanical made itself manifest at a very early age. Bicycles held a peculiar fascination for him, and by his bedside he collected a pile of technical magazines dealing with the world of cycling. Also piled up in one corner of the room were hundreds of trade catalogues and pamphlets. Small amounts of the extra money earned were spent mostly on subscriptions to magazines. With the rest he sent for advertised gadgets. The words "Clip this coupon and receive our handsome catalogue" were irresistible bait to him.

Being reared in a rather frugal home where necessity dictated that he earn whatever he required beyond his basic needs, Glenn was no stranger to hard work. Even as a young boy in Hammondsport he had worked in the vineyards tying, pruning, and harvesting the grapes. He also found that another way to get the things he wanted, but could not afford, was to make them himself. He made a pinhole camera from a cigar box, and fastened a sail to a bamboo fishpole to turn himself into a faster ice skater. And a telegraph set—"There was good workmanship in that," he recalled. "I was about fourteen, and a handy boy of fourteen ought to do and usually does a workmanlike job."

Dropping out of his first year of high school, he found employment at the Eastman Company, where for $3.50 a week he stenciled on film backing strips the numbers which could be seen through the red windows on the backs of cameras. After being on the job for only a few weeks, Curtiss became impatient with the tedious process and worked out a simple device which, when later perfected, increased a man's daily output in this operation from four hundred to nearly four thousand units.

On many occasions, when times were slow at Eastman, he rode a bicycle he had built in his spare time, the eighty miles between Rochester and Hammondsport to visit his grandmother. And Grandma Curtiss, who was very lonely in the big house on the hill and often wrote urging him to come, let him know without saying so in words how much she really wanted him to stay. Glenn was tired of "big-city" life and, upon his mother's remarriage, consented to return to his home town.

Back in Hammondsport, his friends and neighbors called him by his initials "G.H." rather than "Glenn." His studious and serious demeanor, and the degree of responsibility which the use of his initials seemed to confer on him, brought happiness to Grandma Curtiss. She drummed into him the importance of being practical, and convinced him that the difference between success and failure was essentially a matter of concentration and hard work, once a vocation had been decided upon.

Curtiss' vocation seemed, for a while, to be in bicycles. James Smellie, a local druggist, ran a bicycle repair shop and salesroom a few doors from his drugstore. He liked Curtiss, and when he found G.H. had returned to Hammondsport to live, he offered him a place in his shop. Just before his twentieth birthday, Glenn made a deal with the druggist and acquired ownership of the repair shop. He put up a sign over the shop that read: "G. H. CURTISS, DEALER IN HARNESS AND HORSE FURNISHINGS, ALSO BICYCLES AND SUNDRIES."

Curtiss became the agent for several well-known makes of bicycles and sales were reasonably brisk, much better than those of "horse furnishings." But Curtiss somehow liked the idea of carrying on his father's line of business, and he did have occasional calls for harness straps or a new side saddle. But he was so successful in his bicycle business that inside of six months he had placed the Hammondsport store on a paying basis, left it in charge of one of his chums, whom he had hired as an assistant, and went to nearby Bath and opened a second store, which he personally supervised. Later there was a third store at Corning, New York. His business expansion seems to have been accomplished without the help of funds. The story is told of how his Hammondsport store was thrown into a state of embarrassment by a customer offering a dollar bill in payment of a 25-cent item. The total change available in the cash drawer, G.H.'s pockets, and those of his staff of two was only 30 cents.

During this period Curtiss spent much time racing his bicycles in various events in central New York State. In those days a bicycle was the fastest thing in the world other than railroad locomotives, and bike races were a phenomenon of the period. G.H., with other Hammondsport young men, would practice at Stony Brook Farm, where Harry Champlin kept a half-mile track for race horses. The fellows would work out all afternoon; then, exhausted, sleep in the haymow; then practice bike racing again at dawn, before going home to their breakfast. They would often ride twenty-five miles or more to a meet, then race in it.

In 1898 Curtiss took time out from racing and the bicycle business to marry Lena Neff. G.H. was just twenty-one, his bride, eighteen. After a short honeymoon trip to Niagara Falls, the newlyweds moved in with Grandma Curtiss in the "house on the hill." Thus Curtiss arrived at man's estate without yet having achieved financial success. In an effort to make more money, he studied the manufacturing costs of bicycles and discovered that the nationally advertised brands he was selling for about $100 could be built complete for $20. The difference between the retail price and the manufacturing cost disappeared in advertising and selling expenses and the manufacturer's profit.

Believing that he could get a larger share of this differential, Glenn contracted with a small shop in the nearby town of Addison to construct bicycles according to his design. This venture, however, didn't prove too successful. Actually, things were so tight financially for Curtiss that C.O.D. shipments for his business often lay for days and even weeks in the Hammondsport express office before he could raise the needed money to bail them out. However, DeWitt Clinton Bauder, president of the local bank, gave him indirect help during periods of financial embarrassment. While Bauder didn't feel justified in loaning the Bank of Hammondsport's funds to an infant business, he made a habit of stopping by to visit the express agent. Looking about he would say, "S'pose you hold that stuff till Glenn can pay for it." He knew well enough that the expressman would take this to imply that sooner or later the bank would, if necessary, see that the payments were made.

Though he experienced some business difficulties, Curtiss was a constant winner on the bicycle racing circuit. His first, only, and last defeat came in a meet held in 1900 at the New York State Fair Grounds in Syracuse. "That was enough for me," he said. "I was through with bicycling and began to look for something faster. I didn't like to be beaten."

About this time Curtiss caught a glimpse of a new horizon when his former employer, Jim Smellie, came into the shop, perspiring and puffing from a bicycle ride to town. "G.H.," he said, "I am going to give this blamed thing up unless you can invent something to push it. It's too much like hard work pumping up these hills. Why don't you invent something to take the place of foot power, then you can simply sit on the seat and ride?"

Curtiss started thinking about small gasoline engines. A few men were tinkering with them and trying to use them to propel bicycles. In 1900 Charles H. Metz and the Waltham Manufacturing Company turned out the first practical commercially built motorcycle, and Curtiss could not resist trying to hitch up an engine to one of his own bicycle frames. He decided to build a suitable engine for the purpose.

Curtiss actually knew very little about expert machine work, but he secured a set of castings by answering a magazine advertisement in the *Scientific American,* had them machined at Frank Neff's Machine Shop, and started to make an engine. It was assembled on a bench in the rear of his bicycle shop. The completed engine was a small air-cooled affair, with a 2-by-2½ -inch cylinder.

Knowing little about carburetion, Curtiss spent much time building suitable carburetors, utilizing anything that he could get for the purpose. Old tomato cans, fitted with gauze screens, served the purpose. Dr. Philias Alden loaned Curtiss a jump spark-coil from a machine he had used to give patients electric treatments for various ailments. This coil was employed as a make-and-break distributor.

Curtiss drove the wheel by a belt running over a friction roller pulley. He first attempted to apply the power to the front wheel, but later changed to the rear when he found that this gave better results and did not interfere with the steering. He experimented with different kinds of pulleys, making them of wood, leather, and rubber. He tried flat driving belts, round ones, and later a special triangular or "V" belt. The machine was also equipped with pedals which were used to propel the vehicle until the engine took hold.

After several weeks of hard work, the machine was ready for its initial trial. Curtiss wheeled the cumbersome, but nevertheless workable outfit out of his shop and onto the street. The engine refused to start, so he pedaled it down to the square around the park in the center of the village. He was being ridiculed by some of his friends when, suddenly, the engine started.

The park lies on a grade so that going up one side posed a slight difficulty, but coasting down the other was "pie," as the boys said in those days. After much sputtering and kicking, the contraption arrived at Sheather Street, with a clear stretch to the lake. Once under way, G.H. realized he had made no definite provision as to where to go or how to stop, but down the hill he went. Finally, realizing that unless he halted before reaching the shore of the lake, he would have to dive for the wreck later, he chose the lesser of two evils and skidded into a tree.

It was the beginning of Curtiss' motorcycle days and a new vocation. Further experiments satisfied him that the machine had insufficient power to make the hills in the Finger Lakes area. So he ordered a larger set of castings from the E. R. Thomas Company of Buffalo, had them machined by the Kirkham Brothers in the machine shop they had set up in an old water mill a few miles up the valley, and again started to build a cycle around them. The new engine was a large one with a cylinder bore of 3½ inches and a piston stroke of 5 inches. The outfit, without the bicycle and connections, weighed 190 pounds, and it proved to be a terror. The engine was so powerful it nearly tore itself loose from the frame, but with it Curtiss was able to secure a speed of 30 miles an hour, and climb the steepest hills in the area.

Whatever time and money he could spare from his bicycle business Curtiss now spent on the design and construction of motorcycles. He carried on his regular duties during the days, but spent most of the nights in his experiments. He wouldn't have said that he worked nights, but that he spent his evenings "doping out" the best way to build something. Actually, Curtiss worked almost all his waking hours. During office and shop periods he did what he *had* to do. At other times he did what he *wanted* to do. Curtiss was different from other people in that he *wanted* to do things they would call labor. Experimental work was recreation to Curtiss, and because of this attitude he was able to stick at a task day and night.

While Curtiss was improving his motorcycles, he began to receive inquiries and even some orders, and business took a decidedly favorable turn. Some capitalists, interested in the manufacture of motorcycles, asked Curtiss to come to Rochester. "He had about made up his mind to go," said Jim Smellie. "He came in the store one day and told me he was thinking of going to Rochester. I asked if he had a contract, and he said, yes he expected to sign one soon. I asked him if he had had legal advice on it, and he said no, but he thought everything would be all right. I suggested to him that he go across to Judge Monroe Wheeler's office and let him look over the proposition. Wheeler, who had taken quite an interest in Curtiss, looked into the matter, and found undesirable features. He therefore advised Curtiss to have these changed before affixing his signature. Curtiss went to Rochester, saw his people and told them of his objections. Thinking to take advantage of his youth and lack of business experience, they told him they had not asked him to come to Rochester to offer objections. All they expected from him was his signature. Curtiss told them that they had all the signature they were going to get and walked out of the office."

With Judge Wheeler leading the way, half a dozen fellow townsmen became interested enough in Curtiss' motorcycle experiments to put a thousand dollars each into the business, and within a short time a little factory was built on the hill back of Grandma Curtiss' house. It was an inconvenient place for a factory, and all the heavy material was hauled up to it with some difficulty, but the light, finished product could be rolled down the steep grade without trouble. In spite of these little obstacles; in spite of the fact that Hammondsport is located at the end of a little branch railroad which seemed to the visitor to run only as the spirit moved the engineer; in spite of every handicap, the G. H. Curtiss Manufacturing Company grew rapidly.

In the beginning his motorcycles and motors carried the trade name of "Hercules." Curtiss fancied the ring of tradition inherent in the name. But when it was discovered that a small California manufacturer of motorcycles had used it first, he was forced to come up with a new trade-mark. One of the factory staff suggested that Curtiss use his own name on his products. Originally it appeared in old English letters, but later it was changed to a facsimile of Curtiss' own signature, and eventually became internationally famous.

Curtiss realized that to keep his motorcycle in the public eye, it would be necessary to win races, and therefore he set about in a very systematic manner to prepare for the large championship events he knew would bring him and his product fame. In the first major race he entered, which was the Ocean Boulevard Handicap held in the streets of Brooklyn, Curtiss finished second. But in the beginning of his racing career, even when he won, he sometimes failed to receive proper recognition. On May 30, 1902, for instance, he entered a Curtiss machine in an event promoted by the New York Motorcycle Club, and won the gold medal and silver loving cup. When the cup was delivered, it had been engraved "GEORGE H. CURTISS" because when he was asked to repeat his initials over long-distance telephone he had said, "G. H.—G. like in George." And George was the name he was known by in the early days of his racing career. On another trophy the "G.H." appeared correctly, but his last name emerged as "CURTICE."

Fortunately, however, it didn't take long for racing committee officials to learn the correct spelling of the name of the lanky man from Hammondsport. And the prestige and fame of the product he manufactured grew in direct ratio to his success in winning racing events. Few of his competitors realized that he only was just past twenty-four and that the factory equipment he had was so crude. But, in spite of the shortcomings of the Curtiss Company as a manufacturing concern— little financial underpinning, lack of experience in the business field, and a "green" labor force—the other firms in this fast-growing industry were imitating his designs and following his smoke on the race courses.

On Memorial Day, 1903, he entered the big National Cycling Association's meet. The affair featured two important events: a hill-climbing contest at Riverdale in the morning and the national championship race at the Empire City Racetrack in the afternoon. At Riverdale he won with ease. But not satisfied with this, a few minutes later he remounted his wheel, rode to the race track, and there won the gold medal which gave him the N.C.A. championship. He established the world's record for a single-cylinder motorcycle at Providence, Rhode Island, the same year, covering a mile in 56⅖ seconds.

While Curtiss raced excitingly and was always a crowd pleaser, he was not considered a devil-may-care driver. Actually, his racing style was characterized by a calculated daring which weighed the risks, assessed the competition, and withdrew if the odds were too great. He was not above "outsmarting" a competitor with a faster motorcycle if he saw an opportunity. In one Providence event, for example, he studied the race course very carefully and noted that, after climbing Francis Hill, the rider approached the finish line just beyond a right-angled turn across the trolley tracks where the road came to a dead end. While common sense dictated that he throttle down before reaching the turn, he knew that his major rival, Stanley Kellogg aboard an Indian (the model name of Curtiss' major competitor), had a more powerful machine and thus would lead him on the hill climb and into the home stretch.

Curtiss decided that in spite of the danger he would take the final turn at full speed and head for the 8-inch curb on the far side of the street. He would attempt to scrape the curbing sideways with the iron bands of his wheels and so check his speed to a stop in front of the judges' stand.

Everything went as Curtiss had planned; Kellogg led him slightly up the Francis Hill and started to throttle down to make the turn toward the finish line. Curtiss, after streaking up the incline, made the right-angle turn wide open and struck the curbstone with his wheel. Unfortunately, his forward momentum was too great and his machine rolled and bounded over the sidewalk. His daring move brought him across the finish line a few seconds ahead of all the other contestants, but in the excitement of his spill the timers forgot to stop their watches. Although he got there first, the prize according to "good" racing practice was awarded to Kellogg.

While the year 1903 was a very successful one for Curtiss' racing career, it also brought tragedy to him. He lost his Grandmother Curtiss, less than a year after the death of his little son, Carlton N., only eleven months old. More grieved by the two deaths than it was in his nature to show, he buried his grief in hard work. He gave scant attention to anything except engines and motorcycles, orders, bills, and races. In the years from 1903 to 1907, the shy, diffident youth became a frowning, taciturn man, while continuing to remain reticent and uncommunicative.

Hammondsport also changed during these years. Magazine writers and newspaper reporters from New York City, as well as inventors and engineers, began to make frequent visits to the Curtiss factory. The town took a new lease on life, and the "factory on the hill" kept growing. From a small two-story shed back of the house, it gradually expanded into a low rambling structure, which stretched farther and farther across the hillside, as the business made new additions necessary. More men were employed. New families came to Hammondsport. New houses were built. The town became known as one of the centers of the motorcycle industry.

Hammondsport, however, was soon to have another industry. In the spring of 1904, Thomas Scott Baldwin, well known as a builder of balloons, daring aeronaut and showman, started the construction of a dirigible in California. Called "Captain" by his fans, he was a skilled handler of spherical balloons which he had shown in almost every country on the globe, and it was his boast that he had never failed an audience. He wanted a new attraction, but one on which he could place entire dependence.

After some experimental work, Baldwin came to the conclusion that the motor was the one weak spot in the dirigible, and that he must therefore secure a gas engine of proved reliability and light weight. He examined all the engines on the market, but couldn't find one that was just right. Then one day, while on a street in Los Angeles, his attuned ear picked up the beat of an efficient-sounding engine. He recognized it as a 2-cylinder motor and followed it until he came upon a young boy astride a motorcycle. A series of questions divulged the fact that the engine had been made by the G. H. Curtiss Manufacturing Company of Hammondsport, New York.

The story is still told of Baldwin's long efforts to procure his engine. His first step was, of course, to write the company requesting information on an engine similar to the one he had discovered on the youngster's motorcycle but suitable for installation in an airship. This communication received an immediate and polite reply. He next placed his order and was assured that delivery would be made as quickly as possible.

Weeks passed during which many constant reminders failed to produce an engine. But Baldwin, being an intrepid and persevering soul, would not be put off. One bright day he arrived in Hammondsport, where only a few moments were necessary to convince him that lack of finances, not negligence, had held up his engine. Cash with order would have produced almost immediate results. Baldwin was able to pierce Curtiss' reserve more quickly than most men, and production was shoved ahead on the 2-cylinder, 5-horsepower engine that was to power his new dirigible, the *California Arrow*. But he decided to stay in Hammondsport just to make sure that there were no further delays in the building of the power plant he needed. When it was finished, Baldwin took it back to California.

During an exhibition at Oakland, California, on August 3, 1904, Baldwin scored an aeronautic "first" aboard the *California Arrow* when he made the first circular flight by a lighter-than-air craft on this continent, if not the first in the world. The Associated Press reported that "under the intrepid direction of Captain Thomas S. Baldwin, a giant airship has made a successful nonstop flight on a predetermined circular course against the wind and returned to its starting point in Oakland. Thus was born the dawn of a new age—the age of successful flight through air. When asked the chief factor of his success, Captain Baldwin replied: 'It was the motor. The *California Arrow* could not have made the flight without it.' " He promptly placed an order for a bigger and more powerful engine—cash in advance this time—with the Curtiss plant.

The *California Arrow* was next taken to the Louisiana Purchase Exposition at St. Louis in 1904, where it defeated an impressive number of similar aircraft. Many airships or dirigibles had begun to make their appearance in the United States. They were known by the people as "rubber cows," and were long, cigar-like, and generally pointed at both ends. These early ships were kept straight by a bamboo framework installed under the balloon skin. A spine or longitudinal member was usually included. By moving forward along this spine, the pilot was able to point the nose down to gain altitude. Many of the early aeronauts used this strip for stunting, hanging by their feet, knees or hands, depending on their daring.

Baldwin also built the *City of Portland,* which was usually flown by his young assistant, Lincoln Beachey. In building the power plant for this ship, Curtiss is said to have gone completely overboard. It was a huge affair—7 horsepower. On its maiden flight during the Lewis and Clark Exposition of 1905 at Portland, Oregon, Beachey took off from the fair grounds, landed on the roof of the Chamber of Commerce Building, passed over the post office, dropped a message at the *Oregonian* newspaper office, and landed back where he started. This trip established a new milestone in airship progress and development.

However radical Curtiss may have been in his power plant designing for the *City of Portland,* he surpassed all previous efforts in building the engine which powered Baldwin's next airship, the *City of Los Angeles.* This contained two banks of cylinders installed in "V" formation and produced 18 horsepower. Baldwin's enthusiasm for this engine was so strong that it brought quick response from other aeronauts in the form of orders to Curtiss. All of them wanted motors with increased power, better cooling qualities, improved lubrication, and lighter weight, than anything the Curtiss plant had turned out before. One after another these requirements were met.

During a series of airship flights at Dayton, Ohio, in September of 1906, Captain Baldwin asked Curtiss to send a man to make some repairs on the *City of Los Angeles'* power plant. Curtiss went himself. While the repair work was being done, Baldwin, who knew Orville and Wilbur Wright well, arranged for Curtiss to have two short, friendly talks with them. They told him of their first flight of a heavier-than-air craft in December of 1903, and displayed a number of photographs of flights they had made over the previous two years. Curtiss' request to view one of their aeroplanes * was refused. The Wrights, however, did answer the majority of his questions about the operation and flight of their heavier-than-air craft. Actually, Captain Baldwin, who participated in both discussions, thought that the Wrights "had the frankness of schoolboys in it all and had a rare confidence in us."

One of the things they discussed was more efficient propeller operation. The Wrights made several suggestions and even contributed several sketches, which Curtiss took back with him to Hammondsport. He lost no time in utilizing this information and, on September 22, wrote the Wrights that the suggested modifications in the *City of Los Angeles'* propeller had been made. The result was a marked improvement in the airship's performance.

In this letter, too, Curtiss offered to build an engine especially for the Wrights, but he stated flatly that he himself wasn't interested in powered flight. No reply was ever received from the brothers.

During the fall of 1906, a fire in Baldwin's West Coast factory destroyed the *California Arrow* and the *City of Portland.* So disastrous was the blaze that no equipment was saved, and it seemed expedient to Baldwin to transfer his headquarters to Hammondsport, where the *California Arrow II* had already been shipped for engine installation.

Other airships were built by Baldwin with Curtiss engines

---

* This original spelling is used throughout this book because it was customary at the time of Curtiss' period in aviation. The preferred American spelling of "airplane" was adopted at about the end of World War I.

from time to time, and used in giving exhibitions throughout the United States and Europe. Actually, Baldwin became the number one airship builder in America. This drew many other aeronauts to Hammondsport, and before long a whole colony of these early flight enthusiasts had gathered on the shores of Lake Keuka. Thus Hammondsport became the leading center of the airship industry.

While building engines for Baldwin and other aeronauts, Curtiss continued motorcycle racing, setting records wherever he entered. During 1906, at the Syracuse State Fair, he established a new world's mile flat-track motorcycle record: a minute and one second. The excellence of his motors brought him the highest award of the Lewis and Clark Exposition, and his business was so flourishing that the G. H. Curtiss Manufacturing Company was incorporated for the manufacture and sale of Curtiss motors, Curtiss motorcycles, and accessories. R. G. Hall, A. B. Pratt, and Curtiss were the directors of the new corporation, which had a capital stock of $40,000.

Because of his shy, reticent nature, Curtiss made friends very slowly, but those he made were life-long. Many of his bicycling and motorcycling racing friends, including Leonard "Tank" Waters, Will Damoth, and Albert Cook, and early business associates—Claude Miller, Charlie Kirkham, Damon Merrill, Ed Clark, John Osborn, Graham Palmer, Harry Genung, and Henry Klecker—were associated with Curtiss for almost his entire business life. Of this group, however, the last two are possibly the best known. Harry was his first plant manager and then his business manager. Kleckler was hired as a shop foreman in 1907, but soon became Curtiss' trusted "right arm." A self-taught engineer and mechanic, the latter always seemed to have the right answer when G.H. called "Henny," the Dutchman's popular name.

There was always a spirit of pride and cooperation among

the workmen in the Curtiss plant. Fired with enthusiasm by Curtiss' early success, and proud of his continual progress, his workmen began to take as much interest in the welfare of the company as he himself did. Their industrial life and social activities revolved around the Curtiss plant.

Curtiss and the townfolk, of course, did have their differences. For instance, in order to test the power of the motors he was building for Captain Baldwin, and to determine the efficiency of his aerial propeller, Curtiss constructed a "wind wagon," a three-wheeled vehicle with the motor and propeller mounted behind the driver. When he took this queer contrivance out on the road for its first trial, the town of Hammondsport turned out to witness the fun. The "wind wagon" went scooting up and down the dusty roads, creating a fearful racket. An automobile was sent ahead to clear the way and to warn the drivers of other vehicles. The automobile, however, was quickly overhauled, passed, and left far in the rear by the whirring, sputtering, three-wheeled embryonic flying machine.

Protests by farmers, businessmen, and others quickly followed this experiment. They argued that it frightened the horses, made the roads unsafe, and was "bad for business generally." The machine had served its purpose with Curtiss, and so the "wind wagon" was abandoned. Consequently, all motor and propeller tests were made out on Lake Keuka. Curtiss used an ice boat in winter and a conventional craft in summer.

Not all of Curtiss' experiments took place in Hammondsport. During the winter of 1906-7, Curtiss had built a new motor for Baldwin. Because there was so much snow on the ground, he found it impossible to secure satisfactory results, and so he shipped the motor, which he had mounted in a special large motorcycle frame, to Ormond Beach, Florida, with an automobile tire on the rear wheel and a motorcycle tire on the front.

Motorcycle races were being held at the time, and Baldwin was in attendance. It was suggested that Curtiss enter this motorcycle in the races, but because the machine's radical construction barred it from competition, Curtiss decided to stay in Ormond and do the necessary experimental work to fit it for the road. He worked night and day, shifting the parts so as to secure proper weight distribution, strengthening the frame here and there, and devising ways of securing the tires so that they would withstand the terrific speed which he felt sure the vehicle could attain.

On January 24, 1907, he notified the officials that he was ready to try it out. Without goggles or any special clothing, he jumped on the seat, took a two-mile running start and was off. Those who witnessed the performance say that when Curtiss passed the starting line he was hardly visible, so low had he bent over the handle bars to cut down wind resistance. The machine sped down the beach like a shot out of a gun; a blur and a roar, and it was all over. The officials announced that he had covered the mile in 26 and ⅖ seconds, a speed of 136.3 miles an hour. The pink sports section of the Chicago *Daily News* carried a headline over Curtiss' picture: "FASTEST MAN ON EARTH."

The *News* story pointed out that bullets were the only rivals of G. H. Curtiss. It cited the world's previous records. The next fastest mile was Fred Marriott's 1906 record of 28⅕ seconds in the Stanley Steamer. A mile in 29 seconds flat had once been traveled by a Berlin electric car, and the best authenticated time by a locomotive up to that time was 30 seconds flat, made in Florida over the Plant System.

As people gathered at the Stony Brook Farm of Harry Champlin on July 4, 1908, few realized that the previous achievements of Glenn Hammond Curtiss were little more than a prologue to all that was to come. Or that the fragile contrivance at the head of the race track was going to change their lives—as well as those of most Americans. It was to make Hammondsport the "cradle" of the aviation industry. It was the first of many machines that would make Glenn Hammond Curtiss one of the most famous names in aviation history.

Chapter 1

JUNE BUG SPROUTS ITS WINGS

AT THE 1906 Aero Club Show in New York the G. H. Curtiss Manufacturing Company had displayed a lightweight engine similar to the type used by Captain Baldwin in the *City of Portland*. They had also advertised several new engines which would be ready in the near future. At that show Curtiss met Dr. Alexander Graham Bell.

Dr. Bell had been interested in the subject of artificial flight even before he invented the telephone. In a paper written in 1877 he claimed a heavier-than-air craft was feasible and thought it should be "supported by the revolution of a fan wheel or screw."

He further elaborated on his idea in an unpublished statement dictated to his secretary and entitled "The Flying Machine of the Future—As Conceived in 1892." In this paper, Dr. Bell said: "In order that there may be safe ascent and descent, it seems to me necessary that the machine must have power of hovering in the air at any desired height, and of ascending and descending slowly without horizontal velocity. Also in order that there may be translation from place to place, the machine must be capable of horizontal motion in any desired direction."

These, of course, are the basic characteristics of helicopter flight. Realizing the limitations of the engines of 1890's, Dr. Bell began to experiment extensively with kites, notably the "Hargrave" kites,* in part for his own amusement, but also to acquire basic knowledge of flight. As he inquired more deeply into the science of flight, he realized the practicability of his experiments, and continued the kite flying with a sense of dedication and even urgency.

During the Aero Club Show, Bell sought out Curtiss and described his kite experiments and his plan to install a motor in a man-carrying kite. Further, he invited Curtiss to visit his laboratory and home at Beinn Bhreagh, near Baddeck, Nova Scotia, to see his experiments firsthand. While he gave Dr. Bell a polite "sometime" answer, Curtiss told Henry Kleckler privately that he saw no sense in taking time out for a trip to Nova Scotia, unless it was for a vacation—and he just couldn't afford a vacation now. He did agree, however, to build Bell an engine of specified performance. In the early 1900's there were very few recognized motor experts, and Curtiss had proved his ability to produce the particular type of power plant Bell desired.

When the engine was not received by the spring of 1907, Dr. Bell went to Hammondsport to check why not. Bell found he had made the same mistake that Captain Baldwin had—no cash with the order. Curtiss later admitted to Bell that he thought those who believed in flying machines were a "bit unbalanced," so had not bothered about the engine.

Dr. Bell wanted to see Curtiss' factory and to look over his airship engines. On this visit he again invited Curtiss to visit the laboratory at Beinn Bhreagh and was met again with polite evasion. With the factory going at full production, there was

* Lawrence Hargrave of Australia, who believed in the applicability of kite experiments to the flying machine, employed a cellular construction in the making of his famous kites.

no time for a junket to Baddeck to see a man fly a kite. As he often did in such situations, Curtiss undoubtedly asked himself bluntly what there was in it for him, and found himself thinking, "Not a red cent."

Bell's visit to Hammondsport did serve to get work on the engine started, and it was delivered at Beinn Bhreagh not long afterward. It proved unsuccessful because it weighed more than the original order had specified and did not have the required horsepower. After considerable correspondence, Curtiss agreed to make a new engine and give its construction his personal attention. Dr. Bell also requested that Curtiss make personal delivery of the engine. To make his invitation more attractive, he offered him $25 per day plus expenses. As Curtiss told Kleckler, "Twenty-five dollars a day to sit around on the lawn and talk about aeronautics. Sure I'll take him up on that—easy money and a vacation, too!"

Curtiss delivered the engine in person at Baddeck in July, 1907. From the first time he walked into the big house on lovely Bras d'Or Lake, Curtiss felt completely at ease there. Mrs. Bell was deaf, and Curtiss had learned to form his words with care while speaking to his sister, Rutha. Mrs. Bell could read his lips easily, and this seemed to please them both a great deal.

While there, Curtiss was introduced to Dr. Bell's three young "partners"—Frederick W. (Casey) Baldwin, John A. D. McCurdy, and Lieutenant Thomas E. Selfridge. Baldwin had graduated with a degree in engineering from the University of Toronto and had been one of the best all-round athletes in the history of the school. McCurdy, who had also attended the University of Toronto, had virtually grown up at Baddeck, where he had witnessed the making and flying of the kites before coming to work for Dr. Bell. Selfridge had graduated from the United States Military Academy and, next to Bell himself, probably knew more about the flying of kites than any man in the world. To obtain his service, Bell went directly to President Theodore Roosevelt, asking that the young U.S. Army officer be granted indefinite leave of absence to help with the experiments at Beinn Bhreagh. Roosevelt released Selfridge at once and without reservation—a fine testimony indeed to the esteem in which the great inventor was then held.

At the request of Bell, Curtiss agreed to stay in Nova Scotia until the engine was installed in the giant man-carrying kite known as *Cygnet*. After the day's work was complete, they would gather before the fireplace in the study and discuss aeronautics late into the night. McCurdy, Baldwin, Selfridge, and Bell talked of the work of Otto Lilienthal, Octave Chanute, John Montgomery, and Professor Samuel Pierpont Langley. Dr. Bell admitted that his increased interest in heavier-than-air craft was, to some extent, to vindicate his good friend, Professor Langley.

Professor Langley of the Smithsonian Institution had invited Dr. Bell to witness the first actual demonstration of mechanical flight in Washington, D.C., on May 6, 1896. During the morning, an unmanned "aerodrome" (the name Langley gave to his strange-looking craft) was launched from a catapult on a houseboat. It flew forward over the Potomac River; its flight, steady and stable, gained some altitude and steered slowly to the left, describing three large circles. Finally, after it had been in the air a minute and a half and covered over half a mile, it ran out of fuel and descended gently to the water. After it was picked up and dried, it was refueled and relaunched that afternoon. Its second performance was equally satisfactory, proving the first flight had not been fortuitous. In November of the same year, another aerodrome, similarly constructed but with changes in the engine, propellers, and wing shape, flew 4,300 feet. During these test flights Dr. Bell told an interviewer,

"I have not the shadow of a doubt that the problem of manned aerial flight will be solved within ten years."

Shortly after these aerodrome flights, the United States went to war with Spain. The exigencies of warfare reminded the government of the advantages of aerial observation, which had been known to military science since the French Revolution in 1794, when balloons were used at the Battle of Fleurus. The flights of Langley's models were brought to the attention of President William McKinley, and he laid the matter before the Army's Board of Ordnance and Fortification. The argument was that a military observer in an aerodrome, in which he could direct his course, would be of much greater service than a balloon. Accordingly, $50,000 was granted to Langley for the construction of an aerodrome large enough to carry a man. The work was extremely tedious. Many setbacks occurred, and great difficulty was experienced in procuring a suitable engine. Finally, Charles M. Manly, Langley's assistant, took over a radial engine that had been constructed by Stephen M. Balzer under contract with Langley, but which produced only about 4 horsepower, much less than the power needed. After extensive redesigning and reconstruction, Manly's engine developed 52.4 horsepower at 950 revolutions per minute, and weighed 2.8 pounds per horsepower, a remarkable achievement for 1903, hardly equaled, in fact, for fourteen years.

The first trial of the Langley aerodrome took place in the middle of the Potomac at Tidewater, Virginia, on October 7, 1903. Tugs and launches moved about to lend assistance if necessary. Newspaper reporters and photographers lined the banks and boatsides. The aerodrome was set up on the same type of catapult from which the smaller unmanned models had been launched.

Manly, acting as pilot, climbed into the basket seat, got the engine running at full speed, and released the machine.

It moved along the rails of the track with sufficient headway for normal flight. When it reached the end of the track, there was a violent jerk and the machine fell into the river and sank. It rose to the surface again because of its floats, which were to have been used in landing on the water, and was towed ashore. The pilot escaped without injury.

Gravely disappointed, Langley prepared as quickly as possible for a second launch. It was attempted on December 8. A tugboat towed the houseboat into position, but before everything was ready a gusty wind came up. Since all funds were exhausted, it seemed, as Manly put it, a question of "now or never." Only a successful demonstration would induce the government to supply the funds necessary to carry on the work. Throwing discretion to the winds (largely because he saw no alternative), Manly decided to make the trial regardless of weather.

The engine warmed up, and Manly signaled for the start. Just before the craft reached the end of the launching track, something went wrong. The tail dragged, the machine nosed up steeply and, turning over on its back as it left the rail, flopped upside down in the water, pinning Manly beneath it. Manly fought desperately to free himself from the machine. Only by diving clear of it was he able to save himself from drowning in the icy waters of the Potomac.

The newspapers were quick to cartoon, lampoon, and ridicule what they termed "Langley's Folly," and they blamed the government for wasting public funds on a project that was in direct contradiction to all the laws of God and man. The public was not only skeptical, but extremely touchy about the entire subject of flying. Nine days later when the Wright brothers made the world's first successful powered and controlled human flight in a heavier-than-air craft at Kitty Hawk, North Carolina, accounts of the event were either consigned to editorial wastebaskets or were printed in obscure corners of inside pages. They had done something which no man had done since time began, but aviation wasn't news in December, 1903. Most newspaper editors regarded it as a nuisance.

Dr. Bell, who had witnessed the two failures of the Langley aerodrome, told Curtiss he had strongly resented the public conviction that manned flight was an unrealizable illusion and had decided to combat skepticism with proof. He had begun experiments with man-carrying kites towed by motor and steam launches. Careful and copious notes were made on each experiment, and all were photographed in detail.

While Dr. Bell had designed and tested many types of kites —triangular, polygonal and circular—he had decided upon the tetrahedral cell, because of its strength, as best for his purposes. (Tetrahedral means "bounded by four triangular surfaces.") Baddeck seamstresses covered thousands of these triangular cells with colorful silk, and Beinn Bhreagh's workmen assembled them, honeycomb fashion, within the framework of kites of various sizes.

During December, 1905, he had achieved his greatest success when he flew his giant *Frost King,* made up of some thirteen hundred silk-surfaced cells arranged in twelve layers within a series of light frames. On one occasion it had lifted into the air a total of 288 pounds—a 165-pound man, 62 pounds of rope and rope ladder, plus its own weight of 61 pounds.

When Curtiss heard the Langley story and others, he started to show some interest in manned flight. He was most impressed by the fact that these aeronautical pioneers were fellows who seemed to know what they were about, not dreamers stumbling around in a fog. Curtiss also began to visualize the possibility of such flying machines as another market for his engines.

For the first few nights at Beinn Bhreagh, Curtiss just listened. Later, he asked questions about the various phases of flight, and before very long he entered the discussion with his own thoughts on the subject of flying. When he was asked to join the team as the engine expert, Curtiss, while reluctant at first, eventually agreed to return and become a member of the group as soon as he could make arrangements with the factory and fulfill several motorcycle racing commitments.

In early September he was back at Beinn Bhreagh, and the discussions on aeronautics continued. At Mrs. Bell's suggestion and with her financial backing, the five men founded the Aerial Experiment Association (A.E.A.), to foster aviation in America, to conduct experiments conjointly on aerial locomotion, and specifically to construct an aircraft that could fly under its own power, carrying a man. In the words of Selfridge, the object of the Association was simply "to get into the air." All patents and any profits were to be the joint property of all the members of the Association—Bell, Baldwin, McCurdy, Selfridge, and Curtiss.

On September 13, 1907, a formal agreement was drawn up. The next day the five associates went to Halifax to have it notarized and attested to by the American consul general. The Association was to come into existence on October 1, 1907, for a term of one year. The agreement could be modified only by unanimous vote of the members.

At the Association's first meeting held in the Halifax Hotel, Dr. Bell was made chairman; Curtiss, director of experiments and chief executive officer; Baldwin, chief engineer; McCurdy, assistant engineer and treasurer; and Lieutenant Selfridge, secretary. The following salaries were paid by the Association to its members: Curtiss, $5,000 per annum, receiving half-pay when not actually at the scene of operations or headquarters of the Association; Baldwin, $1,000 per annum; McCurdy, $1,000 per annum; Lieutenant Selfridge, no remuneration because he was an observer for the United States Army on full pay; Dr. Bell, no compensation because he did not wish to measure the value of his services by a salary. The Association had two headquarters: one at Dr. Bell's home, Beinn Bhreagh, and the other at the Curtiss factory in Hammondsport. Curtiss would continue to be the head of his engine and motorcycle firm, which was not to be any part of the Association. While Mrs. Bell had fixed her donation to the treasury at $25,000, she stipulated that they should call upon her for additional funds if needed.

First of the A.E.A.'s projects was to get *Cygnet* into the air. On December 6 it was decided to give it a test flight prior to installing the engine. While the huge tetrahedral kite was being set up on a pair of light pontoons, they proved not to be water-tight. Therefore *Cygnet,* which contained 3,393 cells, was to be started from a large catamaran raft anchored out in Baddeck Bay. Selfridge, who had volunteered for the flight, lay flat in the center of the kite's light framework, and the towing steam launch *Blue Hill* sped forward over the waters of Bras d'Or Lake. When *Cygnet* was released from the raft, it rose steadily to a height of about 170 feet. Since *Cygnet* had no controls, Selfridge was only a passenger and had to depend fully on the alertness of the boat's crew to land him safely on the lake's surface. After about seven minutes aloft, the towboat slowed down, and *Cygnet* sank lower and lower until the pontoons touched the water. At this point a workman aboard *Blue Hill* was *supposed* to cut the towline. Possibly bemused by what he saw, the crewman forgot to sever the *Cygnet's* towrope when it settled gently on the water. As a result, the kite was dragged roughly through the waters and its fragile structure was dam-aged beyond repair. Happily, Selfridge suffered only a chilly wetting.

At the post-mortem that night around the fire, it was decided that, although they would build *Cygnet II* in the near future, it would be best to construct a glider immediately to enable them to gain experience in motorless flight. It was also agreed that for the winter months operations should be shifted to Hammondsport where weather conditions were less severe and the facilities of the Curtiss factory were available. Curtiss left immediately for home to prepare their new headquarters.

Space in the Curtiss factory was made available for the building of a Chanute-type glider, the plans of which were given to Dr. Bell by Octave Chanute. Chanute had also furnished the Wright brothers with a great deal of information on his gliders and had actively assisted them with the early gliders they made. The headquarters for the A.E.A. at Hammondsport was the Curtiss house-on-the-hill. There was plenty of space available to accommodate the entire personnel of the Association, as well as Mrs. Bell. In addition, the square cupola on the top of the house was to serve as the conference room, or "thinkorium," for the group.

When Dr. Bell and three other members arrived early in January, 1908, the first glider was almost completed because of the help given by Captain Tom Baldwin, who was no relation to the Association's Baldwin. While building his dirigibles, he had gained a great deal of experience on light framework and fabric construction.

During the early weeks of the new year, all members of the A.E.A. except Dr. Bell took turns learning to fly the glider. The finished craft, given the name of *Hammondsport Glider,* was a tiny biplane, with a small horizontal stabilizing plane in front. With his body hanging down through an opening in the center section of the lower wing, the pilot supported himself with outstretched arms. To launch the glider, he ran down a hillside into a strong wind and jumped into the air. Even though the slopes the pilot selected generally were fairly steep, a wind of at least 15-miles-an-hour velocity was necessary for a successful flight. Once airborne the pilot's only method of control was to swing the lower portion of his body right or left, backward or forward, according to the exigencies of the glider's attitude. Fortunately, the Finger Lake country hillsides were not only of the right size and shape for gliding, but they were well padded with snow. And because of the crudeness of the *Hammondsport Glider,* a soft landing spot was necessary.

Although Dr. Bell had planned to spend the entire winter in Hammondsport, he proceeded almost immediately after his arrival to their Washington, D.C., home because of the illness of Mrs. Bell, and thereafter visited the associates only occasionally. He kept in touch by correspondence with Casey Baldwin, and he read Selfridge's reports faithfully.

While the *Hammondsport Glider* served a very useful purpose in giving the associates the "feel" of the air, McCurdy and Curtiss felt that they were ready to embark on their primary objective—to get a man into the air by means of a powered aircraft. Selfridge, believing they had not learned enough about the stability of a machine in the air, thought they should build another glider. When the question was put to a vote at their nightly meeting, the majority favored going ahead with the designing and building of their first flying machine.

To avoid confusion and delays caused by too many divergent opinions, it was decided that each member of the group, except Dr. Bell, was to be in charge of one of the four machines they planned to build with the funds available. While Bell, as chairman, and the other three members were to offer ideas freely on all structural details, the associate in charge of the particular machine would be the ultimate judge in every instance and it would be regarded as his vehicle. William F. Bedwin, superintendent of Bell's Beinn Bhreagh Laboratory, came to Hammondsport to act as general coordinator of the

A.E.A.'s projects. Lieutenant Selfridge was named the sponsor of their first aircraft, because he had risked his life in the launching of *Cygnet*. The machine itself was officially designated *Drome No. 1,* because Professor Langley had adopted the term "aerodrome" to designate a flying machine. When Dr. Bell received word that his boys, as he often called them, had chosen to call their craft an aerodrome, he was greatly pleased. He pointed out triumphantly that the A.E.A. members had subconsciously evolved the verb "to drome" from it and would often speak of "droming." He thought, too, there should be a blanket term to include all heavier-than-air craft, and the word "aeroplane" would be inappropriate and incorrect for such machines as tetrahedral kites or helicopters. "Aerodrome" would be the ideal word.

Actually, *Drome No. 1* was started on January 12, 1908. Endless details of construction must have been discussed and settled. And the inventors had so little that was actual and conclusive to go on. There were many failures and a few limited successes in aviation to serve as guides. Chanute's book on gliders, Professor Langley's aerodynamical tables, plus the writings of some of the early pioneers in theory of air flight, were all that was available. Definite practical information was very scarce. Because of this, Lieutenant Selfridge, on January 15, wrote to the Wright brothers, "taking the liberty" of asking for advice on certain points connected with the A.E.A.'s earlier glider experiments, and for some details on constructing wing ribs, and how silk should be fastened to the wing frames. To the surprise of Dr. Bell, the Wrights not only answered the questions, but named journals in which their findings had been published. He suggested that Selfridge obtain a copy of the patent issued to the Wrights on May 22, 1906.

After long deliberation the A.E.A. members decided to build a biplane with rigid wings, similar to their glider. The finished wings had ribs and spars made of spruce, covered with a single surface of red silk, a span of 43 feet and 4 inches, and tapered from a width of about 6 feet at the center to 6 feet at the tips. The total lifting surface was 385.5 square feet.

The seat for the operator, a kitchen chair with its legs removed, was located just above the leading (front) edge of the lower wing and was shielded from the wind by a silk-covered, pointed, rectangular nose supporting the elevator. (This arrangement was an early form of pilot's cockpit.) The nose itself was made of four bamboo poles with internal bracing and supported the bow control, which was a flat surface 8 feet across and 2 feet deep. It was balanced about a point one-third back from its front edge and pivoted at the point of the nose (7 feet in front of the main wings or planes). Yoke ropes connected the bow control to a steering drum just in front of the operator on his left-hand side, and was manipulated by turning either the drum itself or a small spoke attached to it.

Fore and aft stability was also sought by the use of a fixed small-surface tail. It was 14 feet 10 inches across, and 3 feet deep, giving a surface of 44.5 square feet. This surface was placed horizontally 10 feet back of the rear edge of the main wings and was attached by bamboo poles guyed with piano wire. Right and left steering was effected by a square rudder 4 feet by 4 feet which pivoted about a vertical axis above the tail and was controlled by steering ropes which led to a lever just in front of the operator on his right-hand side. No provisions were made for lateral control.

While there were no fixed vertical planes or surfaces in *Drome No. 1*, the fish-shaped uprights of the main truss offered a vertical surface calculated as 19 square feet, and undoubtedly contributed to the stability of the machines.

The engine used was a Curtiss 8-cylinder, air-cooled motor

capable of up to 40 horsepower.* It was almost a duplicate of the one used for the record ride at Ormond Beach in 1907. The engine itself weighed 148 pounds, but the oil tank, batteries, shafting, coil, fuel, propeller, etc., brought its weight to about 200 pounds. The propeller was made of steel, had two blades, a diameter of 6 feet 2 inches, and a pitch of about 4 feet. It weighed 15 pounds and was driven directly (without the use of a belt), the engine and shaft being mounted horizontally. The fundamental idea in the design of the aerodrome was to produce an aeroplane with head resistance reduced to a minimum and power enough to ensure its getting into the air.

As the experiments with this machine were to be conducted over the ice, it was mounted on runners. Two main runners with a tread of 2 feet 6 inches were placed below the center panel and supported nearly the entire load of the machine. A light runner was fixed under the tail and subsequently taken off as the machine retained its balance on the front runners alone. Two light runners were also placed under the second panels from the center in case the machine should come down sidewise in landing. Because the flying surfaces were covered with red silk, *Drome No. 1* was given the nickname *Red Wing*.

Despite everyone's energy and enthusiasm, construction of *Red Wing* was necessarily slow because many new problems had to be solved. Nevertheless, it was finished about March 1, but unfavorable weather put off the first trial. Winter weather around Lake Keuka is very uncertain, and the young men of A.E.A. had a tiresome wait until the wintry gales that blew out of the north gave way to an intensely cold spell. Their opportunity came on March 12. Unfortunately, both Bell and Selfridge were in Washington, the latter having been called

* Engine rating was apt to be more optimistic than exact in those days, and the probability is that *Red Wing*'s engine had an actual horsepower strength of not more than twenty-five.

there on an official Army matter. While the other three men hated to try the new machine in the absence of its sponsor, the ice on the lake wouldn't wait. It had already disappeared from the southern end, making necessary a five-mile trip up the lake to solid ice.

Early that morning *Red Wing* was placed in a wagon for a trip through town and down to the dock. Pulling the cart were Baldwin, McCurdy, and Curtiss, while Bedwin, Tank Waters, and several workmen from the factory did the pushing. Once at the lake edge, the aircraft was placed carefully on the flat deck of the canal steam barge *Springstead,* which would carry *Red Wing* to solid ice.

While the barge, which was used to haul grapes at vintage time, slowly made its way up the lake, the three A.E.A. members ceremoniously drew lots for the honor of piloting the first flight. Casey Baldwin won!

Once the barge arrived at its destination, the job of unloading on the treacherous thin edge of ice proved to be a problem. But there was only one catastrophe. Tank Waters fell through the thin ice while moving the wing portion, and had to be confined to the warm oblivion of the barge's engine room.

Bedwin and the associates made a final check of *Red Wing,* and Baldwin climbed into the seat. Curtiss started the engine, and after making a few adjustments, he nodded to Casey and jumped down. The men who were clutching the tail section and wings heard him shout above the thunderous din of the engine, "Let it go!"

Red Wing slid slowly forward at first, then gathered momentum very quickly, and, much to the surprise of everyone, left the ice after traveling only 200 feet. It arose to a height varying between 6 and 8 feet, and had flown but a short distance when the right half of the tail buckled up, causing the right wing to lower and the aerodrome to turn to the right, at the same time descending. The right auxiliary runner struck first, breaking the strut above it. The machine pivoted about this runner and settled on the ice, facing the starting point. At almost the same moment, the engine conveniently stalled and *Red Wing* came to a stop not far from where it had left the ice. Casey crawled out of the wreckage unhurt, more interested in the statistics of the flight than in his bruised knees and elbows.

Measured in a direct line from the point where the runners left the ice to the point where they first touched down, the distance was exactly 318 feet 11 inches. The actual distance traveled was somewhat greater, since the craft described a curve in the air. The twenty-five or so townsfolk who had driven out the lake road and watched with astonishment the "miracle" being performed before their eyes, dashed out on the ice to congratulate the men of A.E.A. What is more, Harry M. Benner, a local photographer, took a series of photographs to show to the world the first public flight of a heavier-than-air machine in America. It was impossible to make the necessary repairs on the ice, so *Red Wing* was disassembled and brought back to town and the factory.

Baldwin became the seventh man in the world and the third in America to fly in a heavier-than-air craft, and was the first British subject to do so. But the name of Frederick W. Baldwin was practically unknown to the press, and, while his historical flight was given only meager coverage, the majority of the newspaper stories of the feat gave credit to Captain Tom Baldwin.

On March 12 another historic flight took place in Hammondsport, when the well-known typewriter inventor and manufacturer, J. Newton Williams, was able to get his helicopter off the ground. This machine, which was built in the Curtiss shop with the help of the A.E.A. members, had two

16-foot propellers mounted horizontally on concentric shafts and revolving in opposite directions. Below the propellers was a little platform carrying a motor and a shift weight which was designed to tip the machine and supplement the rudder in a given direction. A turn to the right or left was to be accomplished by means of a brake.

While the helicopterlike device had been ready for its test for several days, the flight had to be postponed because of the bad weather. On returning to the Curtiss plant after witnessing *Red Wing*'s success, Williams suggested to the associates that they might try their "luck" in flying his craft. The machine was rolled out to a flat area behind the factory, the equipment set up, and a 115-pound boy mounted the platform to represent a pilot's weight aboard the helicopter. When the engine was started, the device promptly lifted the full length of the short cable attached to it. While they were delighted that the inventor had had the satisfaction of proving that his machine could get off the ground, the four younger members of the Association were not really interested in the helicopter since it could not be released for free flight, nor could it travel from place to place as their *Red Wing* had proved itself capable of doing. Dr. Bell, on the other hand, when he read Selfridge's account of the event, was greatly pleased with its operation since he had described a machine of the helicopter type fifteen years earlier and continued to believe it was the aircraft of the future.

On Saint Patrick's Day, March 17, wearing a green necktie for his Irish blood, Casey Baldwin took the *Red Wing* up again. Again it rose, straightened out, and flew along. But the good Saint wasn't with him. The machine began to tilt to the left, and then suddenly it crashed down on the ice in a tangle of red silk. Although Baldwin was unscratched, *Red Wing* was completely demolished.

That evening the undaunted members met and formally voted to construct a second machine. According to the agreement, it now fell to Casey Baldwin to superintend the design and construction of *Drome No. 2*.

The approach of the four men to the problem was, as usual, thoroughly scientific. Again the field was reviewed, and the collective evidence of groping aeronautical design weighed conscientiously. This evidence was then compared with their own findings and the future course determined. During their short stay at Hammondsport, the A.E.A. had accumulated a small library of current technical reports, with Secretary Selfridge as their chief research expert. He assimilated new data quickly, sifted out whatever appeared to be valuable, and referred it on to his associates. While the members did little drawing of plans themselves, they now had complete detail drawings of the Langley aerodrome of 1903; a skeleton cross-section of J. C. Ellehammer's aeroplane No. 1; and skeleton two-view drawings of Henri Farman's machine No. 1 and Louis Blériot's No. 6. There was also the information which the Wrights had suggested they obtain.

The A.E.A. also gathered a great deal of data on *Red Wing* during its short life. Harry Benner, who again photographed the craft's flight in accordance with Dr. Bell's orders, took a photo of *Red Wing* a split second before the crash occurred, and by studying this picture very carefully the associates found out what problems must be solved next. Baldwin himself noted in his report that once the aerodrome was overtaken by the urge to point one of its wings at the sky and the other at the earth it was impossible for its pilot to level it out again. And as long as there was the slightest trace of wind, emergencies of this type had to be anticipated.

In addition, Baldwin realized that greater consideration had to be given to the placement of controls. In their eagerness to

get the *Red Wing* up, the associates had overlooked the detail
of getting it down. As a thing of minor importance, the engine
switch had been put in an inaccessible place under the seat.
With both hands occupied with elevator and rudder controls,
the pilot was not able to reach down under the seat for the
switch, so there was no way of stopping the engine before *Red
Wing* landed. Also, a system of shock absorbers for landing
had to be provided at the extremities of the craft. Such details
as these were really only minor problems compared with that
of lateral stability.

Even Dr. Bell in Washington stressed the importance of
maintaining lateral control to prevent the aircraft from being
tossed about in the wind. In a letter to Baldwin on March 20,
Bell suggested that *"Red Wing's* disaster" indicated that the
agile shifting of the pilot's weight wasn't enough to keep the
machine stable. He reminded his young colleagues that the
Wrights had had the same difficulty. Selfridge's research
showed that they had solved it by "wing warping," an arrangement that permitted the pilot to twist the outer trailing edges
of the wing structure so as to lift the wings on one side of the
craft and dip those on the other. Although this arrangement
kept the Wright flyers level in flight, Selfridge pointed out that
the "warping" idea as now employed by the brothers had a
major fault, in that it relied upon a single wire to preserve the
strength of the structure.

Bell's suggested solution to the problem of stability for
Drome 2 was a flat flap mounted on each wing tip. If these
flaps were attached by a pivoted lever to the body of the pilot
by a yoke or harness, he could raise or lower a wing tip by
simply leaning to one side or the other. It is not known whether
or not Bell was aware at the time of the similarity between his
idea and lateral-control devices employed in France by Robert
Esnault-Peltérie in 1904 and by Louis Blériot in 1907.

The suggestion's worth was immediately recognized by Baldwin, who added the small hinged-surface flaps to the wing tips of the new A.E.A. craft. Called "ailerons" by Dr. Bell, they produced a turning movement which gave the aeroplane more maneuverability. More important, however, was the fact that if the machine tipped to one side, these small surfaces would bring the craft back into level flight.

Another problem solved in the second machine was the choice of material covering the wings. The experimenters agreed that with wings breaking almost daily, silk was too expensive. Deciding to substitute some other kind of cloth, they chose cotton. However, they discovered that the machine would not leave the ground. For a time they were unable to find the reason, until it became evident that the cotton was too porous and would not support the machine in the air. It was therefore decided to try covering the cotton with varnish. This was done with good results. Not only did it reduce the porosity of the cloth, but it also helped to strengthen it. Incidentally, *Drome No. 2,* in keeping with the color of its nainsook wings, was christened *White Wing.*

The tricycle undercarriage was another important innovation in the design of *White Wing.* The builders realized that the ice on the lake would be melted by the time the machine was completed. They were forced to design a form of wheel running-gear so that the machine could be flown from land instead of from the surface of the ice. This undercarriage consisted initially of two castoring wheels under the center section and a third wheel under the tail. But, before the machine was completed, the third wheel was moved to the nose and made castoring, the two rear wheels being fixed. *White Wing* was the first American aeroplane with a wheeled undercarriage.

During the building of *White Wing,* Dr. Bell spent most of his time in Hammondsport. Every night the members of the

A.E.A. would meet in the thinkorium. After the session was called to order by Chairman Bell, the minutes of the previous meeting were read and discussed. These minutes were religiously kept by Selfridge and eventually sent to each member in the form of a typewritten report. Next, the day's work was gone over in full detail. After all pressing business had been completed, a wide range of subjects was brought up and talked over by the group. Discussion at these sessions was not limited to aeronautics.

Dr. Bell was the source of the most unusual suggestions for discussion—usually things he had given a great deal of thought and time. His opinions on all his hobbies were most interesting. For instance, he had collected a good deal of information on the genealogy of the Hyde family, comprising some seven thousand individuals. This he had arranged in a card index system, in order to determine the proportion of males and females, their relative length of life and other characteristics. Or perhaps the doctor would talk about his scheme to influence the sex of sheep by a certain method of feeding; his early experiences with the telephone, the phonograph, the harmonic telegraph, and multiple telegraphy.

After the formal sessions of the Association members, the courtesy of the floor was extended to anyone who might be present for the discussion of anything he might see fit to bring up. Later they would adjourn to Dr. Bell's room, where he would put himself into a comfortable position, light his inevitable pipe, and produce his notebooks. In these notebooks Dr. Bell wrote down his thoughts on every subject imaginable, made sketches and computations. All these he would sign, date, and have witnessed. It was Bell's custom to work at night when there were no distracting noises, though there were few of these at Hammondsport even during daylight hours. Bell often sat up until long after midnight, but he made up for it by sleeping until noon. No one was allowed to wake him for any reason. Actually, Bell had a strong aversion to the ringing of the telephone during the morning hours.

"Little did I think when I invented this thing," said Dr. Bell, one day when he had been awakened by the jingling of the bell, "that it would rise up to mock and annoy me."

While the doctor enjoyed his morning sleep, the younger members of the A.E.A. were often out at the testing ground, which was Harry Champlin's half-mile race track at Stony Brook Farm on the edge of Hammondsport. This site, the same one used by Curtiss during his cycling days, was one of the few level areas to be found in the vicinity, aside from the surface of Lake Keuka. A large tent attached to the side of a nearby barn was to be employed as a hangar for the aircraft when it was completed.

The finished *White Wing* was nearly a duplicate of *Red Wing*. The new machine was 43 feet 6 inches from tip to tip; the wings were 6 feet 6 inches deep at the center, and 4 feet deep at the outside panel, which gave them a total supporting surface of 408.5 square feet. The weight of the main plane with the engine bed was 133 pounds as against 119 pounds for *Red Wing*. The nose weighed 27 pounds; the tail, including a light wheel, weighed 30.5 pounds. The wheels and the spring frames which supported them weighed 47 pounds. The engine, accessories, and propeller weighed 192 pounds. So the total weight, allowing for a pilot of 175 pounds, was about 606 pounds. This gave a flying weight of about 1½ pounds to the square foot compared with 1¼ for *Red Wing*. The wooden propeller had a diameter of 6 feet and a weight of only about 8 pounds.

The major difference between the dromes, of course, was

Dr. Bell's aileron idea. In *White Wing,* the tips at the extremities of the wings were hinged about their fore edges, and the operator could change the angles of incidence by a system of steering gear. If the machine inclined to one side, the pilot could compensate for this movement by leaning to the high side and thus put into operation a tiller which was connected by steering ropes and increased the angle of incidence of the tips at the lower side while decreasing the angle of incidence of the tips on the high side. The idea was that the pilot would instinctively lean to the high side. The tail was composed of two superimposed surfaces which gave it about the same surface as in *Red Wing,* and it was placed 10 feet (the same distance) behind the main plane (wing). This was to remedy the weakness in the construction of the single-surface tail first used on *Red Wing.*

The operator, as usual, sat just in front of the engine. Right and left steering was provided for by a triangular rudder which moved on a vertical axis behind the after central strut of the tail. The steering ropes from the rudder led to the steering wheel in front of the operator, which worked like the steering wheel of an automobile, a turn to the right putting the rudder to the right and a turn to the left putting the rudder to the left. The bow control was operated by a lever connected directly to the steering post, and not by yoke ropes as in *Red Wing.*

On May 13, 1908, with Lieutenant Selfridge at the controls, an attempt was made to fly Baldwin's *White Wing.* The aircraft had been provided with light pneumatic-tired bicycle wheels to enable it to run over the ground until sufficient headway had been gained to get it into the air. The race track, however, proved too narrow. The wing piece was not raised sufficiently from the ground to escape contact with the raised sides of the track. An attempt was made to start the machine from the grass plot contained within the oval track, but the attachment of the wheels proved to be too weak to stand the strain of running over rough ground and broke before much headway had been gained. The damage was repaired next day.

The next trial, on May 17, also failed because of take-off troubles. When *White Wing* was provided with wheels, no steering gear was attached to them. It was thought that the aerial rudder would control the motion of the machine while on the ground. The rudder proved to be inadequate for the purpose, however, and the machine could not be kept from running off the track to one side or the other. It was therefore decided to make a slight change in the attachment of the front wheel, and provide it with steering gear to enable the operator to keep the machine on the track. No attempt was made to fly, however, until the operators were satisfied that they had the machine under full control on the ground.

On May 18 *White Wing* made a short flight, carrying Casey Baldwin to a height of almost 10 feet. The pressure of the air on the elastic edge of the lower wing caused it to foul the propeller, and the aerodrome was brought to the ground after having covered a distance of 279 yards. The damage was easily repaired. The steering gear attached to the front wheel worked satisfactorily, and there was no difficulty keeping the machine on the race track. The track had been widened by plowing up a portion of the adjoining field and smoothing it with a roller.

On May 19 Selfridge made two flights aboard *White Wing*. In the first, the machine ran 210 feet on the race track before leaving the ground, and made a flight of 100 feet in 2 seconds at an elevation of 3 feet, and ran 201 feet on rough ground after landing, without injury to the running gear. The flight was impeded by loose guy wires which caught in the propeller, but no damage resulted. In the second experiment the machine made a beautiful and steady flight of 240 feet, at an elevation of at least 20 feet, but landed badly in a newly plowed field. *White Wing* itself was uninjured, but the frame carrying the front wheel dug into the ground and was damaged. The trouble, however, was easily corrected. These two flights made Thomas Selfridge the first United States officer to pilot an aeroplane.

Selfridge's flights were witnessed by the Bells, who had come from Washington. Mrs. Bell was thrilled by the experience, and Dr. Bell was greatly impressed because the flights indicated that ample power and adequate control were now available, so that only skill on the part of the aviator was necessary to accomplish longer flights.

Before the next flight, the original front elevator of *White Wing* was replaced with a narrower surface split in the middle to insure better visibility for the aviator. Then, on May 22, Curtiss took the pilot's seat for the first time, and in his A.E.A. report, described his experiences as follows:

> The engine was started in the usual manner and after it had speeded up well, I gave the signal to let go. Upon being released the machine darted forward and sped down the track at a speed of perhaps 25 miles per hour. After about 300 feet, I inclined the control expecting to feel it rise into the air, but it failed to do so, and as I was nearing the end of the stretch, I shut off the power and grasped the lever of the steering wheel, guiding the machine around the curve until it came to a stand still. Upon investigation we found that the engine had not been given the usual dose of oil, and that it had been running a little dry, and not giving power enough to push the machine into the air.
>
> The drome was then taken back to the starting point, and after being given the usual dose of oil the engine was again started. Upon being released, the machine started down the

track faster than before, and raised with the front control in the normal position. It glided for a short distance gradually rising to a height of 12 feet, and then seemed inclined to settle to the ground. I pulled back on the steering wheel thereby raising the front controlling plane slightly when the machine immediately rose and would probably have gone on to an indefinite height had I not reversed the plane again and brought it down, but as is usual in any balancing act, the novice overdoes matters, and I came down too far. As soon as I realized this, I again raised the control slightly. I afterwards learned that it touched the ground on this dip. By now I realized that the vertical control was a very delicate thing, and although I did my best to keep on a constant level, there was more or less pitching up and down through the entire distance.

In the meantime, I had steered slightly to the left in order to make sure of clearing a vineyard which had been worrying us and which was directly in front of the start. When I found myself clear of the vineyard, I again turned to the right and on a line parallel to the track. There seemed to be no trouble in steering in this direction.

When the machine first raised, the right side began to tilt down which was easily corrected by the use of the adjustable tips which were operated by leaning to the high side and engaging a lever with the shoulders. This control seemed to work very well indeed. After the plane was restored to its normal position the machine did not vary again.

I don't know just why I landed but I found myself so close to the ground that a landing seemed inevitable and rather than take any chance on trying to get up again, I shut off the engine, raised the front control to the limit, grasped the tiller of the front steering wheel with my hand and steered straight ahead out into the ploughed field until the machine came to a stand still. The machine was found to be in good order and nothing broken. A bolt in the rudder had jarred loose and might have interfered with the steering had I gone farther.

Curtiss' first flight covered 1,017 feet and took 19 seconds. That would make his speed about 37 miles an hour. Later in the evening at the thinkorium, Curtiss told Dr. Bell, "Although I have given the subject of aviation much thought, it wasn't until I flew *White Wing* today that my ideas of how to operate a heavier-than-air flying machine are really tangible enough to be of any service to another." He went on, "The art of flying, even though but the short distance of a thousand feet, gives a person something to work from, and his ideas follow on a more practical course."

Jack McCurdy made his first flight aboard *White Wing* on May 23. Five hundred and fifty feet were covered in 10⅗ seconds, but with quite a strong quartering wind blowing, he failed to correct for his lateral controls. This caused the machine to careen and strike the ground with its right wing tip. It then turned turtle, pivoting on the nose and finally resting on its top wing with the engine and wheels in the air. The center panel was so strongly built, however, that it remained intact, and the engine stayed fast in its bed. Neither operator nor engine was in the least injured. But *White Wing* was so badly damaged that the Association decided at the meeting that evening to salvage all the parts it could and start *Drome No. 3,* under the supervision of Curtiss.

During the building of the first two aerodromes, Curtiss contributed little in the way of original ideas. He did, however, work hard to keep the engine in top-notch condition. He also did a great deal of listening and learning. His background and nature, of course, placed him at a disadvantage, either real or imagined. The other members of the A.E.A. came from fairly well-to-do families and had been to college, while Curtiss had not finished high school. He had built his own business from nothing, and being a practical man, he had the prevailing prejudice of the time against book-learning university boys and impractical theoretical scientists. The fact that G.H. wasn't an engineer by training often made him immune, of course, to some of the caution and preconceptions which technical wisdom entails. On the other hand, intimate contact with their more educated point of view was of immeasurable help to him with his rule-of-thumb background. His ability to visualize a detail—to "sketch it up" on paper—had been adequate for engines and motorcycles. But, in coping with something as speculative and essentially complex as aerodynamics, he required exactly what his association with the other four, over a period of months, had given him. Now, as they tackled the aerodrome which he himself was to sponsor, he abandoned many of his former inhibitions about the group and really became a fully participating member of the A.E.A.

The most radical change in the third aeroplane involved the position of the movable wing tips. In *White Wing* they had been set so that when not in use they were inclined at the same positive angle of incidence as the wings. The result was that when they were moved, one assumed a greater angle of incidence than the other, and the increased drag on one side pulled the plane off its course unless the rudder was used to counteract this effect. In *Drome No. 3* Curtiss placed the tips at a neutral angle. When one was raised and the other lowered, they had identical angles of incidence; there was no differential in drag, and the turning or unbalancing tendency disappeared, thus eliminating the need for the corrective use of the rudder.

The same three-wheel running gear was used, but the wheel base was extended 2 feet. It was also greatly strengthened by two large wooden runners situated fore and aft which could be used as skids in case the wheels broke down. The wings were made so that they could be easily removed from the engine-bed section, and their surfaces were varnished with a mixture of gasoline, yellow ocher, paraffin, and turpentine in order to make them airtight—the yellow ocher so that it would show up in any photographs taken of the aerodrome. The total working surface of the third machine was reduced from 408 to 370 square feet. Switch and spark controls were placed on the front steering wheel. Actually, 5 square feet were added to the area of the front control, its total spread being now 13 feet 10 inches as compared with 11 feet 6 inches of *Drome No. 2*. The nose was now wedge-shaped instead of pointed and was left uncovered. The tail was made spar-shaped from side to side to conform to the general shape of the main surfaces. The vertical surfaces of the tail were removed and the area of the vertical rudder increased from 27 to 36 square inches.

The same engine that had been used in the other two dromes was employed in *No. 3*. But the wood propeller was cut from 6 feet 2 inches to 5 feet 11 inches and the blunt ends rounded slightly. This change resulted in an increase of rpms from 1,050 to about 1,200.

Thanks to the researching of Selfridge and the construction abilities of Baldwin and Curtiss, the A.E.A. acquired some equipment for ground-testing various parts of the aerodrome. Some styles of elevators, for instance, were extensively "ground-checked" to determine how they would react to the moving air. The chassis of the aerodrome, equipped with motor and propeller and three-wheeled undercarriage, was the testing device on which the experimenters raced back and forth in their newly constructed open-air wind tunnel. To test other control surfaces in advance, variations of the Curtiss wind wagons of 1906 were contrived.

Just a month, lacking a day, after Curtiss made his first flight aboard *White Wing,* he made three successful ones as the pilot of *Drome No. 3.* The first flight was 456 feet; the second, 417 feet; and the third, the longest yet made in public in America, 1,266 feet. The public also saw the first sideslip performed. As he was desperately trying to avoid coming down on the menacing grape stakes of a vineyard directly below him, Curtiss turned the wheel and the craft answered its rudder. It came around in a flat sideward turn, away from the dangers of the vineyard.

The flight of this machine reminded Dr. Bell of that of a June bug, a very common insect in the Finger Lakes region. Following his suggestion, *Drome No. 3* was officially christened *June Bug* on June 19. It was also decided by the associates that Curtiss only should pilot *June Bug,* to profit from the experience gained in repeated flights and to avoid the damage which almost surely would occur if all members took turns as flyers.

Two days of bad weather stopped testing until June 24, when Curtiss made two short flights. Owing to a strong side wind the machine made considerable leeway, but showed no tendency to tip. The field in which the tests were being conducted was somewhat restricted by various obstacles. In order to clear these the machine had to rise to a greater height than the experimenters deemed prudent at this time, and as the draft caused by the machine necessitated flying over instead of around these obstacles, the tests were postponed till next morning.

At 6 A.M. on the twenty-fifth, Curtiss made a beautiful flight of 2,175 feet in 41 seconds at the rate of 36.2 miles an hour, running before a wind that varied between 6 and 8 miles an hour. The machine tipped sharply to port shortly after getting in the air, but was righted immediately by means of the tip controls and kept on an even keel from then until the end of the flight. In the evening of the same day, Curtiss flew *June Bug* for a distance of 3,420 feet in 60 seconds. The flight was terminated because of the trees and a fence which limited the testing grounds. Actually, the aeroplane had to travel on the arc of a circle to make even this distance. The height of the flight varied from 3 to 20 feet.

Immediately after the flight, Selfridge telephoned the Aero Club of America that the Aerial Experiment Association was ready to try for the *Scientific American* trophy, which was to be given to the first aeroplane that *officially* flew the distance of one kilometer in a straight line. *June Bug*'s flight of the twenty-fifth had surpassed that distance by almost 140 feet.

In its September, 1907, issue, the *Scientific American* had carried the following announcement of their award:

> The handsome silver trophy was originated with the idea of stimulating the development of the science of aerial navigation. For many years past, and especially since the development of the dirigible balloon, the aim of all inventors in this line has been to construct a machine which would fly at a high rate of speed without the use of gas to support it. Nearly four years ago the Wright brothers, in this country, announced the successful application by them of a gasoline motor to an aeroplane, and the flight which they made upon December 19, 1903,* was presumably the first one of any considerable distance which has ever been made by a motor-propelled aeroplane carrying a man. After two years of experimenting the Wright brothers finally announced that they had perfected their machine. No public demonstration has ever been made by them, however; and although, according to their own statements and those of eye-witnesses, they have solved the problem, still many people doubt this. At any rate, it is probable that progress in the new science will be made by others, and that in time there will be several kinds of heavier-than-air machines perfected.
>
> It is with the idea of encouraging inventors in this line by giving them a valuable object of art worth winning, that the

* The magazine erred as to the date, which, of course, was December 17.

Scientific American Trophy has been completed and presented to the Aero Club of America.

In conducting the competition for the trophy, the Aero Club of America will vary the conditions of winning it, in accordance with the progress that is being made with flying machines. In view of the fact that Santos-Dumont and other French experimenters have already flown considerable distances in a straight line with aeroplanes, it was decided that to win the trophy the first time, a competitor should be required to surpass these distances; and since there have been no prizes offered for a flight of one kilometer (3,280 feet) in a straight line, this distance was determined upon as the one required to be covered.

Should the trophy be won at this distance, the conditions next year will be changed, so that a longer flight with turns will be required. Should any competitor win the trophy three times in separate years, it will become his property.

It was the hope of the *Scientific American* that the trophy would serve as an incentive to the Wrights to make a totally public flight. True, their first flight on December 17, 1903, was public, but it was witnessed by only five people other than the two brothers. After their first flight, they had established testing grounds at Huffman Prairie, eight miles outside of Dayton, Ohio. In 1904, they notified many of the area newspapers of a trial flight, and over a dozen reporters presented themselves. "Please do not make your reports of this flight sensational," Orville Wright pleaded, "and please take no picture. We want no crowds on the experiment ground."

Before a crowd of over fifty persons and with Wilbur at the controls, the machine moved down the launching track, only to fall ignominiously off the end. The *Wright Flyer* never got into the air that day, and the attempt was so ridiculed by the press and the people of Dayton that the Wrights continued their work in almost complete secrecy. While over one hundred flights are known to have taken place at Huffman Prairie in the years 1904-5—one of some 38 minutes' duration—they were seen only by a few special guests of the brothers and passengers on an interurban trolley line that passed their flying field. Even when they returned to Kitty Hawk in 1907 for tests, their flights were open to invited guests only. Reporters and the general public were not permitted near the flight area.

Nine months had passed since the *Scientific American* made its offer, and no one had attempted to capture the beautiful $2,500 trophy. However, when the A.E.A. made known its intentions, there was reluctance among some of the Aero Club officials to make the 300-mile trip from the "big city" to the "sticks." Selfridge and Curtiss pointed out that the rules specifically provided that the contestant could choose his own site. Finally, after several hours of haggling, the Aero Club agreed to send a team of observers and judges to Hammondsport on July 4.

Before the trophy trial, it was decided to revarnish all surfaces so that they would be completely airtight for the long flight. This increased the plane's efficiency to such an extent that, when Curtiss tested it on July 2, the engine developed too much power even with the spark fully retarded. Curtiss finally had to move his weight forward to implement the operation of the front control and keep the machine from climbing. Despite this it reached a maximum height of 40 feet. Curtiss decided to discontinue his flight, shut off the engine, and glided to the ground. No damage was sustained.

On the morning of July 3, Curtiss took *June Bug* up for what was to be the final check before the "big day." But after he had traveled about 90 feet at above 15 feet off the ground, a sudden puff of wind caught the aircraft and dashed it to the ground. While the pilot was unhurt, *June Bug*'s left wing and one wheel were broken. For a while it looked as if the affair on the fourth would have to be scratched. But, with everyone performing mechanical miracles, *June Bug* was repaired, and by seven o'clock that evening Curtiss made a flight of ¾ of a mile in 68½ seconds, at 38 miles per hour. The machine traveled a semicircle.

On the early morning train of July 4, a galaxy of observers, scientists, and "gentlemen aeronauts" converged on the little town in the vineyard country at the head of Lake Keuka. Allan R. Hawley, Augustus Post, and Charles M. Manly represented the Aero Club of America, and Stanley Y. Beach the *Scientific American*. Others who made the "long" pilgrimage from New York City were Simon Lake, the inventor of the submarine; Karl Dienstbach, representing the Imperial German Government; George H. Gary of the New York Society of Engineers; Ernest L. Jones, editor of the *American Journal of Aeronautics;* Wilbur R. Kimball of the Aeronautical Society of New York; and Augustus M. Herring, an eccentric individual who had been identified with flying experiments for nearly twenty years. And as this was the first publicly advertised flight in America, a large number of newspapermen had also come to Hammondsport for the trial.

Business was at a standstill, the town flooded with visitors. All the farmers for miles around had come in to see the sight. As early as five o'clock in the morning the roads leading into Hammondsport were lined with hurrying vehicles. They came early, bringing baskets of food and taking their place along the hillside in full view of Harry Champlin's race track in the valley. In other words, everything was in festive order that Saturday—except the weather.

The clouds which had hung low and dark all morning

finally discharged their contents in early afternoon showers. Many who had come to see the flight returned to town or went home. Some of the visitors from the big city and newspapermen found their way to the nearby wine cellars of the Pleasant Valley Wine Company, and soon the bubbling flow of the fruit of the vineyard put them in a good frame of mind. Harry Champlin had told his employees to give the newspapermen plenty of his Great Western champagne to drink so that if the flight was a failure, they wouldn't be fit to write bad things about "our G.H.," as they had of Langley.

While most of the spectators were somewhat skeptical, they wanted to see a successful flight—except, perhaps, Beach and Herring, who had seemingly come to witness a failure. Both these men had a negative attitude to the entire *June Bug* affair.

Around four o'clock the rain stopped, but the wind continued to blow quite strongly. The crowd that remained grew impatient, and those who were skeptical were sure that this fellow Curtiss couldn't fly. In spite of audible asides from people like Beach and Herring, Curtiss remained determined. He simply would not fly "until the wind was just right."

At about seven o'clock, however, the weather broke and patches of blue sky appeared in the west. The *June Bug* was rolled out of its tent, where it had waited shrouded in mystery during the rain. Henry Kleckler and several mechanics wheeled it through the wet grass and placed it in its starting position at the head of the back stretch. Quickly, Hawley and Manly officially measured off the one-kilometer distance (0.621 miles) straight down the field and marked it with a red flag on a tall pole.

When all was ready, Curtiss started the engine himself. Then, quickly, before it had a chance to overheat, he scrambled into the pilot's seat and took his place at the controls.

With a wave of his hand to the men holding the tail section, he started *June Bug* down the muddy race course, while a breathless silence fell over the crowd of about a thousand persons. The aeroplane rose into the air, swayed and dipped a little and, less than half a mile from the starting point, settled back to the ground. Everyone was rather disappointed, except, of course, Beach and Herring, who rushed triumphantly about shouting, "I told you he couldn't make it. I told you . . ."

But, undaunted, Curtiss and his crew dragged the *June Bug* back to the starting point. After a short discussion with Selfridge, the angle of incidence of the tail section was changed slightly and the front control was rewired. Once again Curtiss started the engine and took his place at the controls. On its second attempt, *June Bug* bumped over the muddy ground, past the 25-, the 50-, the 75-foot markers. Just before the 100-foot marker, it rose hesitantly a few feet in the air. Then this time more surely and steadily, it swiftly gained an altitude of about 20 feet. As the machine passed the half-mile mark, Lena Curtiss cried out pleadingly, "Oh, why do you fly so high, Glenn?"

As the *June Bug* passed over the red flag denoting the full kilometer, pandemonium broke loose among the now enthusiastic crowd. And still Curtiss continued down the valley past the limits of the field. Then he banked into a half-turn to avoid a vineyard before gracefully landing the machine. A major portion of the crowd joined in the cross-country race to congratulate the smiling young man, who was examining the *June Bug*'s engine when they arrived. Even Beach seemed to appreciate the efforts of the A.E.A. to build a plane that would fly.

After the turmoil had subsided slightly, Hawley and Manly set out officially to measure the distance covered and found it to be 5,090 feet, or 1,810 feet more than the required kilometer. However, Herring, who was neither an official judge nor observer, protested the committee's decision as to the exact distance. Hawley quickly silenced him by saying, "I'm acting president of the Aero Club. I *saw* Curtiss make the flight over the required distance, and I know he *made* it."

Hammondsport went wild, and from the little telegraph office in the back of Sandler's store there went forth the following Associated Press story which was quickly clicked around the world:

HAMMONDSPORT, N.Y., *July 4.* The Aerial Experiment Association's Aerodrome No. 3, Curtiss' *June Bug,* today earned the right to have its name the first inscribed on the *Scientific American* Trophy, by making an official flight of one kilometer in a straight line measured from the point where it left the ground. After passing the flag marking the finish, the machine flew 600 yards further and landed at the extreme edge of the field near the railroad track, after crossing three fences and describing a letter S, 2,000 yards in all, in 1 minute 42½ seconds at a speed of 39 miles per hour. This followed a 900 yard flight in 56 seconds.

The machine never behaved better and the long flight could have been continued at the will of the operator had he cared to rise over the trees which bounded the field. Though quite possible, it was not deemed wise to attempt it at the present stage of the aviator's development. There was hardly a breath of air stirring during either flight. This trial is really of the utmost importance as it is the first official test of an aeroplane ever made in America and there are only two other machines which have traveled further in public; Farman's and Delagrange's. The Wrights though have undoubtedly far outflown it in private, so that America is not so very far behind France as might be supposed. The last flight today was the 15th made by the machine, all having occurred under far more adverse conditions than those encountered by the French machines.

One of the A.E.A.'s most important figures, Dr. Bell, was not present at the flight because of his wife's renewed illness. But Mrs. David Fairchild immediately wired her father in Canada the good news and received an exuberant wire in reply: "Hurrah for Curtiss! Hurrah for *June Bug!* Hurrah for the Aerial Association!"

The celebration continued late into the night and began again early the next morning. A boat ride and luncheon, with large quantities of Finger Lakes champagne, were given to the distinguished visitors and Curtiss' local friends. On the boat's arrival back in town, the band and most of Hammondsport turned out to greet its "hero-son," and the men carried him ashore on their shoulders. The usually reserved Curtiss shouted at the top of his lungs, "Out to Stony Brook Farm."

Once at the testing grounds, he ordered *June Bug* taken out of its tent and made ready to fly it. After going about a half-mile in a straight line, Curtiss attempted to turn the aeroplane around. To do this, he steered to the right with the rudder and simultaneously inclined the right wing tip down by the movement of his shoulders. While it was a rather awkward turn, he finally got *June Bug* around and headed back toward the starting point. But finding himself flying toward a vineyard, Curtiss decided to bring the machine down, which he did with slight damage to the front control and the right wing. The flight and maneuver were considered a great success, it being the first 180-degree turn seen by the public in America.

Later that evening the visiting aeronauts and press climbed aboard a sleeper for the "big city," a little weary but happy that their mission had been accomplished. For the first time in America a heavier-than-air machine had been flown on a scheduled date before the general public. The flight of *June Bug* shattered the barrier of silence, skepticism, and outright derision that had followed the Wrights' pioneering triumph. The American people began to believe that man could fly like the birds after all, that time and space could be conquered. The United States was back in the "air race" with Europe, and Hammondsport justly became "the cradle of aviation."

Chapter 2

THE *GOLD BUG* ADDS ANOTHER LEG

M ONDAY was a normal workday for Curtiss and his associates. The broken strut in the right wing and the damaged front wheel had to be replaced. Two days later *June Bug* was back in the air, but its performance was erratic and flight was terminated after a distance of 900 yards.

On July 10 a flight lasting 1½ minutes was made in another effort to complete a 180-degree turn with the craft and return to its starting point. The maneuver failed because as it finished the turn the machine lost headway and came down. The distance of the flight was very close to one mile. The aerodrome seemed to be better balanced from fore to aft than ever, but otherwise it was quite erratic and swayed a good deal. The front control at full speed was quite effective. That evening, Curtiss received a cable from Dr. Bell requesting that he not fly *June Bug* again until A. J. Cameron, his Washington patent attorney, could go over the entire machine to determine all patentable items aboard it.

The next day Cameron arrived in Hammondsport, and after going over the *June Bug* carefully, he found a number of patentable features, including the wing tip controls, three-wheel running gear, the combination steering by ground wheel and rudder, and the shoulder movement controlling the wing tips. He took all the data with him back to Washington, but suggested that the A.E.A. not fly *June Bug* until all these items had been cleared for patents.

The *June Bug* was put in its tent and the members of Aerial Experiment Association decided to continue their work in two locations. Lieutenant Selfridge and Curtiss remained at Hammondsport to work with McCurdy on the fourth machine, while Casey Baldwin went to Nova Scotia to assist Dr. Bell on his tetrahedral structures and a new Association project—a hydroplane.

With the A.E.A. members in two widely separated places, close daily association and personal discussion were no longer possible. To minimize these disadvantages, Dr. Bell, on July 13, prepared the first issue of the weekly *Bulletin of the Aerial Experiment Association,* to replace Selfridge's typewritten A.E.A. reports. So that each group would keep the other fully informed, Dr. Bell insisted that no detail of the Association's work was too small to record, and required that a bulletin reviewing their activities and accomplishments be published weekly. As editor of the publication, Dr. Bell abandoned his campaign to use the word "aerodrome" rather than "aeroplane," when it became apparent that the former had come to mean not only the machine but the shed (hangar) which housed it and the inclined track along which it ran. When it was possible to say: "The doors of the *aerodrome* were opened and the *aerodrome* was wheeled over the *aerodrome,"* it was time, he declared in one issue of the *Bulletin,* to call a halt. Thus the word "aeroplane" found its way into Dr. Bell's vocabulary.

Among the congratulatory wires and mail, following the July 4 flight, Curtiss found the following letter:

DAYTON, OHIO
July 20th, 1908

MR. G. H. CURTISS
HAMMONDSPORT, NEW YORK

Dear Mr. Curtiss:

I learn from the *Scientific American* that your "June Bug" has moveable surfaces at the tips of the wings, adjustable to different angles on the right and left sides for maintaining the lateral balance. In our letter to Lieutenant Selfridge of January 18th, replying to his of the 15th, in which he asked for information on the construction of flyers, we referred him to several publications containing descriptions of the structural features of our machines, and to our U. S. Patent #821,393. We did not intend of course, to give permission to use the patented features of our machine for exhibitions, or in a commercial way.

This patent broadly covers the combination of sustaining surfaces to the right and left of the center of a flying machine adjustable to different angles, with vertical surfaces adjustable to correct inequalities in the horizontal resistances of the differently adjusted wings. Claim 14 of our patent #821,393 specifically covers the combination which we are informed you are using. We believe it will be very difficult to develop a successful machine without the use of some of the features covered in this patent.

The commercial part of our business is taking so much of our time that we have not been able to undertake public exhibitions. If it is your desire to enter the exhibition business we would be glad to take up the matter of a license to offer it under our patents for that purpose.

Please give Captain Baldwin my best wishes for his success in the coming Government tests.

Sincerely yours,
ORVILLE WRIGHT

Curtiss immediately forwarded the letter to Dr. Bell, who replied in letter form:

It is obvious that we may expect to be brought into a lawsuit with the Wright brothers, if we make any public exhibitions of our apparatus for gain without an arrangement with them. I do not know exactly the circumstances that led to the adoption of the movable wing tips as I was in Washington at that time; but if, as I have reason to believe, their adoption was due to a suggestion of mine that moveable wing tips should be used, contained in a letter to Mr. (Casey) Baldwin, I may say that this suggestion was made without any knowledge upon my part of anything the Wright brothers may have done. They had kept the details of construction of their machines secret; and I was ignorant of anything contained in their patent. I have no copy of their patent here, and do not therefore know whether their claim covers our wing tips or not. The matter should be enquired into by Messrs. Auro, Cameron, Lewis and Massie, and reported upon by them. They are more competent than we are to determine this point.

In early August, after making a detailed analysis of the difference between the *Wright Flyer* and *June Bug,* plus the report of the attorneys on their study of the Wright patent, Dr. Bell wrote Curtiss:

The wings of the Wright machine are flexible; ours are rigid. To correct tipping, the Wrights warp both wings; this increases the drag on one side and reduces it on the other making the machine turn. The Wright patent provides for conjoint (simultaneous) use of the rudder to correct this turning tendency. In our Hammondsport machine the movable tips are not part of the supporting surface, so they can be turned at a negative angle. In operation the rear of one is raised and the rear of the other lowered at precisely the same angle to the line of advance. No turning effect is produced and the use of the rudder is not necessary.

Dr. Bell completed his lengthy letter with the unequivocal statement: "I am decidedly of the opinion, and Mr. Cameron concurs, that our invention is not covered by the Wright brothers' patent. If we can only grasp and express the essential features, I am inclined to think we may obtain an independent patent of value which will not be subordinate to the Wright brothers' patent in any respect." The other members of the Association accepted this statement of their chairman as valid and proceeded with the work on *Drome No. 4.*

In hope of increasing the interest of the American public in aviation, a group of St. Louis businessmen offered a $24,000 contract to France's foremost aviator, Henri Farman, to give a series of exhibitions in the major Eastern cities of the United States. In addition, the backers offered $10,000 to the Aerial Experiment Association to race the *June Bug* against Farman's Voisin biplane at Brighton Beach, Brooklyn. McCurdy concluded a lengthy letter to Dr. Bell with the following thoughts:

About the Farman-St. Louis proposition. We have not heard of the detailed arrangements yet, but we have been given to understand that we would secure $10,000.00 to cover expenses if we would go. Don't you think that if such a proposition were definitely put to us we could accept, and make the public pay some of our expenses? I think that we could give old Farman a good run for his money, and you would be pleased, too.

When the formal bid to the Farman exhibition was received, it was not accepted by A.E.A.'s chairman because the organization was "for experimental purposes only," and Dr. Bell further pointed out that if they received money they would "lay themselves open to litigation before they were ready to defend." Though ten thousand sounded like a lot of money to the younger members, they reluctantly accepted Dr. Bell's opinion.

The doctor's advice proved to be good. Lieutenant Selfridge and McCurdy went to public flights at Brighton Beach on August 5 and 6, and the latter wrote Mrs. Bell:

> Farman's attempts were very disappointing indeed. The first day he flew 140 yards at an elevation of 3 feet and a rate of 20 miles an hour. He made two such flights and then wheeled the machine back to the tent. The next day there were 3,000 persons in attendance, and as it was too windy he did not attempt to fly at all, much to the disappointment of the crowd. They were, however, given "wind cheques" and told to come again the next day. We thought that we had seen all worth seeing, so Tom [Selfridge] and I left New York Saturday evening for Hammondsport.

While the Farman flights were given a thorough advertising and publicity campaign, the complete tour was a financial failure. Farman's backers had to go into liquidation, the Voisin aeroplane was impounded for debts, and Henri returned to France a rather disappointed man.

While McCurdy and Selfridge concentrated on the work of the new aeroplane, Curtiss spent most of his time helping Captain Tom Baldwin getting a dirigible ready for the Army acceptance tests. In order to meet the specifications drawn up by the War Department, the big airship was required to make a continuous flight of two hours under power, and be capable of maneuvering in any direction. Curtiss realized that a better engine would be needed. He designed and set about building an airborne, water-cooled engine, something which had not been attempted at the Curtiss factory up to this time, and the success of which would be a long step forward. Although Baldwin had built thirteen dirigibles that had been operated successfully in exhibitions, the government contract was his most ambitious undertaking. There was never any doubt about the balloon itself. The question was whether the engine would survive a two-hour endurance test and furnish the necessary power to drive the big airship at a speed of 20 miles an hour.

The engine for the Army's dirigible proved more difficult to build than Curtiss had expected. For several months he worked with Alexander L. Pfitzner, a young Hungarian engineer recruited for the task, and Charles Kirkham, formerly of Kirkham Brothers Shop, until a 4-cylinder engine of sufficient power was produced. On the test block, the engine had an unlimited supply of cold water, but in the air it required a radiator large enough to carry an adequate amount of water yet light enough not to throw the big cigar-shaped airship out of balance. After a great deal of searching—a lightweight aeronautical radiator wasn't an item found in mail-order catalogues—a suitable one was located. The airship, which had been finished for several weeks, was shipped, together with its power source, to the proving grounds at Fort Meyer, Virginia. There, in preliminary tests, it met the speed requirements.

The cabin, or undercarriage, of the dirigible consisted of a very light framework, with a catwalk made of two narrow boards. Curtiss sat in the front of the ship and kept the lightweight, 24-horsepower engine running smoothly, while the portly but agile "Cap" Baldwin sprinted up and down the catwalk to keep the craft on an even keel. In this primitive fashion the airship was kept going for the required time over a given course above the Potomac River and the hills of Virginia, on August 12, 1908. It was the longest flight that had ever been made by a dirigible in the United States, and remained the record for several years.

Army Dirigible SC-1 was officially accepted by the Signal Corps. (The dirigible was also military aircraft No. 1 in the United States.) The following month a dirigible of the same type was sold to Captain W. Hildebrand of the Imperial German Army and shipped on November 30, 1908. The sale was negotiated by Karl Dienstbach, who had witnessed the *June Bug* flight. It was the birth of the aeronautical export business in the United States.

On his return from Fort Meyer, Curtiss went to work on the design of a new engine for *Drome No. 4,* as well as a "real" powerful one for Dr. Bell's *Cygnet II.* Curtiss knew his earlier engine had overheated because of insufficient oil. In the new engine, he planned to attach an additional tank to provide an abundant flow of oil through four different feed pipes.

On the first of September, Lieutenant Selfridge was ordered to Fort Meyer, to be an official Army observer of a series of flights by Orville Wright. After several talks with the Wright brothers, with pressure from such influential Senators as Henry Cabot Lodge of Massachusetts, the War Department had signed a contract with the Wrights for an aeroplane able to carry a pilot and one passenger on a sustained flight over a distance of 10 miles at a speed of 40 miles an hour. In this agreement, dated March 3, 1908, the government agreed to pay a sum of $25,000, plus $2,500 for each additional mile of speed above 40 miles an hour. The completed aeroplane had to pass several public evaluation trials conducted by official Army observers.

While Orville Wright preferred that these trials be conducted under semisecret conditions, he agreed to go along with the War Department's policy that people had a right to see how their money was being spent. Since the flights were to be public, Curtiss accompanied Selfridge and stayed for the first two days of the trials. He wrote to Dr. Bell of the events:

The first flight of the 3rd was rather short as Mr. Wright said he was unaccustomed to the machine, and the levers seemed awkward for him. He made a wrong move and headed for the tent, which necessitated immediate landing. In this landing, with the machine tilted somewhat, one runner struck first causing the machine to swing around sideways and broke the runner off.

The next day he did better, however, and made as fine a landing on its skids as you would make on wheels. The Wright machine, as you know, is launched on a mono-rail by means of a weight in a derrick-like tower. But this catapulting device includes the tower, and a big weight drops to operate the pulleys and rope to give the machine its initial velocity after the engine has been started. The system, however, doesn't seem to be very well liked by the Army people here. I believe that all who have seen our machine and the Wrights prefer our method of starting on wheels to skids. I think in a few years all machines will be using wheels and skids will be a thing of the past.

I had some talk with Mr. Wright and nothing was said about his patents on adjustable surfaces. He has nothing startling about his machine and no secrets.

On September 9 Orville gave exhibition of great flying skill and on the second flight of the day remained in the air for 1 hour, 2 minutes, and 15 seconds. (This was the world's first flight of over one hour.) That same day Lieutenant Frank P. Lahm of the Signal Corps was also taken aloft to become the Wrights' first "official" passenger. (Orville had taken up his mechanic, Charles Furnas, on May 14, as an experiment before undertaking an official passenger flight.) It was estimated that up to ten thousand people witnessed the trials on the ninth.

At the suggestion of Dr. Bell, the Smithsonian Institution created the Langley Medal "for special services in connection with the science of aerodynamics" and made the first award to the Wright brothers. On September 11, Bell sent this telegram to Orville Wright:

"On behalf of the Aerial Experiment Association allow me to congratulate you upon your magnificent success. An hour in the air makes a historical occasion."

On September 12 the second "official" passenger, Major George O. Squier, was taken aloft for 9 minutes. Later that day Orville set a new endurance record of 1 hour, 14 minutes, and 20 seconds, at an altitude of 250 feet. This flight, equivalent to a distance of almost 50 miles, received good press coverage, and *Wright Flyer Model A* quickly replaced the *June Bug* in the minds of most Americans. While Orville may not have intended it, his flying record (over 6 airborne hours) during the Army evaluation demonstrations brought home to the American public that the air had really been conquered.

On September 17 Lieutenant Selfridge, who along with Lahm and Squier were the *official* Army observers at the trials, requested to be taken aloft. At first Wright flatly refused to do so because of his connection with A.E.A. When he was reminded by Major Squier, who was in charge of the tests, of Selfridge's official capacity, Orville reluctantly consented and they took off.

For about five minutes the plane performed faultlessly. Wright made three and one-half turns about the parade ground. Then spectators heard a cracking sound, saw a splinterlike object fall to the ground. The machine pitched forward, hesitated, and then dove 50 feet, burying its nose in the ground at an angle of not more than 10 degrees from the vertical. The aeroplane hit with such impact that Lieutenant Selfridge was fatally injured and Wright received a fractured thigh and four broken ribs. This was the first fatal crash in powered aviation.

A study of the wreckage revealed that the propeller had fouled in a tail guy wire which had worked loose. Then the propeller had snapped, the control mechanism had been demolished, and with only 50 feet in which to maneuver Orville had been unable to bring his machine out of its fall.

The Bells received the news of Selfridge's death the next day at Beinn Bhreagh. Realizing the profound effect this event might have on "her boys," Mrs. Bell wrote Baldwin, Curtiss and McCurdy:

> I can't get over Tom's being taken. I can't realize it; it doesn't seem possible. Isn't it heartbreaking? And yet it is better for him than die as Langley did.* He was so happy to the very end. I know he would have said he was having the time of his life, and, though he must have really realized his danger in those last few seconds, he would still hope to escape, and he had no time for unavailing regrets. It was the happiest way death could have come to him now, but why need it have come now when he was ready to put to his country's use all the results of his long, patient preparations? . . .
>
> I am so sorry for you in this breaking of your beautiful association. But it was beautiful and the memory of it will endure—Bell, Curtiss, Baldwin, Selfridge and McCurdy. It was indeed a "brilliant coterie," as one newspaper said. Do anything you think best, but let the A.E.A. be only these to the end, and then take some other name.

The end of the Association was scheduled for September 30. A formal meeting was called in Washington on September 26 to discuss what should be done. Edward R. Selfridge represented his son since unanimous consent of five members was required if the group was to continue. After he said that he

---

* Langley died broken-hearted over lack of success and ridicule.

knew his son would have voted to extend the term of Association, the following resolution was passed:

> *Resolved:*—that the Aerial Experiment Association be continued for another period of six months ending 31 March 1909, the Association then to be dissolved unless other plans are unanimously agreed upon by the members.

The members also voted to admit William F. Bedwin as a member of the Association to replace Lieutenant Selfridge, and McCurdy was named Secretary. Bedwin had helped in the construction of both *Red Wing* and *White Wing* at Hammondsport, and the building of the *Cygnets* at Beinn Bhreagh. Charles J. Bell, a cousin of Dr. Bell and President of the American Security and Trust Company, was appointed Trustee of the Association. Still another Bell, Gardiner H. Bell, was made assistant editor of the *Bulletin.* Of course, Mrs. Bell provided the additional funds, up to $10,000, so the A.E.A. could continue.

On Curtiss' return to Hammondsport after the meeting, approval came from the attorneys in Washington that the *June Bug* could be flown again. All patentable items such as ailerons, shoulder movement for their control, tricycle undercarriage were recorded. But, rather than fly it as it was, Curtiss decided to take off the wheel landing gear and substitute pontoons fashioned from canoes, in order that the craft might be flown from the surface of the water. This idea had apparently been in his mind for some time, as is suggested by a letter written by him on August 19, 1908, for the *Aerial Experiment Association Bulletin:*

> I have read the last two *Bulletins* with great interest. The scheme of starting a flying machine from, and landing on, the water has been in my mind for some time. It has many advantages, and I believe can be worked out. Even if a most suitable

device for launching and landing on land is secured, a water craft will still be indispensable for war purposes and if the exhibition field is to be considered, would, I believe, present greater possibilities in this line than a machine which works on land.

An arrangement of floats to support the flyer when at rest would be necessary. Then small hydroplanes to carry it up out of the water and to catch the shock of landing. I do not think the problem is difficult.

Besides, the lake would afford an ideal flying place, and what was more important still, a fall, or a bed landing would not nearly so likely result in injury to the aviator.

Accordingly, McCurdy mounted *June Bug* on two 20-foot, flat-bottom floats built something like a catamaran, and re-named it *Loon*. It required some time to construct the light and strong floats, and it wasn't until the beginning of November, 1908, that they were ready for the first attempt to fly from water ever made in this or any other country.

The addition of the pontoons to *June Bug* added weight to the ship and, of course, increased the air resistance. It was found impossible to attain a speed greater than 25 miles an hour on the surface of the water. With McCurdy and Curtiss alternately at the controls, it could glide over the water but could not leave its surface. The suction which held down the machine was much greater than they had anticipated. They concluded that the air-cooled *June Bug* engine was not equal to the task of lifting the *Loon,* which now had a total weight of 1,000 pounds. They decided to repeat the experiment with the newly designed water-cooled engine. Though the pontoons lifted slightly out of the water in the second trial, there was still too much drag. The best speed they could make was 25 miles an hour, which was not enough to "break" the suction and permit the aerocraft to rise from the water.

After reading in the *Bulletin* about the *Loon*'s difficulties, Casey Baldwin wrote a letter to McCurdy suggesting that shorter and lighter pontoons be used. Following Baldwin's specifications, a new set of canvas-covered pontoons were substituted for the ones previously employed. But on the first trial one of the pontoons caught in the dock, tearing a hole in the fabric covering. Curtiss reported: "McCurdy, who was riding the machine, did not know of the accident. He made a circle on the lake and returned to the starting point. Then the *Loon* sank."

That same night, which was the second of January, 1909, this dejected message went to Dr. Bell in Nova Scotia:

GAVE VAUDEVILLE PERFORMANCE TONIGHT BY MOONLIGHT WITH LOON FIRST HYDRO TEST SUCCESSFUL, SECOND AERODROME TEST FAIRLY SUCCESSFUL, THIRD SUBMARINE TEST MOST SUCCESSFUL OF ALL. EXPERIMENTS ENDED.

CURTISS and MCCURDY

Curtiss, with the assistance of several of his factory workers, managed to raise the *Loon* from the lake, and the next day it was dismantled for the winter.

Drome No. 4, however, proved to be entirely successful, and its first flight was made by McCurdy on December 6, over the Stony Brook flying field. Because of the experience gained in the construction of the first three machines, the new craft was a very professional-looking job. Loaded weight, including pilot, was about 800 pounds. It was powered by a 35-horsepower, 8-cylinder, water-cooled engine.

The wing span of the new machine was 49 feet, and the wing area 420 square feet. The wings, which tapered from 6 feet at the mid-section to 4 feet, were covered with a rubberized, nonporous balloon silk that was impervious to air.

It had a silver finish on one side, prompting McCurdy to dub his machine *Silver Dart*.

After several other successful test flights at Hammondsport, *Silver Dart* was crated and shipped to Baddeck early in January, 1909. On February 23 Dr. Bell was able to telegraph to the London *Times* that the first aeroplane flight in Canada and the first by a British subject anywhere in the British Empire had taken place on that day. J. A. D. McCurdy had flown a distance of half a mile, about 30 feet above frozen Bras d'Or Lake. A few days later, McCurdy flew the *Silver Dart* 8 miles in about 11 minutes.

While the *Silver Dart* was being built, an unexpected visitor stopped at the factory in Hammondsport. He was Augustus Herring, the man who had voiced loud objections to the rulings of the judges in the *Scientific American*'s trophy award. But this time his attitude was completely different. He was very friendly, and even assisted McCurdy with many suggestions and ideas on the construction of *Silver Dart*. Herring, of course, had twenty years' experience in the field of aeronautics, during which he had worked with many of the great pioneers of early manned flight—Lilienthal, Montgomery, Langley, and Chanute. With the latter he had made over two hundred glider flights. In 1898, working on his own, Herring built a Chanute-type biplane glider, on which he mounted a compressed-air engine. He insisted that after several trials he had made a flight of a few seconds, but this claim was never verified or accepted.

In the evenings Herring and Curtiss had many discussions in the thinkorium. One of Herring's favorite subjects was the financial rewards to be had in this new field. He said that if the G. H. Curtiss Manufacturing Company, for instance, started building aeroplanes immediately, it would have no problem making money. But, he stressed, "The time is now, before the Wright brothers create an air trust."

After Herring left in late October, Curtiss did a great deal of thinking about the future. It was something he had seldom done in the past. Almost everything that had happened to him up to this point in his life had been due to circumstances rather than planning. Based on his conversations with Herring, plus his own observations, Curtiss began to believe that money could be made in aviation. The Wrights' patents were not airtight, according to Herring, and even Dr. Bell's lawyers said that there were no conflicts between those held by A.E.A. and the Dayton brothers. Why not exploit aviation before the Wrights had everything their way?

Early in January, Dr. Bell wrote Curtiss, stating:

> Time passes rapidly, and the day assigned for the dissolution of the Association will be upon us almost before we know it. So much work has been done by other people upon plans for aerodromes having the general features of our first four aerodromes, *Red Wing, White Wing, Jung Bug,* and *Silver Dart,* that it is extremely doubtful whether patents of any great value can be obtained to represent our work at Hammondsport. We are liable to come into contact with numerous patents; and should any patents we obtained turn out to be subordinate to other patents already granted, the owners of these patents, not being affiliated with the Association would be liable to make trouble.
>
> When the Association finally dissolves the only way in which the members can obtain any substantial reward for their labors will be by the manufacture and sale of aerodromes embodying features produced by the Association. This means either that the Association must be converted into a manufacturing corporation, or that the Association will sell out its rights to some manufacturing company for a consideration in shares or cash. Now no company will give the Association

anything for its inventions unless they are patented, or at least patentable. What we would sell to such a company would be patents or patentable inventions. Anyway patents would be involved and it should, therefore, be the special object of the Association during the remaining months of its existence to work—not simply, as formerly "to get into the air" by any means we can—but to get into the air by new means of a patentable nature. Upon our success in doing this will depend whatever future the Association may have before it. The Association cannot be continued indefinitely upon the present basis on account of the expense incurred without reimbursement.

It would then be for the Association to decide what should be done with the proceeds:—

(1.) The Association might decide to distribute the proceeds in accordance with our agreement of organization and dissolve the Association.

(2.) It might decide to continue the Association indefinitely putting the proceeds into the treasury of the Association for the support of its experimental work.

(3.) It might also decide to enlarge the membership of the Association and establish it as a permanent institution or society to promote the art of aviation.

This third plan would be my desire. . . . I would, therefore, urge that we should all have this great object in view, and bend all our efforts to the development of practical improvements of a patentable nature to the end that we may be reimbursed sufficiently to enable us, or some of us, to endow the Association and extend a helping hand to others who may be seeking to advance the art of Aviation by experimental methods.

Curtiss made his sentiments known on the Bell proposal in an interview with a New York *Herald* reporter on January 21, 1909, at the Auto Show, where he had a motorcycle exhibit. When asked about dissolution of the group, he said, "It is true that the Aerial Experiment Association will probably disband in March because we have accomplished what we intended to do."

The next day Curtiss signed a contract with the Aeronautic Society of New York to build for them an aeroplane for the sum of $5,000. This Society, the first organization in the world formed for the practical pursuit of mechanical flight by man, decided it needed a flying machine to carry out its objectives. A committee was formed to approach the Wrights for the purchase of one of their planes. When the brothers flatly turned down the Society's proposal, Ernest Jones and Wilbur Kimball, who both had witnessed the flight of *June Bug,* suggested they approach Curtiss with their offer. After several conversations early in January, he agreed to deliver a machine in May that would be "in many ways different from the aerodromes of the Aerial Experiment Association." Curtiss agreed to hold the Society immune from any costs or damages that might arise out of any suit brought on the ground that the machine infringed other patents. In return, Curtiss requested that the existence of this contract be kept secret until he had severed his connection with the A.E.A.

The secret leaked out, however, and when Bell learned of it, he wired Curtiss to learn how it affected the Association. Curtiss promptly replied that he believed it wouldn't affect the aerodrome arrangement Dr. Bell favored, adding that if a commercial organization emerged from the A.E.F., the order would be turned over to it; otherwise the order would be taken up by the G. H. Curtiss Manufacturing Company.

On January 29 Curtiss went to Beinn Bhreagh to discuss the matter fully with all members of the Association. He urged that the A.E.A. should become commercial. He thought that the United States Government wouldn't purchase aeroplanes from anyone but the Wrights for some time to come, but possibly the Canadian Government might be induced to invest in a flying machine or two, especially if built in Canada, in Baddeck. Many private persons and organizations might be ready to purchase aerodromes as well.

Curtiss also pointed out that exhibitions could be profitable if handled by someone who knew how to obtain contracts and how to collect the money after the contracts were fulfilled. He predicted that many alluring prize offers would be made both in America and abroad. Thus it seemed feasible to him to include "prize chasing and exhibition work" in one branch or division of the business. Curtiss also said that he believed schools would be needed to teach the great numbers of people who would like to fly. This would, of course, create another market for the sale of aeroplanes.

Dr. Bell, while agreeing with Curtiss that aviation would someday be a profitable enterprise, suggested, as he had previously, that, without patents or assured prospects of obtaining them, it would be extremely difficult to obtain outside capital to organize such a firm. Since they lacked the patents and the Patent Office operated very slowly in issuing them, Bell concluded, and the Trustee concurred, that A.E.A.'s only possible course of action was to organize a company with money contributed by themselves and their friends. He asked Curtiss for an estimate of the amount that might be necessary for a year's operation.

After much discussion, the week-long meeting adopted Bell's plan for the organization. Under it, the American Aerodrome Company, with headquarters in Hammondsport, would be formed as a joint stock company with nominal capital of $100,000 divided into 10,000 shares of par value $10. The A.E.A. would transfer all its property and patents to this new company in return for the money spent on experiments, in the form of paid-up stock.

After a great deal of figuring, Curtiss estimated that a sum of $10,000 would be required as working capital for one year. Mrs. Bell immediately offered to subscribe $3,500 to the new concern, but Dr. Bell insisted that each associate must invest $1,300 of his own money in the project. The American Aerodrome Company, of course, meant the end of the Aerial Experiment Association.

While the other A.E.A. members remained at Baddeck, Curtiss returned to Hammondsport to take care of some pressing matters that had arisen in his engine business, and to consider whether or not he wished to invest his future and money in a concern he thought subject to the dictatorial powers of one man—Dr. Bell. While in the early days of the Association, G.H. seemed to hold unvoiced reservations respecting much that was done or planned by the group, he now let his feelings be known. And, all too often, they seemed to conflict directly with those of Bell's.

A few days after his return from Nova Scotia, Cortlandt Field Bishop, president of the Aero Club, approached him with the suggestion that he form an aircraft corporation with Augustus Herring. Bishop pointed out that Herring had been conducting aeronautical experiments for twenty years and was looking for a young man with mechanical know-how. He reputedly had an array of aeronautical patents, some of which were supposed to antedate those of the Wrights. He also had obtained from the U. S. Army, at the same time as the Wrights, a $50,000 contract for an aeroplane utilizing his patents. In addition, Bishop showed Curtiss newspaper reports that French, Belgian, and German syndicates were trying to lure Herring from the United States with offers of over $100,000 for exclusive rights to manufacture his machine.

After several meetings with Bishop, and then with Herring himself, in late February and early March, terms were drawn up for a new company. Curtiss was to give up control of the G. H. Curtiss Manufacturing Company and become vice president and general manager of a new corporation of which Herring was to be president. Herring would assign the Army contract, patents of undetermined value on automatic stability devices and other valuable aeronautical devices. Bishop, Allan Hawley, Cooper Hewitt, and several other "big-city financiers" would put up the necessary capital—about $45,-000. On March 15 a charter was obtained by the Herring-Curtiss Company to manufacture aeroplanes, motorcycles, automobiles, and various kinds of engine-drawn vehicles. It was capitalized at $360,000.

Curtiss told friends that he selected the Herring deal over the A.E.A. one because all that he had to put in the new organization was his company—no cash! In addition, Herring had all the patents necessary to build aeroplanes without any worry from the Wrights. He notified Dr. Bell of his decision and invited all members of the Association to join with him in the Herring combination. Thus, with the defection of Curtiss, plans for the American Aerodrome Company were abandoned and, on March 31, a year and a half after its formation, the Aerial Experiment Association was dissolved. During its existence it had received from Mrs. Bell two donations totaling $35,000, one for $25,000 and another for $10,000. Its liabilities totaled some $3,000, the cost of issuing the A.E.A. *Bulletin,* which Dr. Bell had carried and now wrote off. In other words, the Association functioned for eighteen months and built four successful aeroplanes for an over-all cost of $38,000.

Dr. Bell agreed to meet all the other liabilities that still might be remaining in return for the aerodrome *Silver Dart,* the hydroplane boat *Query,* the tetrahedral kite *Cygnet II,* and the tools and equipment at Beinn Bhreagh. The physical assets of the A.E.A. at Hammondsport, including the aerodrome *June Bug,* tools, and other apparatus, were given by Bell to Curtiss. All records of the Association were turned over to its Trustee. In the last issue of the *Bulletin,* Dr. Bell wrote: "The Aerial Experiment Association is now a thing of the past. It has made its mark upon the history of aviation and its work will live."

One month after the dissolution of the A.E.A., the first aircraft manufacturing company in Canada, the Canadian Aerodrome Company, was formed at Baddeck, comprising Bell, Baldwin, Bedwin, and McCurdy, and backed financially by Mrs. Bell. Five aircraft were designed and built by the company, two of which, *Baddeck I* and *Baddeck II,* were very successful. The latter was tested by the Canadian Army at Petawawa in the summer of 1909. Because of the unlevel landing field, the wheels couldn't stand the sudden jar of the rough terrain, and the *Baddeck II* folded up when it landed. As a result, Army officers decided that the aeroplane was impractical for military purposes, and they refused the support that the members of the Canadian Aerodrome Company had hoped for. Not long after, the company was disbanded. This event virtually marked the end of aviation experiments at Baddeck, except in 1912 when Dr. Bell was able to prove to all skeptics that a power-driven tetrahedral kite could fly. This man-carrying kite, called *Cygnet III,* was smaller than the others in the series and was powered by a 70-horsepower Gnome engine. With McCurdy acting as operator, *Cygnet III* took off under its own power and made a number of short straightaway flights over the ice of Bras d'Or Lake on March 9 to 17.

Two days before the disbandment of the A.E.A., announcement of the formation of Herring-Curtiss Company was made to the newspapers. The press announcement contained a sentence stating that Herring, while with Octave Chanute, had helped the Wrights in the design of their gliders and their first aeroplane. This claim was quickly denied by the Wrights, and Wilbur revealed that Herring had written them in June of 1908 explaining that he, too, had many patents on aeroplane designs, and wanted to join forces with them, taking a one-third interest. They never replied to his letter.

When Mrs. David Fairchild visited Hammondsport to pick up items left there by her father, Dr. Bell, she wrote him that she was sorry that the A.E.A. couldn't continue with its work. She went on:

> Mr. Herring was especially enthusiastic over tetrahedral construction which he believes is going to be a great feature in flying machines. He has promised to call you over the long distance telephone to discuss it. It will be interesting to hear your opinions about him. Mr. Curtiss says he's an authority on all kinds of aeroplanes, but all others without exception (the ones I talked to) were uncertain as to whether he is a genius or a fool.

While Dr. Bell never expressed his comments on Herring in public, he stated to close associates that Curtiss was moving into "pretty fast company" and that he hoped the young man could hold his own. He wired Curtiss to please arrange his business affairs so that he could be present at the last meeting of A.E.A. on March 31. Curtiss did not attend.

Bell was "hurt," according to friends, by Curtiss' actions during the disbandment of the A.E.A., but his goodwill toward G.H. continued. Seven months later, on October 30, 1909, he telegraphed Curtiss from Washington, "Wish you would come here for conference with Charles Bell before I return to Baddeck. Want to go at once but would wait a day or two for you. Come right to my house and shake a paw for auld lang syne." Again, Curtiss didn't take up the invitation.

While the expansion plans of the new corporation were being formulated by Herring, Curtiss started work on the Aeronautic Society's flying machine. With delivery date the first week in May, an exhibition was fixed for May 22 on word from Curtiss that he would be ready. Later, however, he asked for an extension of another week, and the date was changed to May 29. But again the exhibition was postponed, and the Society decided that no new date would be fixed until its "star" attraction arrived in New York.

The machine was finally delivered on June 11, and the exhibition was scheduled for Saturday, June 26, at Morris Park Track in the Bronx. The location seemed ideal. The 327-acre track had not been used for horse racing for some years, but automobile races had been held there, and both the track and the infield had been kept in very good condition. Except for the posts marking the old race courses, which could be moved, it was free from obstructions, and seemed made for a perfect aerodrome. It was within a short walk of the subway at West Farms or Bronx Park. Trolley cars ran up to it. It lay within a forty-minute, five-cent journey from the center of Manhattan. But the New York press didn't pay too much attention to the goings-on at Morris Park. Although the newspapers in England and on the continent of Europe eagerly printed details of the upcoming exhibition, the attitude of the papers at home was: "Wait till they fly an aeroplane!"

While the total attendance may have suffered through the postponements and lack of press coverage, almost twenty thousand people came to see the first exhibition of *all* types of aeronautical devices ever held in the United States. The charge for admission was one dollar, but only a small proportion of the visitors passed through the turnstiles. During the years the race track had lain unused most of its fences had been broken down. The payment of admission proved a matter of almost Quixotic courtesy. Commissioner J. E. Bingham, who was at the head of the Police Department, very kindly lent the assistance of a large staff of men, both on foot and mounted, who performed excellent service. But not even a regiment of soldiers could have kept out the swarming crowd from so great an unfenced space.

The program opened with the performance of a wind wagon. It was a crude type of automobile driven by a large propeller in front of the machine just near enough to the driver to make the thing look very dangerous. It moved rapidly, making a fierce clatter, and it pleased the crowd as it went sweeping around the mile course.

Next there were several short, straight flights by Curtiss in the Society's new aeroplane, and then a contest of automobile-towed gliding machines, during which W. H. Martin, of Canton, Ohio, came within a hair's-breadth of losing his life. The Martin machine was a grotesque type of monoplane, and both he and his wife had made some very remarkable flights in it out in Ohio. There it had been hauled into the air by a farm horse. During the exhibition, an automobile was used, and it provided too much speed. The glider failed to get into air before it crashed into a fence.

While other events were taking place, certain officials of the Society complained to Curtiss that he wasn't making the flights of which his machine was capable. At their insistence, he promised to make another flight as the last event of the day. When his machine started from a point a quarter of a mile from the grandstand, thousands of men and women were lounging listlessly upon the lawn, expecting to see another straightaway flight. As the motor began to purr and the machine came sweeping down the course, it was evident from his velocity and altitude that he had started on a longer journey than before, and as the aeroplane darted past the grandstand, and past the

point where he had ended his previous flights, the crowd rose
and began to cheer. Then the machine, checking its speed a
trifle, tilted just a little, swerved gracefully to the left and
darted in between the judges' stand and the scoreboard. On
sped the aeroplane toward the other side of the track, moving
so swiftly that an automobile on the track was unable to keep
up with it. In a few seconds it had reached the opposite side
of the track, and was darting in and out between clumps of
trees, but keeping an even keel and a steady, rapid pace.

It was dusk, and as it sped away on the farther side of the
field, at times only an occasional flash of the propellers and
the constant humming of the motor told that it was still in
the air. Men with field glasses tried to follow its course, and
some in their enthusiasm started pell-mell across the infield
to see where it landed, while three large automobiles went
dashing in pursuit of it. It was something new to a New York
crowd. Aside from the flights of Orville Wright at Fort Meyer,
and flights at Hammondsport, nothing of the sort had ever
been seen in the United States.

In a special meeting held immediately after the exhibition,
the Society members decided that a race between two aeroplanes would be the most appealing event to the public. But
where could they obtain another aeroplane? After consulting
with Curtiss, he suggested that while *June Bug* wasn't capable
of any future flights, why not contact Dr. Bell? He knew that
McCurdy would be most happy to "race" him in *Silver Dart.*
In a telegram, the Society offered Bell one-half of the net receipts of all exhibitions in which the former A.E.A. aeroplane
took part.

A few days later, the Society received a reply in which Dr.
Bell stated that the Canadian Aerodrome Company would not
exhibit *Silver Dart* or any of their aeroplanes in the United
States. In leaving this market wide open to Curtiss, Bell told

his partners that at some future time they could request that Curtiss refrain from putting on any exhibitions in Canada or Great Britain.

On July 3 another exhibition was organized by the Society, but even after dropping the admission charge to 50 cents, it too resulted in a financial loss. W. H. Martin remained with his glider and Curtiss made a flight similar to the one on the previous Saturday. Some motorcycle events were added. After this meet, the directors of the Society decided that it was inadvisable to risk the considerable cost of the exhibitions, and not only because of the condition of the fences at Morris Park. It had been their hope that the exhibitions, while stimulating the interest of the public and encouraging inventors, would also encourage the formation of an experimental fund out of which the Society could provide more workshops and sheds, buy more motors for the use of members, and acquire testing devices and other useful aids. It was very much to their regret that this hope was unfulfilled.

Immediately after the first trial of the Society's aeroplane, Stanley V. Beach, one of the organization's directors, sent a cable to Cortlandt Bishop of the Aero Club of America, who was then in France, informing him of the showing the machine had made and suggesting that Glenn Curtiss at once be named to represent the United States in the Great Aviation Week to be held on August 22 to 29, 1909, near Rheims, France. For the first time in history, flyers and flying machines would be gathering from all over the civilized world to compete in altitude, endurance, speed, and distance races. Climax of the occasion was the $5,000 Coupe Internationale d'Aviation purse to be presented by James Gordon Bennett, publisher of the New York *Herald*.

When the International Aeronautic Federation and the Aero Club of France were arranging for the Rheims meeting,

After being partially disassembled, *Red Wing* was loaded aboard the canal barge *Springstead* and taken about five miles down the lake to solid ice.

A close-up of the wing section of *Red Wing* aboard the canal barge *Springstead*.

The canal boat *Springstead,* about ready to leave the dock at Hammondsport, thus to become the world's first "aeroplane carrier."

Ken Ingraham, Harold Glover and William Bedwin (left to right) keep watch over *Red Wing* as it moves up the lake aboard the canal boat.

Reassembly of *Red Wing* is almost complete, and the aerodrome is about ready for its first flight.

A skid was built so that the aerodrome could be taken off the barge.

Red Wing was put ashore, then moved on its skids to the solid ice of Lake Keuka.

A close-up of *Red Wing*'s engine and its air-cooling fan. The small projectile-like object above the engine is the fuel tank. The batteries (electrical system) can be seen in the lower right corner.

Rear view of *Red Wing* showin͏
the motor portion and the propelle͏

Curtiss sits in *Red Wing*'s cockpit prior to the
first flight.

William Bedwin checks the wing section after *Red Wing* was reassembled on the
ice of Lake Keuka.

Actual flight of *Red Wing* on March 12, 1908. The overall distance was 318 feet and 11 inches.

The final results of the first flight. Baldwin was unhurt, and all the parts of *Red Wing* were saved. Five days later *Red Wing* flew again.

Curtiss, kneeling and with the hat, working on J. Newton Williams' helicopter-type aerial machine. It made its first successful "rise" on March 12, 1908.

The wing section of *White Wing* being transported from the Curtiss plant in town to the trial site at Stony Brook farm.

The first wheeled undercarriage in America as it appeared on the A.E.A.'s second aerodrome, *White Wing*.

White Wing about to take off on its first trial flight with Lt. Selfridge at the controls.

Another view of *White Wing* just before take-off. Note how close the wing bottoms are to the raised sides of the track.

Dr. and Mrs. Bell (far right) leave the Stony Brook race track after a successful flight of *White Wing*. In the design of *White Wing*, Dr. Bell suggested the method of lateral control—hinged-surface, wing-tipped flaps—which became known as ailerons.

The A.E.A. members (left to right—Baldwin, Selfridge, Curtiss, Bell and McCurdy) with another air pioneer, August Post, far right. McCurdy was using crutches, following a motorcycle accident. *White Wing*, at left, shows a close-up view of the first aerocraft ailerons in the United States—the triangular panels at the wing tips.

Curtiss testing the engine and front elevator design of *June Bug* in his "wind machine."

Curtiss sits at the controls of *June Bug,* on June 12, 1908. A few minutes after this picture was taken, Curtiss flew this craft for the first time.

June Bug just prior to its famous July 4th flight. Curtiss, in tie and white shirt, is standing behind the craft.

June Bug in one of its trial flights. Curtiss is at the controls.

The Scientific American trophy which was first won by Glenn Curtiss for the *June Bug* flight on July 4th, 1908.

The U.S. Army's dirigible *SC-1,* flown by its builder
Tom Baldwin (rear), with Curtiss (forward) to run
the engine, successfully fulfilled all requirements in a
"phenomenal" flight at Fort Myer, Virginia, on August
12, 1908.

June Bug is shown winning the Scientific American Cup for sustained public flight over a measured mile, July 4, 1908, at Hammondsport.

People gathered on the shore to watch the trial, but were disappointed when *Loon* would not take off from the water.

John McCurdy and Curtiss took the wheels off *June Bug,* equipped it with two floats or pontoons, and re-christened it *Loon.* Above, Curtiss is checking the engine before McCurdy takes *Loon* out for a test flight.

Later Curtiss took over the controls, but the results were the same. A few days later, *Loon* sank without warning because one float was waterlogged.

Silver Dart prior to the installation of the landing gear.

Silver Dart ready for its trial take-off. It was the last of the four A.E.A. aerodromes.

Alexander Graham Bell's *Cygnet II* on the ice of Baddeck
Bay, Nova Scotia, on February 22, 1909. This powered glider
never flew.

Curtiss (back to-
ward the camera)
talks to several
visitors in front of
his hangar at the
Rheims Air Meet.

The rear view of the first Gordon Bennett Cup winner, *Golden Flyer*. (Official U.S. Navy photo.)

Curtiss in flight during the Rheims Air Meet in 1909.

The Coupe d'Aviation Gordon-Bennett which Curtiss won and which crowned him champion aviator of the world.

Golden Flyer being rolled back to its hangar after winning the Gordon Bennett Cup at Rheims.

Curtiss coming in for a landing in a standard biplane (*Golden Flyer* type) on Lake Keuka during the winter of 1910.

it was supposed that the United States would be represented
by the Wright brothers. They were very popular in France.
In 1908, while Orville Wright was demonstrating the *Wright A*
to the Army, Wilbur went to France and made a series of
public exhibition flights at Hunaudièrs, Auvours (both near
Le Mans), and Pau. Some of these lasted two hours, and on
one flight he gained a record altitude of 360 feet. The American was the talk of France, the hero of the hour, and the
newspapers were filled with enthusiastic accounts of his public
exhibitions. The main purpose of Wilbur's journey to France
was accomplished when he sold the brothers' patent rights to
a French syndicate who planned to launch a European company and manufacture Wright biplanes for the commercial
market. It paid $100,000 for these rights, but under the
agreement Wilbur had to teach three Frenchmen to fly the
Wright A aeroplanes.

The refusal of the Wright brothers to participate in the
French contests prompted the Society's recommendation of
Curtiss as the sole representative of America. When the
Rheims race committee drew up the meet rules, it was specified that in certain circumstances planes might touch their
landing wheels to the ground without being disqualified. The
Wrights were furious. Everyone knew that their planes didn't
have wheels—they were launched from catapults and landed
on skids—and the famous brothers took the rule as not only
discriminatory but insulting. (The vast majority of European
aeroplanes employed wheels rather than skids.) Horrified, representatives of the Aero Club of America pleaded with the
meet officials, who agreed that the rule could be changed. But
the Wrights were angry. Deaf to apologies and appeals alike,
they flatly refused to have anything to do with the meet at
Rheims. When newspaper reporters pressed them for the
reason, Orville Wright expressed the opinion that *all* flying

machines of the future would start from tracks or special apparatus such as their catapult. He stated that the system of pneumatic wheels, used in Europe and by the A.E.A., had not proved satisfactory except in very large fields and it would probably be easier to provide small tracks than large fields. But, when especially asked by the newspapermen for their reason for not entering the Gordon Bennett race even after the rules had been amended to suit them, the Wrights went into their shell of secrecy, which meant no public flights or statements. The United States appeared to be left without representation in the Rheims meet.

Actually, Bishop had never considered his business associate, Curtiss, as a possible entrant in the affair, and he went to France in the hope of explaining away the fact that America would not participate in the Bennett Cup race. On receipt of the Aeronautic Society's cable, he promptly communicated with Curtiss, but the latter was too engrossed in the affairs of his new company to give the Rheims matter serious thought. "I'm not a professional aviator," he said, "and fear that I would stand little chance with these great flyers of Europe. Besides, I have only one machine completed, and that isn't built for great speed."

Bishop was insistent. He cabled again, urgently, sounding the call of patriotic duty, and also suggesting that it would be very good for the Herring-Curtiss Company. Curtiss knew, from his motorcycle racing days, the effect winning such an event could have on the new company's sales. Further, Bishop guaranteed to reimburse Curtiss personally for all expenses incurred in case he failed to win any of the $40,000 prize money. Bishop, however, assured him of his faith in the Curtiss machine and its pilot to carry off high honors for the United States. Rather reluctantly, Curtiss gave in.

So at the last moment Curtiss was officially named by the

Aero Club of America. This was early in July, and less than six weeks remained for him to prepare for the big contest. To fulfill his contract with the Aeronautic Society it was necessary for him to make a certain number of flights with the new machine and to teach two of its members to operate it, and since these duties kept Curtiss in New York during the greater part of July, he supervised the building of the machine for the international air meet by long-distance phone calls and telegrams.

The Morris Park location was too small for proper testing, and Curtiss asked the Society to find some suitable area in the city, otherwise he would take the craft back to Hammondsport. The group's secretary, Augustus Post, knew a land developer who owned or controlled a major portion of Hempstead Plains, a large level piece of land lying near Mineola, Long Island. After permission was granted for its use, Curtiss took the aeroplane from Morris Park to Mineola by truck and stored it in Peter McLaughlin's barn.

McLaughlin's Hotel soon became the "unofficial" headquarters of the Society. Many of the meetings were held late at night. As one of the members said, "Many is the time that I sneaked in at half past nine, under the cover of darkness, so that my neighbors wouldn't know that I was a member of such a flying organization. I am a businessman in New York, and didn't like to have anyone question my sanity. So we all kept the whole affair as secret as possible until finally the activities of the Society became so talked about that we could let our wives and neighbors know that we were the crazy ones who had been financing such an enterprise."

The first Society Herring-Curtiss biplane, which was called *Gold Bug,* mainly because the wing covering was unbleached linen with a filler, or niad cloth, which looked golden in the air. It contained most of the features of *June Bug,* but was somewhat smaller so that greater speed could be obtained. The wings were straight and uniform in width instead of tapering, as in the A.E.A. machines, and they measured 28 feet 9 inches in spread and 4½ feet in width. They were spaced 4¾ feet apart and had an area of 258 square feet. Herring suggested, from his glider experience, that instead of hinging the ailerons on as tips of the main wings, the balancing surfaces be mounted on the struts between the wings. Curtiss followed his partner's advice and thus the between-wing aileron made its first appearance.

Outriggers were placed 12 feet from the wings fore and aft, which bore an elevator forward (24 square feet), with a triangular fin between (and extending a little above) the two surfaces. The tail unit was made up of a fixed tailplane 15 feet square and a rudder 6½ feet square. Bamboo was used for the tail and rudder, while the remaining construction was of Oregon spruce, put together in sections. The wing ribs were light laminated spruce sections spaced about a foot apart. They projected beyond the rear structure of the frame and wings, and ran through tucks on top of the fabric. A wire ran through the rear framework of each surface, and was tightened over the end of each rib, thus serving to lighten the cloth.

The 4-cylinder engine developed better than 30 horsepower at 1,200 revolutions per minute. The propeller was 6 feet in diameter, with a 5-foot pitch. Control was by a wheel on a horizontal rod (turning the wheel to turn the rudder, and pushing or pulling the unit to operate the elevator) and a shoulder yoke which operated the interwing ailerons. A new simplified type of tricycle undercarriage proved to be standard for several years to come.

The members of the Society chosen to take flying lessons from Curtiss, in accordance with the terms of the sales contract, were Charles F. Willard and Alexander Williams. They flipped a coin to see who would be the first student. Williams, who won, was given ground instruction on what to do in the air. Since in the early days of aviation an aeroplane could carry only one person, flying instructions had to be given on the ground and demonstrated in the air by the instructor. Then the student went up and did the best he could alone. He also had to learn to take off and land, the two most difficult operations in flying, before he had mastered the aeroplane in straight flight. Without learning the first he couldn't leave the ground, and without mastering the second he couldn't keep out of the morgue.

Alex Williams did take off on his first flight, but soon after, he became rattled and pulled the controls back so far that he stalled the machine and crashed. While he didn't land in the morgue—he only was slightly injured—the aeroplane was badly damaged.

When the *Gold Bug* was repaired, which took almost two weeks of feverish work, Curtiss taught Willard to fly it. While giving the machine its final checks before turning it over to the Society, Curtiss decided to make an attempt to win the second leg on the *Scientific American* trophy, offered to the first person who flew 25 kilometers (15.5 miles) around a triangular course. The Aeronautical Society was very happy to lend him the *Gold Bug* for this purpose.

Under the watchful eyes of Charles M. Manly, official representative of the Aero Club of America and observer for the *Scientific American,* a triangular course was set up on Hempstead Plains measuring 1⅓ miles. It was necessary for Curtiss to circle the course twelve times to win the trophy.

At a quarter after five on the morning of July 17, Curtiss made his first flight. This was for the Cortlandt Field Bishop Prize of $250 and the President's Cup offered by the Aero Club of America to the first four Americans in 1909 who should fly one kilometer in public. It took just 2½ minutes to win this prize, and immediately afterward Curtiss started after the *Scientific American* trophy.

The flight was rather uneventful. The motor functioned perfectly, the weather was most favorable. Round and round went the *Gold Bug*, steadily down the straightways, banking steeply at the corners. On the completion of the twelfth lap, Curtiss decided to keep right on flying until his gas gave out. But on his nineteenth trip around the course, he made a turn too near the ground and a gust of wind forced him to land. The flight took 52½ minutes and covered an official distance of 24.9 miles, though the actual distance was well over 33 miles. Thus, a year and thirteen days after his first "official" flight in *June Bug*, Curtiss was awarded the second leg on the *Scientific American* trophy for his flight aboard the *Gold Bug*.

Chapter 3

COUPE INTERNATIONALE D'AVIATION

O<small>N</small> his arrival back in Hammondsport, on August 1, Curtiss found his factory staff working frantically on the finishing touches to the aeroplane which was to take part in the Gordon Bennett race.

This new machine, named *Golden Flyer,* was almost a duplicate of the *Gold Bug* except that the diameter of the wood propeller had been increased from 6 to 7 feet, making it necessary to raise the entire structure a foot higher from the ground so the blades might swing clear. The wings themselves were constructed in sections to facilitate disassembly and shipment. They had twenty-two laminated spruce ribs. Bracing was by woven cable instead of the piano wire commonly used, and the control wires were passed through bamboo tubes to prevent chafing. A new position had been found for the outriggers that supported the elevators and for the rudder control. The ailerons, however, were again operated from the struts.

The major difference between *Golden Flyer* and its predecessor was its added power. An 8-cylinder, V-shaped, water-cooled engine, rated at 50 horsepower, was built for the new aeroplane. So close was the margin of time before shipping that engine testing was limited to a single day's running on the test block. *Golden Flyer,* which was never given a flight trial, was shipped to New York on August 4 in a couple of large parcels, like oversized suitcases, and was carried for safety as personal luggage by Curtiss and his favorite mechanic, "Tod" Shriver, aboard the S.S. *Savoie.* Ward Fisher, who was the sales agent for the Curtiss motorcycle in central New York State, accompanied them on their overseas trip. Unfortunately for the three, the ocean voyage was a rather rough one and Fisher remembered that Curtiss remarked, during a period of seasickness, that he would devise a way of crossing the Atlantic by air.

Curtiss' reception in France was less than enthusiastic. While Bishop knew him very well, Gordon Bennett, the sponsor of the feature event, took one look at Curtiss and his face soured. Curtiss was a small-town mechanic and looked it. Round-faced and shy, dressed in an ill-fitting suit, awkwardly twisting in his hands the shiny visored cap, like a chauffeur's hat, that was his favored headgear, he looked more like a country bumpkin than a spectacular speed king. However, Bennett received him cordially and complimented him on his fine sportsmanship in entering the meet on such short notice. But when he learned that Curtiss' aeroplane had fitted nicely into the trunk compartment of a limousine and that his only spare equipment consisted of an extra propeller, Bennett later admitted that he muttered to Bishop, "I have grave doubts about America's chances."

With sighs of resignation, the two gentlemen packed their best and only aviator off to Rheims. Here lodging had been arranged for Curtiss and his two mechanics at the home of a Roman Catholic priest, who spoke English and had once visited the United States. After being welcomed by their host, the men hurried out to view the flying field where the races were to be held.

The three Americans from Hammondsport were flabbergasted by what they saw. Just outside the medieval city of Rheims, on a stretch of farmland known as the Bethany Plain, an elaborate layout of grandstands for over fifty thousand spectators, a restaurant to seat six thousand, hangars for the various aviators, and offices was arranged along the west side, near the Neufchâtel-Rheims road and the railroad. The race course (La Piste) was laid out in an oblong shape, 3.750 meters parallel to the grandstands and 1,250 meters in depth away from it. Thus one lap around the course was 10 kilometers or 6.2 miles. A tall, black-and-white-striped pylon was placed at each corner of La Piste.

Originally the meet had been scheduled for the month of March at Monte Carlo, and it was to have been sponsored by the French Government. Since the area available was so limited that the contestants would have been obliged to fly out over the Mediterranean Sea, most aviators did not want to fly in such a risky location. The project was therefore transferred to the ample Bethany Plain and was sponsored by champagne firms in the region. By moving the date of the meet up to the end of August, the list of prospective contestants was considerably lengthened. Curtiss would not have been able to enter in March, and Louis Paulhan did not learn to fly until June. By August most of the famous flyers in the world were on hand, eager to compete in altitude flights, distance contests, and other trials of endurance, skill, and daring.

Each type of aeroplane had a hangar assigned to it, and one hangar was reserved to house the Curtiss machine. It still looked alarmingly empty after the single American plane had been unpacked and assembled by Curtiss and his two assistants. Many of the aviators, especially the French, had been out on Bethany Plain for several days and were thoroughly acquainted with the course. In addition, many of them had ample facilities to repair damages, make changes in motors, and do all the experimental work often necessary on the eve of a race. Curtiss believed that he had a larger and better power plant than any of the Frenchmen. He soon learned, however, that Louis Blériot had taken out his smaller engine and installed an 8-cylinder of 60 horsepower.

Blériot, who had recently topped off his long list of impressive achievements by making the first flight across the English Channel, was considered the number one French aviator in the meet. The picturesque new flyer, Hubert Latham, also occupied a warm place in French hearts. Shortly after the London *Daily Mail* had announced a prize of $5,000 for the first flight across the Channel, Latham had proceeded to Calais. He started on July 19, but his motor balked when he was only 6 miles out, and he came down safely on the water. Nonchalantly smoking a cigarette, he was picked up by the destroyer detailed to follow him. He was ready to make another attempt when Blériot took off on July 25 and landed safely near Dover, England.

There were other Frenchmen at Rheims who had won flying fame since the South American Alberto Santos-Dumont, in August, 1905, flew the first heavier-than-air craft off European soil. Henri Farman, who had made exhibition flights in America, was there with his Farman biplanes; Louis Paulhan, who had already captured one of the Wright brothers' records in his two months of flying experience, was preparing to enter the events in a Voisin biplane. Though the Wrights themselves were absent, three of their machines, made in Dayton and assembled in Europe, were entered and were to be flown by Wilbur's three star students—Eugene Lefebvre, Paul Tissandier, and Comte de Lambert. Another Wright pupil, Alfred LeBlanc, had entered a Blériot. Other formidable French flyers were F. de Rue (a pseudonym used by Captain Ferdinard Ferber when flying as a civilian), Jean Gobrun, Henry Fournier, Henry Rougier, Étienne Bunau-Varilla, Georges Legagneux (all flying Voisin biplanes); Roger Sommer flying a Farman biplane; Louis Breguet in his own Breguet I biplane; and Maurice Guffroy in an R.E.P. No. 2 monoplane. Englishman George B. Cockburn had entered the meet in a Farman biplane.

After making a tour of hangars and inspecting the aeroplanes on the flying field, Curtiss thought his biplane was speedier than the other biplanes—the Wrights, Voisins, and Farmans. Santos-Dumont's *Damoiselle* and Léon Delagrange's special craft seemed to be too light to offer any serious competition in the speed events. The recent feats of Blériot and Latham indicated the monoplane type had definite points of superiority. Blériot had five of his planes at the meet, while Latham had three Antoinettes. Aviation experts were convinced that the big speed event would be a contest between these two Frenchmen, and their monoplanes.

In the few days left before the meet, Curtiss and his mechanic worked hard to finish assembling their plane. It was a demanding task, requiring more than usual care, for under the rules no replacement parts would be allowed. Once the meet began, if any vital part failed or was broken, the aeroplane would be out. That was why Blériot, Latham, and others had more than one craft at Rheims. Rainy weather also plagued the flyers prior to the opening of race week.

During one of Curtiss' infrequent trial flights, a collision was narrowly averted when, for the first time in history, three planes were in the air at the same time. Henri Demanest, in an Antoinette monoplane, approached *Golden Flyer* at right angles and at the same height. "Quick as a flash," according to the newspaper report of the incident, "Curtiss realized the danger. He elevated his plane and his machine instantly shot upward and soared safely over the Frenchman." Observers below applauded wildly. The third machine in the air was flown by Paul Tissandier.

While landing on a bumpy portion of the field Curtiss was thrown out of the machine and sprained an ankle. After that, he always tried to land back at the place where he had started, in front of his own hangar, in order to avoid a long tramp across Bethany Plain on his injured ankle.

During the time prior to the meet, while making explanations to eager Americans who could not understand why Curtiss did not fly all the time, Tod Shriver attracted attention from the French who visited the hangars because he worked in his shirt sleeves. They thought Tod picturesque because he did not wear the French workman's blouse. Shriver used to say that if he were picturesque in shirt sleeves, there were about fifty million perfectly good Americans across the Atlantic who formed the most picturesque crowd on earth. A born showman, he was an excellent workman, and the kind of man who was invaluable in getting the machine to the field on time and in top operating condition. One thing that impressed Curtiss, Shriver, and Fisher was their ability to communicate with the French people without the bridge of a common language.

Long before opening day, hotel rooms in the town were booked solid for the meet week at prices ranging up to $500. To make matters easy for the many visitors, signal flags were to be hoisted on various public buildings in the city—black meaning "no flights"; white, "flights probable"; and red, "flights on."

The opening day of La Grande Semaine d'Aviation de la Champagne (as the meet was officially called), Sunday, August 22, was disappointing. But in spite of the black flags flying in Rheims from early in the morning, the grandstands were filled with spectators, among them the President of France, Armand Fallières. The planes were ready and the flyers eager, but for most of the day flying conditions were almost impossible. All day Saturday it had rained; Sunday morning the rain let up, but the field was a quagmire. Mud stuck to the wheels of the machines on take-off and made the exhibition flights look like a combination aviation meet and potato race.

By midday, the weather improved enough for the meet to start. The first event was the French Elimination Trials for the Gordon Bennett Cup race, which was to be held on Saturday, August 28. There were twenty entries and lots were drawn for starting order, each plane being allowed a quarter of an hour to get away. Lefebvre, Blériot, and Latham won the right to represent France. Among the favorites who couldn't get off the ground were Captain Ferber (de Rue) and Maurice Guffroy.

Lefebvre won the *Tour de Piste,* the daily speed trial of one lap, in 8 minutes 58⅕ seconds, while Tissandier captured the *Prix de la Vitesse,* a three-lap speed trial. Before starting a given performance each competitor had to announce to the organizers which event he was entering, and his performance counted only for that particular event. The result was that the organizers had to devise a system of signaling from a flagstaff with yardarms. Signs of different colors and shapes, representing numbers, told the onlookers what event was being competed for, who was competing for it, whether the record had been beaten or not, whether a good or bad start or landing had been made, when a landing had been effected without accident, whether the aid of mechanic was needed, whether a competitor had touched the ground during a flight, or had incorrectly negotiated a corner tower that marked the course, as well as whether flying was probable, there was no flying, or there was about to be flying. The whole signaling system was most ingenious, and could convey any amount of miscellaneous information. For example, a white disc, a red pyramid, and a white oblong meant, "Attention! Flights are about to commence." A white disc, a white oblong, and another white disc, representing the number 171, meant that a motor breakdown had delayed the start. A white disc, a white oblong, and a red pyramid meant that the aeroplane had sustained damage to a wing. A white disc, a white oblong, and a red oblong, representing the number 179, announced that a propeller had been changed; and the arrival of the President of the Republic, a Minister, or a foreign sovereign, could be similarly conveyed by the sign staff.

As the President made ready to leave his box near the end of the first day, nine French aeroplanes took off, one by one, and all nine were in the air at once for a few short moments. This was unprecedented. The spectators gasped with amazement. To what new extravagances would this new art of flying not go?

What a contrast to the opening morning was the second day's dawn! On Monday morning all was fair and calm. Both Blériot and Curtiss flew in the daily *Tour de Piste*. The Frenchman did very well, completing the required one lap in 8 minutes, 42⅖ seconds. But Curtiss' biplane buzzed around the oblong course at an astonishing pace, touching down for a new world record of 8 minutes, 35⅗ seconds. Suddenly, unbelievably, it appeared that this one-man team from the United States might be a formidable contender.

Monday was also the day of the qualifying trials for the *Grand Prix de Champagne,* a contest to see who could fly the greatest distance around the course. One condition of this event was that competitors had to fly a reasonable distance on or before Monday to qualify for the trials on Wednesday,

Thursday, and Friday. Eighteen actually qualified, but Curtiss was not one of them. Since he had come to France especially for the Gordon Bennett Cup race, he planned to enter no other events, except the daily speed trial, until after Saturday. The French flying fans seemed to commend his caution; after all, the man had only one aeroplane while the other leading contestants had several.

Black flags were hoisted on Tuesday morning; the strong winds made flying out of the question. Very late in the day, when conditions improved, Blériot smashed Curtiss' new record by a full 31 seconds, touching down in 8 minutes, 4⅖ seconds in the daily *Tour de Piste*. Other events for the day were canceled. Curtiss did not attempt to fly at all, and spent most of his time working on *Golden Flyer*'s engine.

On Wednesday, weather conditions were better and Latham won both the *Tour de Piste* and the *Prix de la Vitesse,* but in neither did he break record time. The *Golden Flyer* made its worst time of the meet, taking 9 minutes, 31½ seconds for the 10 kilometers. To correct this, Curtiss and his crew streamlined their aeroplane as much as possible, removing every extraneous wire or strut. *Golden Flyer*'s large gas tank was removed and a smaller one installed to lessen wind resistance. Curtiss also tried a new propeller. His French competitors were highly interested in *Golden Flyer*'s wooden propeller, but were thoroughly convinced of the superiority of their metal ones. In fact, Lucien Chavière, who supplied propellers to Blériot, built one especially for the American plane. This sportsmanlike gesture touched Curtiss deeply, but after several ground tests and one air flight, he decided to continue using his own homemade wood propeller.

The feature of the day was the start of the *Grand Prix de Champagne.* Late in the afternoon, during this event, the duration record of 2 hours, 20 minutes, and 23 seconds set by Wilbur Wright at Auvours on December 31, 1908, was broken by Louis Paulhan. He stayed aloft for 2 hours, 43 minutes, and 24⅘ seconds and traversed a distance of 83 miles.

On Thursday, during which a steady and persistent rain fell, Latham traveled 96½ miles in 2 hours, 17 minutes, 21⅖ seconds, thus topping Wilbur Wright's mark of 87 miles set seven months previously at Auvours. Thursday also found Blériot winning the *Tour de Piste* in a record time of 7 minutes, 52⅘ seconds. Curtiss' time for the lap was 7 minutes, 56⅗ seconds, or 3⅘ seconds behind the winner. None of the other contestants came close to these times.

Both Blériot and Curtiss, or "Koor-tess" as the French called him, did not race on Friday. The *Tour de Piste* was won in slow time by George Cockburn. But it was Henry Farman who really captured the headlines that day. At 4:25 P.M., his biplane took off and started around the triangular course at about 30 feet. The sun went down and the dusk closed in. Men climbed the pylons and hung lanterns from their tops. Automobiles moved onto the field to train their acetylene headlights at the sky. At 7:30 P.M.—some 3 hours, 4 minutes, and 56⅖ seconds after he had taken off—the officials declared Farman winner of the *Grand Prix de Champagne* and set his distance at 112 miles. Actually he flew for ten minutes longer before he "fluttered out of the night" and landed. The official results of the *Grand Prix* were:

1. Farman (Farman biplane)—112 miles (3 h., 4 m., 56⅖ s.)
2. Latham (Antoinette monoplane)—96½ miles (2 h., 17 m., 21⅖ s.)
3. Paulhan (Voisin biplane)—83 miles (2 h., 43 m., 24⅘ s.)
4. De Lambert (Wright biplane)—72½ miles (1 h., 50 m., 59 s.)

On the evening before the Gordon Bennett Cup race, the five contenders—Blériot, Latham, and Lefebvre of France; Cockburn of England; and Curtiss of the United States—were called together before the committee and heard the rules explained. Flights for the prize could be made at any time between the hours of 10 and 5:30. Each entrant might make as many trial laps as he desired, but he must notify the judges when ready to start the official flight.

Saturday dawned hot and clear. Well before ten o'clock the enormous grandstand was packed with people to see the *pièce de résistance* of the first international flying competition. Down on the field some morning mist persisted, though it was fast being burned away by the sun.

It was assumed that no one would fly until the last of the mist was gone, but in front of the United States hangar Curtiss was seen in animated talk with his mechanic and a few Americans. At ten o'clock precisely he broke off the talk with a gesture of command. The plane was wheeled out, and he prepared to make his preliminary run.

To the spectators, it was an exciting but puzzling flight, the plane making the round of the course at an altitude of about 40 feet, but pitching and bucking as if the flyer were experimenting with his controls, an odd thing to do at such a time. Immediately upon landing, however, Curtiss signaled readiness to fly his race. He took off. If spectators thought his preliminary flight was strange, his actual race pulled their hearts into their throats.

Zooming upward from in front of the grandstand, Curtiss approached the first pylon at a height of 45 or 50 feet, leveled off, and then, as he began the turn, dived as if heading straight into the ground. The crowd gasped. But, no—completing the turn he leveled off, no more than 10 feet from the earth, a wing tip almost grazing wheat shocks in the adjacent farm field. He began to climb. Nearing the second pylon, he was again at about 50 feet. And again, going around the turn, the plane dived sickeningly. The watchers stared in horror. Obviously, something was seriously wrong. But he kept on. At the last two pylons he was again at 50 feet—and again, making both turns, came the awful plunge nearly to the ground.

Many in the stands thought him insane, but still he kept on. As he passed the grandstands, climbing toward the first pylon to begin his second round, the crowd stared in silent awe. Down on the field officials were staring, too. Ups and downs or no, the lunatic's time for the first round was under 8 minutes.

Curtiss' second round was a repetition of the first. By the time he finished, the crowd was exhausted from excitement. Around the finish line swarmed other flyers who had come out to watch him. He touched down, and his time was taken. The United States entry had finished the race, 20 kilometers nonstop, in a sensational 15 minutes (a roar of astounded cheers), 50⅗ seconds, a spectacular new world record.

Near the French hangar, Blériot, no longer smiling, stood near his big No. 22. Mechanics were working on it. Earnestly the French star conferred with them. The work continued while other flyers took off to fly their races. At noon Blériot made his preliminary flight. Landing, he conferred again with the mechanics, who started to work on the plane some more. The race went on.

Cockburn on his first lap dropped so low on a turn that he crashed into a haystack and was out of the race. Latham and Lefebvre completed their laps, but they didn't threaten the American's time.

As the afternoon wore on, the eyes of the crowd turned more and more toward Blériot, still hovering over the mechanics at his plane. It was close to five o'clock, almost the final allowable minute, when at last, to a roar from the crowd, the great Frenchman climbed into his plane to take off, Europe's only hope now for the Gordon Bennett. As soon as he was off, Cortlandt Bishop and David Wolfe Bishop, his brother, took Curtiss in their automobile to a position near the judges' stand.

Blériot flew magnificently, blazing from pylon to pylon, to complete the first round in even faster time than Curtiss had —7 minutes, 47⅘ seconds, a new record for the *Tour de Piste*. But on the second round he went wide on one turn. He recovered swiftly, but the slight loss of time made results in doubt.

Leaving Curtiss in the automobile, Bishop rushed over to the judges' stand. There he found Tod Shriver clutching his stop watch and gesticulating wildly. He had an idea one of the judges was preparing to hoist the French tricolor and announce a victory for Blériot. "Tell them we win!" he pleaded when he saw Bishop. Then the official times for the Gordon Bennett Cup race were made known:

1. Curtiss (Curtiss biplane)—15 minutes, 30¾ seconds
2. Blériot (Blériot monoplane)—15 minutes, 56½ seconds
3. Latham (Antoinette monoplane)—17 minutes, 32 seconds
4. Lefebvre (Wright biplane)—20 minutes, 47⅖ seconds

Bishop ran back to the automobile shouting triumphantly, "America wins. The judges find you have beaten Blériot's time by twenty-five and three-quarter seconds."

A crowd of hysterically excited Americans rushed over to Curtiss—Ambassador Henry White, accompanied by Mrs. Theodore Roosevelt and her daughter Ethel and her sons Quentin and Arthur, Commander F. L. Chapin, plus many other American visitors to France. Ambassador White said, "I came to see you win, and you have done it." He congratulated Curtiss in the name of the government and the people of the United States.

Overcome with embarrassment, the aviator climbed out of the automobile. But the resolute Ambassador took firm hold of his arm and said, "Why, my dear fellow, you can't run off now. I'm taking you out on the field to meet the official representatives of the Republic of France." This prospect staggered Curtiss. Searching frantically for an excuse, he muttered something about getting off a cablegram to his wife. The newspapermen assured him the news had already been flashed to the ends of the earth.

He was led protesting to the base of the tall pole in front of the main grandstand on which the victor's national colors were run up after each event. The American flag was hoisted and the band played "The Star-Spangled Banner." There followed a short ceremony during which the victor was only a little less uncomfortable than he would have been had he understood what the French officials were saying about him. Curtiss remarked later that this was the longest ten minutes of his life.

There was a reason beyond mere patriotism why the Americans felt so happy over the results. It meant that the next international race would be held in the United States, and that the best foreign machines would have to come across the ocean to make a try for the cup the following year.

The newspapers indulged in an orgy of superlatives in telling the story of that day's victory. But it's doubtful if more than a handful of people, including the flyers, understood just how Curtiss had won it. By flying early in the day he had taken advantage of the layer of cool air that still lay near the ground, and that gave his engine more power than hot air could, and his wings more lift. And the dives at the pylons, so frightening to look at, were a sort of aerial adaptation of an old motor-cycle-racing trick, a way of gunning into turns for sharp cornering under full power and at maximum speed. It was risky, and in the warm air later in the day would probably have been impossible.

The other important event of Saturday's program was the *Prix des Passengers,* which was won by Farman. With two passengers he made the circuit of *de Piste* in 10 minutes, 39 seconds, and with one passenger, 9 minutes, 52⅖ seconds. The passengers with Farman were newspaper reporters, one sitting on the other's shoulders. His single passenger was the Marquis de Polignac, president of the committee in charge of the Rheims meet. Lefebvre, who finished second, carried Herbert Ward, the world-famous sculptor.

With the contests for the two big prizes over, Sunday was earmarked for the finale of the *Prix de la Vitesse* and the daily *Tour de Piste,* plus the height competition. Ideal weather prevailed, and an exciting duel was anticipated between Blériot and Curtiss for the three-lap *Prix de la Vitesse.* Curtiss placed himself in front by completing the course in 24 minutes, 15⅖ seconds. (He had to submit to a 5 percent time penalty because he had not entered either of the two qualifying races held on the previous Sunday and Wednesday.) In the first lap, Blériot pushed his famous No. 22 to a speed of 47.85 miles per hour, but soon after starting the second one he disappeared from view below a hillock. A rush was made to the spot as soon as smoke was seen, and the machine was found to be in flames. A fuel line had broken and caught fire. Although the gas tank had exploded, Blériot was only burnt about the arms and face. Also on the last day of the meet—which could be called jinx day—Léon Delagrange's propeller flew apart in mid-air, but he was able to glide his craft safely to earth. Henri

Fourneau wrecked his aeroplane, but walked away from it; so did Louis Breguet. The official results of the *Prix de la Vitesse* were as follows:

1. Curtiss (Curtiss biplane)—26 minutes, 40⅕ seconds (this included the 5% penalty time)
2. Tissandier (Wright biplane)—28 minutes, 59 seconds
3. Lefebvre (Wright biplane)—29 minutes
4. De Lambert (Wright biplane)—29 minutes, 2 seconds
5. Latham (Antoinette monoplane)—29 minutes, 11⅖ seconds
6. Paulhan (Farman biplane)—32 minutes, 49 seconds

A world record was broken when Hubert Latham, during the *Prix d'Altitude,* mounted into the sky to the awesome and unprecedented height of 155 meters—about 508½ feet. (Latham claimed 1,200 feet, but the more conservative judges, who had no really accurate way of determining the exact height, told him that he had been up only 508½ feet.) Farman was second in the altitude event with 110 meters (361 feet), Paulhan third, and Rougier fourth.

On each day during the week attempts were to have been made for the *Prix des Aéronauts* (dirigible prize), a race over five laps of the circuit, but it was not till the last day that the *Colonel Renard* made its attempt. Its time for 50 kilometers (31 miles) was 1 hour, 19 minutes, and 49 seconds. The *Zodiac* was unable to better this time, so the *Colonel Renard,* flown by Paul Kapferer, secured the prize. Lefebvre won the *Tour de Piste* on Sunday. But Blériot was awarded the *Prix du Tour de Piste* for having the week's best time (7 minutes, 47⅘ seconds); Curtiss placed second with his 7 minutes, 56⅗ second lap on Thursday.

The total of Curtiss' winnings for the week was over $8,000. But the Gordon Bennett Cup was far and away the main event at Rheims, and Curtiss' victory made him a European celebrity overnight. The New York *Herald,* whose publisher hadn't thought too much of Curtiss as a flyer a few days before, called him "The Champion Aviator of the World—the fastest man of the earth and skies." (His mile on a motorcycle in 26⅖ seconds in 1907 had not yet been beaten by any ground machine.) Thus the star of the meet which was initiated, promoted, and financed by the champagne industry of France was a man from the leading champagne area in the United States.

There followed several elaborate ceremonies in honor of Curtiss. Possibly the most important was the dinner given by Ambassador White at the Embassy in Paris. The New York *World,* however, correctly estimated his sentiments when it said, "Curtiss fears ceremony more than he fears the most perilous flight. He was not intending to go to the dinner, but when he had been solemnly promised that no one would call upon him to speak, he came."

The Europeans at the dinner were impressed with the singular indifference with which Curtiss accepted applause, not realizing that his apparent poise was actually embarrassment. When he was back home Curtiss told his own story of the banquet: "I could eat off the gold plates all right. But when they wanted me to stand up and make a speech, I was lost. If only they would let a fellow talk sitting down it might not be so bad."

Thirty-eight aeroplanes had entered the Rheims meet. Twenty-three had been flown by twenty-two pilots, some sharing aircraft, some flying more than one. There were 87 flights of more than 3 miles, and 7 of over 62 miles, the longest being 112 miles. The best speed obtained was nearly 48 miles an hour, and the highest altitude was over 508 feet. La Grande Semaine d'Aviation was an unqualified success, both technically and financially. Some 250,000 spectators saw the world's first aviation meet. And for all its primitive aspect compared with modern-day flying, it went far toward stimulating the development of aviation. England and Germany, consistent laggards in the early days of aviation, were given a sharp prod. As a result of the Rheims meet, Germany set about building her first power-driven heavier-than-air machine.

The newspapers of Europe also devoted considerable space to the event. Because Curtiss had won with a biplane against monoplanes, many of the publications predicted the wide use of this form of craft. The New York *Herald,* Paris edition, said that the race had rehabilitated the biplane, that while the lightness and birdlike lines of the monoplane had appealed to the crowd, "the American aviator proved that the biplane not only possessed qualities of carrying weight and undoubtedly of superior stability, but that, if need be, it can develop speed equal to, if not superior to, its smaller rival."

However, *Flight Magazine,* in its September 4, 1909, issue, gave the best comparison of the types of aeroplanes when it stated:

> The Rheims meeting has not shown biplanes as a class to be pronouncedly better than monoplanes, or the other way about. The Antoinette has, perhaps, shown itself to possess more automatic fore-and-aft stability in flight than the little Blériots, that seemed to have the better speed and lift for their wing area and horsepower; the Curtiss doubtless displayed the best speed of the biplanes, and proved the quickest to launch into flight; the Farman shone for weight-carrying, length of flight and ease of alighting; the Wrights made their mark as to quickness in executing turns; the Voisins showed strength and a certain degree of automatic stability, and so forth. Thus it is good for the movement that no one machine should possess a monopoly of good points.

The Curtiss party, however, received some bad news in the midst of all their joy. On August 25—three days before the cup race—the Wright brothers had filed a patent suit against Glenn H. Curtiss and the Herring-Curtiss Company, asking injunctions in the sale and manufacture of Herring-Curtiss aeroplanes. The bill of complaint set forth that the Wrights as "the true, original, first and joint inventors of new and useful improvements in flying machines" had created an invention of "great value."

Curtiss didn't learn of the impending court action until August 30. The European newspapers gave so much coverage to the events at Rheims that they failed to carry the story. And Curtiss' associates in Hammondsport decided it was best not to notify him until after the big race. When Curtiss received the cable from Herring informing him of the possible patent litigation, he was greatly disturbed and wanted to sail for home immediately. But Bishop, who had been besieged by aviation delegates from most of the cities of Europe to have Curtiss fly at their meets, assured him that there was little to worry about, especially since his company had Herring's patents. In addition, he would build more good will for the Herring-Curtiss Company and for the United States if he would stay in Europe for a while and enter some of the really important affairs such as Royal Aero Club of Italy Meet at Brescia, scheduled for the second week in September.

Curtiss agreed to enter the Italian meet and accepted Bishop's invitation to drive him there. Shriver and Fisher went by rail with *Golden Flyer*. The ride across the Alps to Italy was a memorable one for Curtiss. He sat on the back seat with the chauffeur, and Bishop never realized that the intrepid flyer had the door of the auto open a dozen different times ready to leap for his life. Like many good drivers, he was a craven passenger.

In Italy Curtiss was received with such enthusiasm that he decided the French people were phlegmatic compared with the Italians. No flights had previously been made in that part of the country, and when the first contestants took to the air there was much excitement. Soldiers and policemen managed to confine people to the grandstand during a flight. But when a flyer nosed down for a landing, they rushed out on the field to acclaim him, oblivious of the danger. Because of this, Curtiss had to rise up quickly from an attempted landing five times during a trial flight one day. Finally he was forced down in a nearby field, outside the flying area, with an empty fuel tank.

The leading contenders were Curtiss, the Frenchmen Blériot, Guffroy, and Lefebvre, and the Italians Lieutenant A. Calderara, Mario Faccioli, Umberto Cagna, Alessandro Anzani, and Guido Moncher. In the major event, the *Grand Prix de Brescia,* Curtiss had little trouble winning the 100 kilometers (ten laps of the airfield) race, mainly because Blériot was handicapped by his burnt arm, which was still in bandages.

Curtiss also won the Passenger Prize, given to the aviator who carried a passenger around one lap of the field in the best time. His passenger was Gabriele d'Annunzio, the celebrated Italian poet, author, and soldier. A board was wired to the top of the lower wing, and Italy's first flying passenger clung precariously to the struts and wires. The crowd below shouted and waved ecstatically as the pilot landed the *Golden Flyer* near the grandstand. D'Annunzio jumped from his perch and declared enthusiastically, "Until now I have never really lived! Life on earth is a creeping, crawling business. It is in the air that one feels the glory of being a man and of conquering the elements. There is the exquisite smoothness of motion and the joy of gliding through space. It is wonderful! Can I not express it in poetry? I might try."

And he did some time later. But enterprising Tod Shriver, a man of the moment, grabbed the narrow board on which d'Annunzio had perched, chopped it up, and auctioned off the pieces. D'Annunzio later learned to fly and became one of Italy's "aces" during World War I.

On his return to Paris, Curtiss received a personal invitation from the Kaiser to visit Germany. Learning that a temporary injunction had been issued against him and the Herring-Curtiss Company, he embarked immediately for America, with a feeling of distaste for the financial difficulties ahead. He was greeted at the dock by an enthusiastic group of admirers. Delegates from the Aero Club of America and other organizations showered him with congratulations; dinners and luncheons in his honor kept him busy for a few days. Although he received invitations from other cities, and protests from the members of the Aero Club against his short stay in New York, Curtiss left for Hammondsport as soon as he could.

Here the real celebration began, the one which Curtiss liked best of all. He found many people waiting for him at Bath, at the junction of the small branch railroad to Hammondsport. Despite the driving rain which had arrived just in time to spoil an elaborate fireworks display, the crowd escorted him to the special train chartered to take him home.

In Hammondsport the "champion aviator of the world" was led from the train to a coach of honor with a twenty-manpower team ready to draw the vehicle up the hill to the Curtiss factory. As it moved slowly along, Curtiss' friends rushed up to shake hands and express their pride in him. Skyrockets fired from under umbrellas lit the way. The citizens of Hammondsport had worked around the clock to give their local hero as warm a welcome as Dayton earlier in the year had given the Wrights.

The coach passed through an especially made triumphal

arch in front of the factory, and Curtiss was led inside the plant's largest room, which had been cleared and decorated for the occasion. While no formal program had been planned, Judge Monroe C. Wheeler, a long-time friend, delivered an impressive oration. Then, after several cries of "Speech, speech!" Curtiss said rather shyly, "Ladies and gentlemen, I'm back from France. Had a very nice time. Had a whole lot of luck and a little success. As you know, I just had a common school education and I didn't learn any words big enough to show you my appreciation of my welcome home."

The biggest welcome of all came in the house on the hill. A score of times in the past year Mrs. Curtiss had felt her heart sink when she saw him flying. Now, however, her husband was home with the world's most important cup in aviation, several thousand dollars, and a bagful of souvenirs for their friends.

When Curtiss left Hammondsport for France, Lena Curtiss had gone with him. She accompanied him to Mineola the day before he left on the steamer, to test *Gold Bug* just once more. They walked side by side out to the Hempstead Plain, he in his silent manner and she just as quiet. But as they trudged along she kept her hand thrust into his inside his coat pocket. When he stepped into the aeroplane, she gave his shoulder one little pat and said, "Be careful."

The next morning when he boarded the steamer, there was another little pat on the shoulder and again she whispered, "Be careful." There were no tears, no impulsive embraces, no impassioned adieus. She wasn't that sort of woman. Only the expression in her eyes as they followed her husband up the gangplank showed how deeply she felt.

"I should think you would want to go with your husband," said an acquaintance as the ship steamed away down the harbor.

"I would very much like to go," she answered, "but I want to help him and I can best do that by not going. He would like me to go just as much as I would like it, but with the new machine and the short time he has to get ready for the races, he'll be very, very busy, and I know that I could not avoid being a hindrance. So I'm not going."

Chapter 4

THE AEROPLANE GOES TO COURT

WHILE Curtiss was in Europe, members of the Aeronautical Society of New York had decided to form the Aeronautical Exhibition Company to put on flying exhibitions around the country. Having purchased the first commercial aeroplane in this country, *Gold Bug,* they saw no reason why they shouldn't capitalize on their property. But on August 16, 1909, the Society received a court order restraining it from exhibiting *Gold Bug* and requiring it to reimburse the Wright brothers for any financial losses incurred because of exhibitions already held.

Nine days later similar papers were served on Mrs. Curtiss and L. D. Masson, secretary of the Herring-Curtiss Company. Judge Wheeler, as counsel for the firm, immediately issued the following statement to the press:

> These suits will be defended, and it will be the policy of the defense to disprove all claims of infringement by showing that many of the infringements alleged were fully covered by patents taken out by Mr. Herring and his associates in the Curtiss-Herring Company before the Wrights applied for patents. While the plaintiffs in the case are without doubt acting in good faith in their allegations, the records of the patent

116

office, which will be produced by the defense, will easily and satisfactorily adjust what at first was regarded by the public as a stupendous litigation.

It was Wheeler's plan to base his entire defense on the patents Herring claimed he held. Unfortunately, since Curtiss' return, the Herring-Curtiss Company was a house divided, with Herring assuming an aggrieved attitude. He deeply resented Curtiss' conduct in "arbitrarily" withholding some of the money collected from the Aeronautical Society in payment for *Gold Bug*. Of the total sum of $5,000 plus the $150 paid for repairs to the machine, Curtiss had only deposited $3,000 in the company's treasury. To him this seemed a "fair amount" since he had delivered *Gold Bug* and done all the instruction and exhibition work with it. In addition, the engine used in the aeroplane had been built by his firm prior to the formation of the Herring-Curtiss Company.

To further aggravate the hostility between the two men, Herring, without informing Curtiss, had contracted with Wanamaker's Department Store in New York City to exhibit *Golden Flyer* for four months for $4,000. This amount, plus all Curtiss' European prize monies and any further money he might earn in exhibition or prize flights, should, according to Herring, be a part of the corporation's assets. Curtiss, on the other hand, insisted his position was that of demonstrator and public relations man for the firm and, as such, he was fully entitled to his salary plus any prize money he should win. Curtiss planned to become a professional aviator and take full advantage of his popularity. When word of his success at Rheims had reached the United States, Curtiss was flooded with cablegrams and letters. Apparently thousands of people wanted to see him fly, dozens of promoters wanted to exploit him, and hundreds of ambitious young men wanted to learn to fly aeroplanes. Two exhibition contracts had been signed while he was still in Europe.

When Herring continued to press his view, Curtiss lost his temper and suggested that Herring should have the privilege of risking his neck for like gains. He added, "What the hell have you done for the company?"

Curtiss' question was valid. What had Herring done? While he had offered a great many ideas, few were tried out, and none—except the intrawing ailerons—had proved of value. The factory staff, accustomed to taking orders from Curtiss, often resented Herring's suggestions. Although a controlling interest in the firm had been issued to Herring, principally in payment for his patents, he had never turned them over to the company. These patents included features it was expected he would utilize in the machine he was to deliver to the U.S. Army for $50,000. But, wishing to avoid involvement in the forthcoming patent litigations, the Army revoked its contract with the Herring-Curtiss Company in late September.

With the company in a mess, both financially and legally, Judge Wheeler requested that Herring turn his patents over to him so that he could study them carefully before the impending patent case. When Herring refused, action was brought in the State Supreme Court to compel him to turn over his patents and other property in the company, and an injunction was obtained to restrain him from disposing of any of his stock. When notice of the action was served on him at a directors' meeting, he and his lawyer disappeared.

With the entire village tracking down clues to what the Hammondsport *Herald* called a "sensational getaway," the story was pieced together. Young Rumsey Wheeler was hired at Bath by an unknown third person, who obviously did not know his driver was Judge Wheeler's son, to drive to the Hammondsport Hotel and pick up a stranger, evidently Herring's attorney. Then the young man was directed to proceed slowly down the west side of the lake. There a large man—who was undoubtedly Herring—popped up out of the bushes. At this point the driver decided he was involved with a sinister band of criminals and, in a panic, dumped the two by the roadside while he fled back to Bath. The two stranded men apparently walked the eight miles to the Bath railroad station and took the early morning train to New York City.

Locally, of course, Herring was cast in the role of villain, especially after the papers reported that he had gone into the enemy's camp and given testimony in support of the Wrights' claims. It was generally conceded, though, that "G.H. should have had better sense than to accept him as a partner." Certainly Curtiss realized what a grievous mistake he had made that spring and recognized how feeble were the weapons with which he had armed himself to combat the Wrights' patent suit.

Curtiss turned to the company directors for help, particularly his friends Captain Tom Baldwin and Judge Wheeler. Wheeler found a way out, for the time being at least, by having the temporary restraint order lifted so that Curtiss could proceed unhampered with his flying. Late in the month of October, the court ruled that Herring must turn over his alleged patents to the company, but when he complied with the order and the papers were carefully examined, they turned out to be merely old patent *applications* dating back to 1895, none of which had ever been allowed. Thus, as a last resort, an involuntary petition of bankruptcy was filed by the directors. In the course of a personal letter to the editor of *Aero Magazine* Curtiss stated:

> The newspapers, as usual, have things somewhat mixed. Our business is in the hands of a receiver, but is not shut

down. Our trouble is due to our connection with Mr. Herring, who organized the company, but did not put up any money or goods. He, however, acquired a controlling interest, and threatened to assume control of the business last fall. In view of this, no money could be raised to carry on the business, and, together with the undesirable publicity from the injunctions, we were unable to meet our bills, and were forced into the hands of a receiver.

As soon as the bankruptcy petition was filed, Herring brought a suit against Curtiss and the other directors. The legal verbiage stated that "because of his difficulty of adjusting his attitude of mind to the requirements of a corporate business which was not solely his own, as his old company had been," Curtiss had been guilty of a "breach of his fiduciary duties" toward Herring as a stockholder.

Originally the suit also named Cortlandt Bishop, who in his answer united with the plaintiff, whereupon the charges against him were withdrawn. This came about because of a serious argument between Curtiss and Bishop; the latter felt even more bitter about Curtiss' "thickheaded" determination to enter professional flying than he did about Curtiss' arbitrary attitude on the subject of his corporate fiduciary duties to the various stockholders who had contributed money to the venture. He felt, too, that it was unethical of Curtiss not to stick to his bargain. Accordingly, he aligned the said stockholders, who were himself and his brother, David, on the side of Herring.

After leaving Hammondsport, Herring associated himself with W. Starling Burgess, a successful Marblehead (Massachusetts) yacht builder who wished to enter the aviation business. The first Burgess Company aeroplane appeared on February 8, 1910, and it closely resembled the type originated by Curtiss, but with skids in place of wheels and without ailerons. To obtain lateral stability without infringing the

Wright system of control, Herring mounted six (later eight) fixed triangular fins, each about 3 feet high, on top of the upper wing. Essentially, this was a modification of the Voisin principle. The Voisins in France were the only aeroplane builders in the world who had adopted a method of balance that could not possibly be construed as an infringement. They simply built their huge "flyers" like cellular box kites with closed or boxed ends. As they rocked in ordinary air currents, these vertical surfaces supplied the increase or decrease of wind resistance necessary to maintain lateral balance. The Voisin brothers once stated that their principles of control were free to all for "the good of aviation," and thus Herring did not have to worry about infringement. His stay at the Burgress Company, however, was a very brief one.

Herring's complaint against Glenn Curtiss was dismissed when it came to trial in the lower court, but the case was appealed and it dragged on through the courts until long after the Wright patent litigation, which had precipitated the situation, was settled. In fact, a final determination in the Herring-Curtiss case was never made.

In November of 1909 the Wright Company was organized with a capitalization of one million dollars, turning Curtiss' battle from one with two men of his own financial status into a highly professional contest against a seemingly invincible group—one not only financially and politically powerful but composed of men of immense public influence and social prestige. On the board of directors, together with Orville and Wilbur Wright, were Frederick A. Alger, August Belmont, Edward J. Berwind, Robert J. Collier, Andrew Freedman, Howard Gould, Morton F. Plant, Allan A. Ryan, Theodore P. Shonts, and Cornelius Vanderbilt. The Wright brothers received stock and cash for all rights to their patents in the United States and future royalties of 10 percent on all aeroplanes sold. The company had its administrative office in New York City and its factory in Dayton, Ohio.

The new company met with almost immediate defeat when Judge T. P. Coman of Utica, New York, on December 6, vacated the original injunction against Curtiss and the Herring-Curtiss Company on the grounds that the terms, upon examination, were inconclusive and indefinite.

The rejoicing in the Curtiss camp was short-lived. On January 3, 1910, the first opinion in the history of jurisprudence directly involving the aeroplane was issued by Judge John R. Hazel of the United States Circuit Court at Buffalo, New York. According to his ruling, the Herring-Curtiss Company was restrained from the manufacture and sale of aeroplanes infringing on patents "for improvements in a flying machine granted May 22, 1906, to Orville and Wilbur Wright and subsequently assigned to the Wright Company."

On May 30, 1899, Wilbur Wright had written the Smithsonian Institution requesting such pamphlets and references as would aid him in his search for knowledge about manned flight. Largely because Dr. Langley was then head of the Smithsonian and had been studying the literature of flight and experimenting with his large unmanned models of aerocraft, the Institution was able to recommend such authoritative books as Octave Chanute's *Progress in Flying Machines* and James Means' *Aeronautical Annuals,* and to send several pamphlets reprinted from the writings of Lilienthal, Mouillard, Montgomery, and other pioneers, including Langley himself. From the material received, the brothers started to build gliders.

Having been successful with gliders and anticipating similar success with their power aeroplane, the Wright brothers filed their first application for a United States patent on March 23, 1903, while their first *Wright Flyer* was still under construction. In due time their patent attorney, H. A. Toulmin of Dayton, received formal notice that the patent examiners had rejected the application because it covered a device that was "inoperative." If the machine did prove operative, they could then reapply.

Even after their December flight, they could not get all the patents they requested. The examiners claimed the requests were too "all inclusive" and covered a much wider range of principles than those established in their application. Toulmin warned them of the danger of allowing their machines to become public property before their patent rights were adequately covered, and so the brothers became the mysterious hermits of the early aero age. Thanks to some Congressional help, they obtained patents on what was believed to be a "foolproof" combination of aeroplane design specifications in 1906. Eighteen claims from their original March 23, 1903, patent application, which had been too "all inclusive" for three years, were suddenly allowed with the issuance of Patent No. 821,393.

Toulmin succinctly phrased the reason for the granting of the patent: "Although men have been experimenting since 67 A.D., the Wright brothers discovered the secret whereby aeroplanes, or sustaining surfaces, could be steered and controlled through the air."

Nearly all of the early aviation pioneers, including the Wright brothers, had discovered that by increasing the lift on one side of the plane and decreasing it on the other, simultaneously using the rudder at the rear, they could control the balance of the machine and keep it flying safely even in cross winds or when making turns. But the Wright patent was so broadly and loosely worded that it could be interpreted to refer to any method of providing lateral stability by using the rear rudder in conjunction with the balancing surfaces. Apparently the Wrights were not sure just what they had claimed.

On August 16, 1908, Orville wrote to Wilbur in France: "If you have a copy of our American patent I wish you would look it over and give me your opinion of the claims that cover the Curtiss machine; i.e., one using separate pieces on the ends of the wings that can be adjusted. I think Claim 14 was intended to cover this point."

The weight of the brothers' legal attack was directed against the aileron method of providing lateral stability. First used in the United States by the Aerial Experiment Association at the suggestion of Dr. Bell, the supplementary surfaces were hinged to the tips of the wings. The aileron patent was filed in the name of the A.E.A. by its trustee and each of the members had the right to use it. The A.E.A. patent was ultimately granted on December 5, 1911, despite the Wright patent of 1906 and the prior use of ailerons by Esnault-Peltérie in 1904 and by Blériot in 1907. (Two other aeroplane patents of a similar nature, held in the name of Casey Baldwin and Dr. Bell, were later sold to Curtiss for a token sum.) Beginning with *Gold Bug,* Curtiss located the ailerons between the main wings, first attaching them to two of the forward struts, then to two of the rear struts. Today the ailerons are universally placed at the trailing edge of the wings.

It was the claim of Curtiss and other so-called "infringers" that the aileron differed radically from the wing-warping method, since when the wings were warped, or bent, the rudder had to be employed simultaneously, while the ailerons and the rudder were not interdependent. It was the question of this link between the two parts of an aeroplane which formed the crux of the bitter controversy and legal battle.

In addition, the defendants argued that the aileron system lent greater strength to the aeroplane, since a wing that could be warped was necessarily weaker structurally. Blériot, for example, had used the wing-warping method in his earliest machines, but had discarded it to assure greater wing strength. The Aerial Experiment Association had considered using wing-warping, but had decided against it because they were convinced that hinged supplementary surfaces would offer a more dependable means of obtaining lateral stability and control.

The Curtiss factory at Hammondsport tried to discover a substitute for the aileron. Idea after idea received a fair and unprejudiced trial. A miniature machine with a control system similar to Langley's, with the wings set at a dihedral angle, was built. In flight, its wings swept backward and rotated around a vertical shaft mounted on ball bearings. It resembled a monstrous butterfly. Dr. Bell's original idea of a vertical fin set over the center of the upper wing was tried, as well as a small vertical plane surface attached to the rear spar at the extremity of each wing. A pair of tiny dihedral wings was placed about the upper wing with a lever to give them a slight rotary motion, and the elevators were divided so that they worked separately on either side of a wide tail.

A friendly group of aerial designers cooperated in the work. Among them was Alexander Pfitzner, who had helped Curtiss with the engine for the Army's first dirigible. He built one of the first successful American monoplanes, a low-wing machine similar to the Curtiss biplane, but very different from the European monoplanes. He maintained lateral equilibrium by means of sliding panels at the ends of the wings. They were so adjusted that one pulled in as the other thrust out to increase or decrease the wing surface for banking. Six times he crashed in trial flights. On January 12, 1910, he made a successful flight, and announced that anyone was free to copy his invention.

Experiments were also being carried on elsewhere. In France Louis Paulhan had the stabilizing surfaces which ordinarily hung from the rear of the upper wings removed from his Farman machine, and installed a stabilizing device of his own in the Farmans and two Blériots he brought to America for exhibition flights. But Paulhan's foresight went for nought. He was served with an injunction upon landing, allowed to fly only under a high bond, and on February 29, 1910, was restrained from any further flights in this country. His contract with the promoter of his flights, rumored to be for $24,000 a month, had to go by default.

The progress of aviation appeared to be completely stymied. After August 16, 1909, whatever anyone did required plenty of courage. Nor was this condition limited to the United States. The Wright brothers had filed patent claims in most of the civilized countries of the world, and their company was prepared to prosecute infringement anywhere on the face of the earth.

Typically, the press seemed to be more interested in the patent dispute than in the progress of aviation. Newspapers which had refused to devote space to Curtiss and Wright flights in the past gave front-page coverage to their legal battles. The patent dispute received broad coverage in Europe, too. For instance, the New Work *World* for March 6, 1910, published this item as a cable dispatch from Paris:

> There seems to be much indignation in France about the attitude of Wilbur and Orville Wright over their patents. Some of the adverse opinion is real, some manufactured. On the other hand there is much public sentiment in the Wright's favor. This is voiced in *La Liberté,* an evening newspaper, which says:
>
> "The Wrights ask only for royalty which certainly is due them. They have a perfect right to protect their patents. Sympathy should go out to them as inventors and pioneers, not as mere chauffeurs or mechanicians who learn to pilot aeroplanes."

(The distinction probably goes back to a remark made by Orville Wright that "We are no mechanics, we are scientists.")

One thing certainly could be said for the Wrights: their sense of abuse was sincere. They felt that they alone had brought about the age of flight, and let anyone beware who sought to encroach upon their financial rewards. They looked on flyers of aeroplanes other than theirs as chiselers, who by using bootleg machines sought to avoid the payment of license fees justly due them. The brothers were extremely successful in arousing widespread public sympathy. Of course, one of the first things the new Wright Company did was to hire two former newspapermen to act as intermediaries between Wilbur and Orville and the press. It was their task to make sure that the Wrights' side of the patent dispute was thoroughly covered in the newspapers and that one of the brothers was quoted on all important aviation events. This was a major departure from a 1907 statement by Wilbur Wright: "We do not need newspapers to tell us of our successes, for we, and those whom we desire, know we have accomplished all we claim."

The nation's press seemed evenly divided on the Curtiss-Wright issue. Most Eastern and Southern newspapers were in the Wright camp, while those in the Midwest and Far West sided with Curtiss against the giant "Wall Street Air-Trust." Several injustices were done to Curtiss in some press reports of Judge Hazel's decision. Hastily reviewing the case, one news agency circulated an article stating that the court found Curtiss had copied the Wrights' system of control, while another asserted Curtiss had not equipped his aeroplanes with ailerons until after he had seen the Wright flights. This was a gratuitous and malicious invention. The court decision, far from suggesting that Curtiss had copied the Wrights, stated that when an already broad claim is liberally construed an infringement is established. Prior to the A.E.A. public flights made at Hammondsport in March and April, 1908, neither of the Wright Brothers had made a flight in considerably more than two years. Nor did they make their first *public* flights in the United States until several months after Curtiss' demonstration, in which an aileron system had been used. The irony of the whole situation is that, of all the A.E.A. members, Curtiss had shown the least interest in Dr. Bell's proposal of the aileron.

The major complaint of "air" scientists was that such a highly technical case had been handled by a nontechnical court. Judge Hazel admitted that he had never seen an aeroplane and knew very "little" about the theory of flight. He based his full decision, as a judge should, entirely on the evidence presented in court. Actually, the decision was very brief and afforded little satisfaction to those interested in what was a very complicated case. It simply stated that the Wright patent was a valid one, and continued: " 'That the third claim, when liberally constructed, has been infringed' and 'that during some part of their flight defendants' machines used the rudder synchronously with the wings so that by their joint action lost balance may be restored, etc.' "

The interpolation of the three words "when liberally constructed" seemed to leave the case, so far as the moral issues were concerned, exactly where it started. As for the decision on the use of the rudder, men with a technical knowledge of the subject held that the court seemed to have failed to take into account the marked difference between the use of the rudder of necessity and its use as a matter of expediency. For example: a bicycle is balanced by steering of necessity; a sailboat may be righted by steering as a matter of expediency, though the same end would be served, and perhaps as a rule more quickly, by easing off the sheet. These points, however, involved technical questions that for years had puzzled men closely in touch with aviation, including Octave Chanute, who was considered the senior statesman of aviation. In an interview with a Chicago *Daily News* reporter, he stated:

Wilbur and Orville Wright are entitled to a reward for their efforts, that is to say, for the things they actually performed. I know that they thought, at the end of the year 1908, that they were so far ahead of the rest of the world in aviation that they could not be caught up with for from three to five years. Suddenly they discovered that their world's records for speed, duration, distance, altitude, and carrying capacity in the air were not so far in advance that they could not be duplicated or surpassed.

Now, as to the wing-warping patent, under which they claim damages from others for alleged infringement, this is not absolutely original. On the contrary, many inventors have worked on it, from the time of Leonardo da Vinci. Two or three have actually accomplished short glides with that basic warping idea embodied in their machines. Several of the ideas were patented, but I believe the patents have now expired.

Mouillard, a Frenchman, in 1896, tested his glider near Cairo, Egypt. He found at first that his machine was not big enough, and he altered and enlarged it accordingly. He made one successful glide, using the warping wings principle as a basis, but he suffered two consecutive strokes of apoplexy shortly afterward, and was unable to carry on his work. I obtained a U. S. Patent for him covering his warped wing principle in 1897.

When the Wrights wanted to start, they wrote to me that they had read my book on gliding and asked if I would permit them to use the plans of my biplane. They said that they did not desire to enter aeronautics for financial reward but for pleasure or sport. Indeed, it was only a year ago they felt almost the same way about it. Instead of hunting or fishing or playing some game during the summer, as other men do, the Wrights took their pleasure in working on gliders.

I turned over all my data which included a copy of the Mouillard patent and information given to me by Dr. Langley and his young engineers Manly, Herring and Huffaker, and made them free of it. I was glad that someone wanted to continue the work, which, because of my lack of mechanical ability, I had been compelled to leave off.

There is money enough to be made in aviation, I think, without lawsuits. But regardless of the merits of the controversy, which must now be left to the higher courts for adjudication, it does seem to me as if it was just a little bit too early in the game for the Wrights to shut off experiments—which are perhaps best carried out by public competition—in the way they have tried to do.

The German courts ruled out the Wright patent claims in that country on the grounds that Octave Chanute, in a lecture at a Berlin University prior to 1906, detailed fully the principle of warping the wings for control of a glider. Whether the Wright brothers told him about this method or whether he had researched it on his own, the disclosure of one of the main features of the Wright patent was sufficient to invalidate the entire thing under a peculiar provision of German patent law which stated that the disclosure of an invention by the inventor, or by anyone else who had knowledge of it, before the application for a patent was filed, was sufficient to render the patent void. Likewise, Curtiss' German patent claim was invalided by the fact that several French aeroplanes used a similar aileron system prior to 1908.

Upon returning from Rheims, Curtiss had seemed deeply disturbed and even alarmed by the prospect of a patent litigation, but after Judge Hazel's ruling, he became strangely unconcerned. He seemed actually to relish the thought of a long court battle with the Wrights and showed amazing resourcefulness in helping Judge Wheeler, his legal counsel, contrive evidence. On January 10 he issued this statement on the aileron to the Associated Press at Los Angeles:

> In the arguments of their lawyers the Wrights proved theoretically to Judge Hazel in the Federal Court at Buffalo that my machines depend on the vertical rudder to maintain equilibrium. I will demonstrate by actual flight that they do not. That will end the action for injunction, for the Wrights' patents hinge on what is called the warping surface.
>
> Their machines have to depend on the vertical rudder to help them maintain their balance. The warping surface of the wings gives the machines a turning tendency which the rudder has to overcome.
>
> The rudders on the Curtiss machines have no such function. This demonstration will prove what I say. We are going to take the decision of the judges before the courts.

To back up his contention, Curtiss made a flight before a dozen or more newspapermen with the rudder tied and sealed, but he was optimistic if he thought such a demonstration would end the suit. While the case was under appeal from court to court, Curtiss was able to continue manufacturing and flying only by posting heavy bonds, which would be forfeited if the Wright Company won the suits and succeeded in wiping out competition by law.

Despite the litigation and receivership, business was fairly good at the plant. Motorcycle sales continued to be a source of revenue even though Curtiss had done little to publicize them since 1907. In January, 1910, the Paris agent of Wyckoff, Church & Partridge sent an order for a *Golden Flyer* type of machine, the model that was soon to become known as the Curtiss standard biplane, for F. L. DeRiemsdyke, a Dutchman who had attended the Rheims meet. It was the first Curtiss, as well as the first American, aeroplane sold to an individual. Another order for a machine for individual use was placed with Curtiss in February by Clifford B. Harmon, a New York City real estate millionaire. Orders were also received from all over the United States and Europe for an engine similar to the one employed in *Golden Flyer*. Curtiss still maintained his cash-with-order policy.

The manufacture of aeroplanes in 1910 was not a highly profitable business. Production expenses were high because each individual part had to be fabricated. Even the wire bracing and turnbuckles had to be made in the plant. Since there were few, if any, blueprints, the factory mechanics generally made what they thought would best do the job, and then named the part. For this reason, no two aeroplanes were exactly the same.

Free flight instruction was also included in the purchase price of the aeroplane, which was usually between $4,000 and $5,000. Even so, the machines were sold at a loss, since the total cost per plane was generally between $8,000 and $10,-000. In the early years most of the machines were sold at the expense of other departments of the Curtiss factory in the hope of a larger future business based on volume production.

Judge Wheeler suggested that one possible way of bringing sentiment to bear on the tangled patent situation would be to show the aeroplane to the American people. By the end of 1909, less than one percent of them had even seen a flying machine. With this in mind, Curtiss became aviation's first *consistent* promoter and chief salesman of commercial flying. To help him publicize his air shows and act as press relations agent, he hired Jerome S. Fanciulli, a former Washington reporter.

Curtiss, of course, had some experience with exhibitions. After winning at Rheims, he had agreed to exhibit his flying ability at the Hudson-Fulton Tercentenary Celebration in New

York during the last week in September, 1909, and to do the same at the St. Louis Centennial the same year.

The Wright brothers had also agreed to participate for the first time in public exhibitions in the United States. Wilbur, of course, had taken part in several exhibition flights in France during 1908 and had even won some cash prizes. Following the advice of their press advisers, they signed a contract to take part in the Hudson-Fulton Celebration.

The celebration committee, eager to introduce as many novel ideas as possible, hoped the Wrights and Curtiss would make flights over the harbor and around New York City. As a grand finale it was proposed that an aeroplane accompany the naval parade up the Hudson River. They already had replicas of Hendrick Hudson's *Half Moon* and Robert Fulton's *Clermont,* and they wanted an aeroplane, and perhaps an airship, traversing the air above them.

Although most people in the United States' largest city had never seen an aeroplane, they believed that flying had reached the point where a man could ascend into the sky at will regardless of the weather. Unfortunately, the fall of 1909 was one of the windiest in the history of the New York Weather Bureau. Neither the Wrights nor Curtiss would attempt to fly in high winds, and Curtiss, moreover, had a contract to fly in St. Louis on October 4. The public grew bored and disenchanted waiting. Just a short flight up the river and a swing around the Statue of Liberty, the Tercentenary committee pleaded, and everyone would be happy.

America's three must famous aviators were encamped on Governors Island. They met on one or two occasions, and spoke briefly but not about aviation or the patent situation. Curtiss took several short flights on the island, and because of the machine's poor performance, he decided to call Hammondsport, hoping Henry Kleckler could come down by train and

put the aeroplane in flying shape. But the long-distance operator reported that everybody from the plant had gone to the
State Fair and would be away for the rest of the week. Even
his wife had gone along. Afterward Curtiss said, reproachfully,
"It looks like somebody would've stayed at home."

Next day, September 29, he decided to leave for Hammondsport, while Fanciulli told the press that after making a flight
around the Statue of Liberty at dawn, Curtiss had packed up
Golden Flyer and left to fulfill his St. Louis engagement. The
reporters were furious, and felt that Curtiss had wronged them
grievously. Two days later, the winds diminished considerably
and Orville Wright made a rather sensational flight up the
Hudson from Governors Island to Grant's Tomb and back.
It was the first flight viewed by the residents of the City of
New York and the Wrights were the heroes of the day.

After a successful exhibition at St. Louis, Curtiss made two
flights in Chicago that proved most popular. As a result he
decided to form a flying exhibition team, consisting at first of
only two machines and two pilots. Charles Willard, who was
Curtiss' first student and whose flying career had stopped when
the Wright brothers enjoined the Aeronautical Society, flew
Gold Bug, and the "boss" flew a duplicate of *Golden Flyer.*
Shortly, the team was joined by others. Jack McCurdy returned from Canada to become a member. J. C. (Bud) Mars
(Aeronautical Society trained pilot), Charles Hamilton (a
former aeronaut), and Eugene Ely (a self-taught flyer from
Iowa) rounded out the group that toured the United States
during the early part of 1910. Some of the exhibitions were
failures, and some of the promoters were more interested in
their own pocketbooks than in fulfilling the terms of their
agreement with the flyers. They failed to provide fields large
enough or smooth and free from obstructions. They often
expected the aviators to take off from the center of a half-

mile race track or from the town's baseball park, surrounded by grandstands, high fences, and horse barns. After Willard cracked up in the rough enclosure at Memphis, and Mars was forced to land on top of a parked automobile in Little Rock, Curtiss refused to permit his flyers to take part in an exhibition unless suitable fields were provided.

Curtiss, because of his success in France and also because he had made the world's fastest mile on the ground, was the major drawing card at the exhibitions. He undertook most of the specialty flying himself—circular flights, quick starts, "high" altitudes, and so on. On a couple of occasions, Curtiss even competed with auto racers. While this stunt was a great crowd-pleaser, the aeroplane was no match for the automobile. But none of Curtiss' exhibition flyers did any actual stunt flying. He wanted to win people over to the aeroplane, not to frighten them off with broken necks and wrecked planes.

Some American "sportsmen" objected to exhibition flights and looked to Cortlandt Bishop, who was still president of the Aero Club and vice president of the Fedération Aéronautique Internationale, "to check the aerial showmen." This champion of all worthwhile causes leaped into the fray. Aviation was a gentleman's sport and he wanted to keep it so.

Bishop told the editor of *Aero Magazine:*

Soon, we shall have the best people in the world interested in flying machines. But, we, the leaders of the aero-age, must make every effort to combat the ruthless destruction of a great enterprise and a delightful sport through an excess of promotional vigor. The ambition to make money in the show business has reached the stage where the average flying machine constructor builds more for the road than for the air. In several instances builders have purchased a show tent before they knew their machine would fly, and engaged a press agent before procuring a motor.

Bishop deeply resented the aviation-stock-promotion and get-rich schemes which were now flooding the market, and he pointed out that one New York City firm was claiming to be capitalized at fifty million dollars. The indignation of the "sports-loving" men of the "aero age" raged on, and they were supported by the Wright brothers, who also felt that exhibition flying was a menace—or at least so said their press agents. Nevertheless, in 1910, the Wright Company formed an exhibition team headed by Roy Knabenshue, a former aeronaut associated with Captain Tom Baldwin.

In spite of the vocal opposition of the "blue bloods of aviation" and the Wrights, almost every American city of any size felt impelled in the winter and spring of 1909-10 to stage an air meet of some sort. It remained for Los Angeles to hold an international-style air meet during January, 1910.

While the Wright brothers were not represented, Louis Paulhan brought two Blériots and two Farman aeroplanes from France, and Curtiss had three machines at Los Angeles. There were also some fairly successful aeroplanes built by enterprising experimenters, including a multiplane that flew with no less than five wings. But, as far as the spectators were concerned, it was a two-man affair. They applauded almost every flight of Paulhan and Curtiss during the eight-day event.

On opening day, January 12, Curtiss thrilled the crowd by flying at a speed of 55.2 miles an hour, breaking Louis Blériot's record set at Rheims. He also captured the passenger-carrying record, which had been Wilbur Wright's since October 10, 1908, when Curtiss carried J. N. Painleve 55 kilometers (almost 35 miles) in 1 hour, 9 minutes, and 45⅗ seconds.

The next day's highlight was Paulhan's flight to a record height of 4,165 feet. On the fourteenth Paulhan and Curtiss held a speed match, which the latter won, though by only 5 seconds, in a flight of 24 minutes, 54⅖ seconds over ten laps of the track (about 18 miles).

Later in the week Paulhan made a cross-country flight of about 47 miles in a time of 1 hour and 3 minutes. Altogether the Frenchman, who was the particular darling of the audience, won more than $15,000 in prizes, while the Curtiss team's winnings amounted to $8,500, although Curtiss' own prize money amounted to only $5,000. When Orville Wright was approached for an opinion on the two stars of the meet, he said, accurately enough: "Aside from Curtiss, Paulhan is probably the most skillful aviator in the world, and really more daring than his American rival."

This statement tends to indicate the absence of any personal animosity, at this time, toward either of the two so-called "infringers" who had been compelled by Wright injunctions to post heavy bonds in order to fly at Los Angeles. The Los Angeles meet was the first successful air competition in the United States. Its gate money was over $250,000, and the organizers made a 25 percent profit.

Thanks to the exhibition flying of Paulhan, Hamilton, Mars, Ely, McCurdy, Willard, Curtiss, and a few others, the American public started to become interested in flying. Many cities, large and small, formed local aeronautical organizations. A number of states had aero clubs as well as area groups such as the New England Aero Club and the Pacific Aero Club. All were looking forward to the fall of 1910 when the international competition for the Gordon Bennett Cup was, hopefully, to be held in the United States, under the sponsorship of Aero Club of America.

While Curtiss' victory was supposed to have ensured the holding of the event on this side of the Atlantic, the outlook for this looked rather dubious. Because of the Wright Company's victory in the first court test of the patent litigation, European aviators, remembering what had happened to Paulhan's aeroplanes in February, 1910, asked the Aero Club of America what guarantee could be offered that they would not be prevented from flying if they brought their machines to the United States. Curtiss and other American flyers wanted the answer to this question, too.

To settle the confusion, a committee from the Aero Club, headed by Cortlandt Bishop, met with Wilbur Wright and Andrew Freedman, of the Wright Company executive committee, and drew up an agreement which was hailed as "an assurance" that the next Gordon Bennett Cup race would be staged in the United States. Under its terms the Aero Club recognized the rights of the owners of the Wright patents and the decision of the Federal courts, and refused to countenance infringement of those patents while the decision remained in force. This, in effect, meant that only Wright aeroplanes, or those approved by them, could take part in the Gordon Bennett Cup race, unless there was a reversal of the court's decision.

The agreement stated further that the Aero Club of America, as the American representative of the Fedération Aéronautique Internationale, would approve only such public contests as were licensed by the Wright Company. The Wright Company, on the other hand, would encourage open meets approved by the Aero Club by granting licenses to those promoters who made satisfactory arrangements to compensate the company for use of its patents. At such licensed meets any aeroplane of any make might participate freely without obtaining further license or permit.

The early flyers were a stubborn lot. The European aviators wrote letters of protest to the Aero Club of America, and most of them stated flatly that they wouldn't enter the international event unless the restrictions were lifted. In this country, the exhibition flyers continued for the most part to fly without licenses from the Wright Company, as prescribed in the official dictum of the Aero Club. It was truly the era of "flying in spite of the Wrights."

Chapter 5

THE FLIGHT THAT MADE
AVIATION IN AMERICA

ON February 4, 1909, Joseph Pulitzer, owner and publisher of the New York *World,* cabled his business manager, Don Seitz, from Europe, ordering him to post a $10,000 prize to be paid to the first man to complete successfully in one stop the trip between Albany and New York City, following the Hudson River. Another condition was that the flight had to be made during the two weeks of the Hudson-Fulton Tercentenary Celebration.

The offer was a revolutionary step. No newspaper had ever made a real effort to foster aeronautics in the United States. Editors had generally demonstrated an "I'm from Missouri" attitude and had given little or no encouragement to the struggling aviators. Even when Curtiss won the Gordon Bennett Cup, which was sponsored by the owner of the New York *Herald,* the paper's United States edition devoted only a single column on the first page to it. The Paris edition, on the other hand, gave the entire first page to the event. Several leading United States newspapers failed even to mention Curtiss' exploits at Rheims. Their only interest in aviation, it seemed, was in the patent litigation between the Wrights and Curtiss.

140

In England, Lord Northcliffe, publisher of the London *Daily Mail*, had consistently encouraged aviation. His initial prize offer of ten thousand pounds for a flight from London to Manchester met with considerable derision when it was first made in 1906, and it was not claimed until 1909. Other *Daily Mail* prizes had been offered, including the one of a thousand pounds which inspired Blériot to make the first Channel flight. Gordon Bennett had donated a cup in Europe for aeronauts and one for aviators, with cash rewards attached. But the New York *World* was the first American newspaper to follow in the *Daily Mail*'s footsteps.

Since there were no "takers" during the Tercentenary week, the *World* extended the contest for a full year and the conditions of the flight were liberalized, as follows:

> To the first person who on or before October 10, 1910, makes the Fulton Flight, from New York to Albany, or from Albany to New York, in a mechanically propelled airship either lighter or heavier than air, *The World* will pay $10,000.
>
> The trip must be made within twenty-four consecutive hours, two landings being allowed between start and finish to replenish gasoline, etc.
>
> This offer is made with no other condition whatsoever, except that the starting point must be somewhere in the limits of New York City and the finish somewhere in the limits of Albany or vice versa, and that intending competition must give at least a twenty-four hour notice to *The World* and to the Secretary of the Aero Club of America of their intention to start. This twenty-four hour notice is required only that proper official records may be made. There are no conditions other than these. And no entrance fee or forfeit is required.

Cortlandt Bishop wanted the *World* to abide by the Aero Club's infringement rules, but Seitz refused, saying that this was no meet and thus was open to all aeroplanes regardless of design.

During that February and March, Curtiss did a great deal of thinking about the possibility of attempting the 150-mile flight. On bicycles, motorcycles, and in the air, Curtiss had seldom missed an opportunity to compete for prize money, but flying the Hudson River presented special problems. The major one was the natural ruggedness of the terrain itself. The lack of suitable landing fields and the possibility of cross winds between the mountains combined with this to make it an undertaking full of hazardous possibilities.

Early in May, Curtiss made up his mind to "take a crack at the *World*'s prize," despite the fact that Mrs. Curtiss was frankly opposed to it. Although she had flown with her husband a few times, she was afraid of the terrain rather than of the aeroplane. While awaiting the completion of a new standard Curtiss biplane, Curtiss continued to work on the plans for the flight. Because he felt that he might be helped by a following wind blowing down the river, and believed that his preliminary work could be better done at the Albany end, Curtiss chose Van Rensselaer Island, in the middle of the Hudson River opposite Albany, as his starting point.

While intending to make Governors Island his final landing spot, Curtiss wanted to be sure there was another place on the northern edge of the city where he might come down if it should prove necessary. He looked all over the upper end of Manhattan Island, and at last found a little meadow on the William B. Isham estate near Broadway and 214th Street. While fairly small, it was within the city limits and, because of its location near the junction of the Hudson and Harlem rivers, could easily be spotted from the air. Minturn P. Collins, Isham's son-in-law, gladly gave Curtiss permission to land there.

To go over the whole route, Curtiss made the trip from New York to Albany by the Hudson River boat with his wife and Jerry Fanciulli. He had some very interesting conversations with the first mate and captain of this craft. At first, neither of them seemed to realize that the flight was actually to be made, and it was clear from their answers that they had little confidence in Curtiss' ability to "do the trick." "Their answers," said Curtiss, "in reply to various questions about the winds along the Hudson and other navigational details were, 'Oh, yeah, I guess so!' and it was not until we went under the Poughkeepsie Bridge, and I was discussing with the captain the advisability of flying under or over this structure that he really began to take an active interest in my plan. From then on, questions about air currents received full and explicit answers."

Curtiss talked with other river pilots, too. While he got as much information as he could from these men, little of it was usable because conditions on the surface of the river and in the air were rather different. As Curtiss once expressed it, "Water pilots and aerial pilots can never belong to the same union. There seems to be nothing in common between us."

On his return from the trip up the Hudson, the new aeroplane had been completed and was promptly christened *Albany–to–New York Flyer* (*Albany Flyer* for short—Curtiss himself always referred to this aeroplane as his *Hudson Flyer*). It was very similar to *Golden Flyer* except for the simple precautions Curtiss had taken to keep his aircraft afloat in the event of an emergency landing in the Hudson River. A slender sausage-shaped tube of rubberized cloth, filled with ground cork, was stretched between the fore and aft wheels of the tricycle landing gear. To prevent the nose wheel from digging in on contact with the water and thus capsizing the machine,

Curtiss placed a horizontal fin—a "hydro-vane"—on the axle. A pair of metal, cylindrical tanks were installed, one on each side of the center section, under the lower wing to keep them from sinking below the water surface. *Albany Flyer*'s 8-cylinder, 50-hp engine was air-cooled. It did not have the Curtiss conventional water-cooling system. This change saved weight, and the total weight of the aeroplane was only 1,004 pounds.

On May 22 Curtiss tested *Albany Flyer* for only a few hours and then concluded that everything was as ready for the flight as it ever would be. One of the most important experiments he made, however, was to determine if the flotation gear would function properly. Selecting a spot close to Lake Keuka's shoreline but in water deep enough to provide a fair test, Curtiss pulled the craft into a fairly steep stall and plunked it in with little or no forward motion. The flotation rig worked, and he pulled the machine ashore unharmed. This test provided him with the comforting knowledge that a forced landing on the Hudson would not necessarily be a fatal one.

Meanwhile other "human birds" were preparing to swoop down the Hudson River with the intent of swooping up the $10,000 purse offered by Pulitzer. Curtiss learned that one of his former exhibition pilots, Charley Hamilton, had notified the *World* that he would be ready to start from Governors Island on June 3. Cliff Harmon, who had just learned to fly, announced he would try for the king-size prize in his recently purchased Curtiss biplane sometime during the week of June 6. Dr. William Greene, a famous former aeronaut, was known to be ready for a flight downriver, but hadn't set the date as yet. Thus Curtiss lost no time in mailing his entry blank, in compliance with the stipulation that a formal notice must be filed at least twenty-four hours in advance. He sent the following letter to the sponsors:

May 23, 1910

GENTLEMEN:

I have today sent my official notification to the Aero Club of America, announcing my intention to try for *The World's* $10,000 prize for a flight between New York and Albany, and making an official entry for that prize. It is my intention to start from Albany on Thursday morning, May 26, 1910.

For over a year I have made exhaustive experiments with the object of perfecting a machine which would start from and alight on the water. It was my intention to give such a machine its first practical test by attempting to fly from Albany to New York over the Hudson River, with the hope of obtaining *The World's* most commendable Hudson-Fulton prize.

While my experiments have proved very successful, they have not been completed. It is my belief that the incentive offered by *The World* to aviators and experimenters has been responsible for considerable activity similar to that in my own case.

If I should be successful in winning your prize, I would have only one regret; that is, that there would be no further inducement for other aviators to make the same flight.

Yours very truly,
(*Signed*) G. H. CURTISS

The next morning Curtiss, his wife, Kleckler, Fanciulli, and several mechanics left Hammondsport along with the crated aeroplane. On arriving at Albany, Mrs. Curtiss and Fanciulli went to get hotel accommodations, while the rest of the party proceeded to Van Rensselaer Island's mud flats to establish their base of operation. A tent was put up to house *Albany Flyer,* and Tod Shriver and Henry Kleckler insisted that they should stay there to "guard" the aeroplane.

On the twenty-fifth, while the machine was being unpacked and reassembled, Curtiss, his wife, and Augustus Post, who had been appointed official Aero Club observer and timer for the flight, caught a morning train for Poughkeepsie to select an ideal midway landing field. In an automobile borrowed from a local newspaper editor, the searching party scurried about the countryside. The first spot they considered was the State Hospital for the Insane, which stands on a hill just north of Poughkeepsie. Dr. E. D. Taylor, the Superintendent, showed the party about the grounds, and when told that Curtiss intended stopping here on his way down the river in an aeroplane, said with a smile: "Why shouldn't he? We get most of the mentally unbalanced people of this state sooner or later."

Notwithstanding the doctor's cordial invitation to "drop in on him," Curtiss decided to go elsewhere since the place had too many trees and rocks. The Vassar College lawn proved equally impracticable, because of trees, and he began to consider the possibilities of landing on the river, being towed ashore and taking to the air from a dock. But there were no large docks in the area, and he needed at least a hundred feet to take off.

South of Poughkeepsie, in the little hamlet of Camelot, they finally found a rather smooth, level field near the river which wasn't too closely bordered by trees. The owner, Farmer W. Gill, was happy to allow Curtiss the use of his meadow as a landing field. A local fuel dealer promised to be on hand with a supply of gasoline, oil, and water.

On their return to Albany, Curtiss found that *Albany Flyer* was not ready to start its journey downriver the next morning. Kleckler wouldn't approve of the flight until he had checked everything himself and tested the engine thoroughly. Curtiss didn't question his trusted friend's wisdom and postponed the start until the following day.

With the New York *World* playing up the event and other newspapers doing likewise, hundreds of seriously interested and merely curious people flocked to Albany. *The New York*

Times chartered a special train consisting of one of the New York Central's fastest locomotives, No. 3840, and four heavy cars to carry the official observers and a *Times* reporter and cameraman down the river abreast the *Albany Flyer*. Thus the stage was set for a train-plane race and the *Times'* first big aviation news beat.

On the twenty-seventh the aeroplane was ready, the pacemaking train was under steam on a siding with the right of way over every train—even the fastest passenger ones— through to New York, reporters were plentifully on hand, and the crowds were waiting. Everything was in readiness for the start, but unsettled weather conditions compelled Curtiss again to postpone his start until the next day. The United States Weather Bureaus at Albany and New York kept him informed of conditions along the proposed route.

Curtiss read in the morning papers the disquieting news that Charley Hamilton was in New York, preparing for flight. He had just announced that regardless of weather conditions, with one exception, he would start not later than Tuesday, the thirty-first, to fly up the Hudson to Albany. The one exception was a strong wind from the north, which would put him at a great disadvantage, with Curtiss flying with the wind, while he flew against it.

The period of waiting almost ended on Saturday morning. *Albany Flyer* was brought out of its tent, groomed and fit, and the special train stood ready. Newspapermen and crowds watched eagerly for the aeroplane take-off on its long and hazardous journey. Then something happened: the wind came up. At first it seemed to be no more than a breeze; then it grew stronger and reports from down the river told of a gale wind blowing upstream. Curtiss gritted his teeth, forced a weak smile and said once more: "No flight today!" *Albany*

Flyer was rolled back into its tent and Curtiss returned to the Hotel Ten Eyck.

The third postponement brought a storm of indignation. Jerry Fanciulli tried to explain: "Curtiss has never had a serious accident, because no matter what the pressure or clamor from the outside he won't fly unless he thinks it's safe. He knows the dangers, and carefully avoids them. He will make the flight." But the attitude of the New York newspapermen on Van Rensselaer Island was already far from friendly. Many of them had not forgotten the so-called "Curtiss Hudson-Fulton Celebration hoax" of the previous September, and some were not sorry to have an opportunity to retaliate. They sent mocking and sarcastic reports back to their papers, accusing Curtiss of publicity-seeking, and predicting that there would be no flight after all. One of the Poughkeepsie papers printed an editorial which said: "Curtiss gives us a pain in the neck. All those who are waiting to see him go down the river are wasting their time."

At 5 A.M. on May 29, Curtiss met Jacob L. Ten Eyck, the official starter for the Aero Club, and Bruce Frost, a correspondent for *The New York Times,* in the hotel lobby for breakfast in an all-night lunch room. During the meal, Curtiss said, "I'm not really anxious to make the flight on a Sunday. I wouldn't like to offend anyone, and many perhaps might think it wrong. But if there is a good chance I don't think I ought to miss it. Real good chances are so rare; I dare say people will forgive me." And as they walked to Ten Eyck's car, he cautioned Frost, "You hadn't better come down to the camp with us this morning. You had better get out to your train. I told Mrs. Curtiss she shouldn't attempt to make the island visit, either."

Driving along with Ten Eyck, Curtiss noted how the smoke hung almost immovable over the chimneys. When they reached the tent in which *Albany Flyer* was quartered on Van Rensselaer Island, all the mechanics were still asleep except Kleckler.

"Everything is good and ready," he reported.

"Let 'em sleep a while," Curtiss said, referring to his other men.

After taking another keen glance around the horizon, and without a word as to his intentions, Curtiss went back to Ten Eyck's automobile and drove away from the island.

Later it was discovered he had rushed back to the hotel and hurried Mrs. Curtiss and her party to the special train. On his return, the aeroplane was run out of the tent and the engine tried without the least sign of haste. The expression on Curtiss' face was inscrutable. However, in spite of the secrecy of his movements, a good crowd of people started to form around *Albany Flyer*.

Once more he got into the automobile and took Kleckler with him, saying that he was going to consult the weatherman. In reality, he was taking Kleckler to the special train so that his chief mechanic would be at the landing place below Poughkeepsie with tools and any supplies that might be needed. Kleckler's tool kit contained a hammer, a screwdriver, a pair of pliers, a couple of wrenches, a brace and bit, a little wire, and some black tire tape.

At the New York Central yards, the train crew that had been on duty at intervals for four days, expecting a flight which had not come, sniffed the atmosphere and seemed to find it just right. H. E. Brown, Assistant Superintendent of the division, who had come up from New York and had already seen three morning "false alarm" starts, did not have to be called on a morning such as this. He was on time, and with him was G. D. Van Schaick, Special Inspector of Motive Power, who had also joined the special train to see that it came through without a hitch.

Charles Lewis, the engineer, fairly leaped into the cab when told it was "going time." Mike Gillaren, the fireman, and Joseph Martin, the conductor, were shoveling coal and giving signals almost before Mrs. Curtiss, Fanciulli, Post, Kleckler, *The New York Times* correspondent, and the photographer could scramble aboard. There were only nine passengers on the special four-coach train.

Using its right-of-way authority, the special moved out of the yards to a siding in clear view of Van Rensselaer Island. A white flag, hung from the top of a building of the Standard Oil Company's plant by one of Curtiss' mechanics, would signal the train to start even with the aeroplane.

On his return to Van Rensselaer Island, Curtiss officially notified the New York *World* representative and the observers for the Aero Club that he was ready to start. While Tod Shriver tuned the engine, *Albany Flyer*'s pilot went into the tent and very quietly drew on his aviation-aquatic suit. He knotted the twine that supported his fisherman's rubber trousers, pulled light cloth shoes over his rubber-covered feet, put on his chauffeur's leather jacket and reversed the peak of his cap. So attired, and presenting a most odd appearance, he carefully went over the whole of his aeroplane, examining especially the controls and the inflated bags that were to support him if he had to alight on the river. Satisfied, he took his seat.

Suddenly one of the mechanics, Lynn Bauder, called out for him to stop, and, hurrying into the tent, brought out the cork life preserver Curtiss was to wear. The four slabs of cork were fastened together so as to make one big slab that the aviator could place in front of his chest. He could not wear it in the ordinary way because it would have interfered with operation of the aeroplane's controls.

Many rushed up to get a last handshake and to wish Curtiss

success. The last to wish him luck was Dr. Greene, who was himself anxious to try for the prize. The engine was started by one swing of the propeller. For half a moment Curtiss speeded up his engine. Then he nodded his head, pulled down the goggles over his eyes, and raised his right hand. His mechanics sprang back from the aeroplane and the machine moved along the ground at a speed of 20 miles an hour, which became 30 within 50 yards and 35 in another 25 yards.

The little crowd of onlookers cheered, then burst into shouts as the aeroplane rose from the ground. There was still doubt that Curtiss was really on his way to New York. He swung a little to the right to cross the boundary of the city of Albany at a point that had been located by Official Starter Ten Eyck. Within half a mile of his starting point, Curtiss was flying at a height of over 700 feet.

The train crew had been warned that the aeroplane could do 50 miles an hour. They had smiled incredulously. Now, however, the train had a real task catching up with the aerocraft; before the engineer could really open the throttle, the aeroplane was way ahead. For four miles the tracks ran through trees, and only now and then could the speck in the blue sky be seen.

Soon the train was gaining, good news to all aboard. Athens, Stuyvesant, and Stockport whizzed past, and the sun flashing off *Albany Flyer*'s varnished surfaces, glimmering through its whirring propeller blades, showed the contour of Curtiss sitting as immovable as any part of his craft. He was looking directly ahead, where all was serene, without a cloud to mar the prospect.

Tivoli, Rhinecliff, Staatsburg—the stations were flying past, and Mrs. Curtiss smiled broadly as she began to realize that it was no longer a question of getting started, but of making a stop at the end of a successful flight.

The Sabbath morning quiet of Poughkeepsie was shattered at ten minutes after eight o'clock by an incessant clamoring of the deep-toned fire bell of the City Hall tower. Twenty-seven times the bell rang out—the signal that Curtiss and *Albany Flyer* had been sighted within 16 miles of the town.

Beds, breakfast tables, and bathtubs were abandoned. Garages were besieged, cranks feverishly twisted, automobiles crowded and put into motion. The city trolley company responded by turning out a squadron of cars—one line going down to the river front, the other winding along rural roads in the direction of the Gill farm.

At 8:21 A.M. Curtiss flew over the Poughkeepsie Bridge and continued down the Hudson until he spotted the American flag and the piece of red cloth Gill had run up on a pole to guide him to his landing spot. Turning inland, Curtiss saw Gill in the middle of the field in his shirt sleeves, flagging him down with his coat. He glided in above the trees at the edge of the meadow, and landed safely 1 hour and 24 minutes after leaving Albany, a distance of some 76 miles.

The *Times* train made a special stop, and the passengers clambered up the embankment to the landing site. Kleckler checked the machine while Curtiss first kissed his wife, then answered questions of reporters and spectators about the flight. One problem had arisen: the man who had agreed to bring the gasoline and oil did not work on Sunday and thus these needed supplies were not at the field. The difficulty was quickly solved, however, when two tourists from Summit, New Jersey, took the quantities needed from the stocks in their automobiles.

At 9:08 Curtiss tried the propellers and, after kissing his wife, he warned the train party not to linger. An automobile commandeered from an obliging spectator took them to New

Hamburg, where the train had gone onto a siding while another passed it.

At 9:20 Curtiss took a long drink of water from a tin pail, tested the controls of his aeroplane, and adjusted his goggles. He looked over the steering gear again, put on his life preserver, and shook hands with several who crowded around him and wished him luck. The crowd began to press toward the machine, and Curtiss with a note of warning in his voice urged them with a gesture to move back. "Lots of room on the side."

At 9:25 the engine was started, and without a farewell word or gesture, Curtiss mounted into his seat. Several men gave the craft a little push. The aeroplane started forward, running lightly over the grass for about 500 feet, and at 9:29 *Albany Flyer* left the ground. After a dip that was somewhat after the fashion of a good-bye curtsy, the machine rose steadily and flew westward on a direct line to the Hudson River.

The train party saw the aeroplane as it loomed above the treetops. This time the crew didn't want Curtiss to get too far ahead of them, and Kleckler and Fanciulli, who had lingered behind the others, promising that they would come in a later automobile, were summarily left behind by engineer Lewis. While feelings aboard the train were running high, everyone knew that the most difficult part of the trip lay directly ahead. Around the hills of Storm King Mountain there could be very dangerous air currents. It was thought Curtiss would fly anywhere from 500 to 800, or even 1,000 feet, in that area. Instead of rising to fight the currents from the mountains, he dipped lower and lower with each contrary gust. Fishkill Gap was passed with evident trouble. Five minutes later Storm King was at hand. The zigzagging motion experienced in the Gap now gave way to pitching and lurching. Mrs. Curtiss held tightly to her window ledge, as she asked how quickly this trouble would pass.

West Point and Iona Island were immediately ahead. As the aeroplane passed the promontory of Storm King Mountain, the lurching reached a climax. Those on the train held their breaths as *Albany Flyer* pitched like a yacht in a hurricane. The machine seemed to be blown back by a head wind that held Curtiss in check in spite of his propeller's thrust. The craft began to settle, and the watchers thought he was going to land. *Albany Flyer* dropped to about 25 to 30 feet above the river bank. Then Curtiss skimmed along for a while before he brought the aeroplane back to above 100 feet.

Once *Albany Flyer* reached the broad bend in the river at Peekskill, there was renewed confidence on the train. "Yonkers," read the sign on the station platform, and the horizon of lower Manhattan, with its smokestacks, tall buildings, and docked liners, came into view. A few moments later, the engineer pulled the whistle valve wide open to announce to the world that Curtiss had passed the city limits, after an actual flying time of 2 hours and 28 minutes. Little did he know that Locomotive 3840 had given the first cry of warning to every complacent owner of gilt-edged railroad stocks.

At the junction of the Hudson and Harlem rivers, the train went inland, on its way to Grand Central Station, while Curtiss, because the aeroplane's oil supply was running rather low, decided to set down at his 214th Street landing site rather than chance a flight all the way to Governors Island. He put down on the grassy lawn of the Isham estate at 10:35 A.M.

After shaking hands with Minturn Collins, owner of the property, he asked if any oil was available and if he could use the telephone. Curtiss immediately called the *World* to notify them of his arrival in New York City.

An inspection of the aeroplane disclosed a leak in the oil tank line. Curtiss quickly repaired it with tape and refilled the tank with oil furnished by Collins. While he was at work, a crowd began to gather on the grounds. Fortunately, a wagonful of policemen arrived at the scene to keep the people in check.

At 11:30 he said, "I guess I'm ready to leave if some of you people will give me a helping hand." Many of the policemen and some half-dozen chauffeurs stepped forward. Curtiss waved the crowd back and took his seat in the aeroplane. He started the engine, and the propeller began to revolve at high speed. The men gave *Albany Flyer* a shove. It ran along on its wheels for a few yards. At 11:42 it was up in the air on its way to Governors Island.

The people of New York City had been eagerly awaiting the flight. They had been watching the Singer Building, Hotel Astor, Pulitzer Building, and other signal points for days. While normally red-balled flags flying from their flagstaffs told New Yorkers that the ice on the ponds in Central Park was skatable, this time they knew the appearance of the fluttering pennants meant that Curtiss was under way.

All morning New Yorkers followed the progress of the flight by means of bulletins posted in front of the Times and Pulitzer buildings and at United Cigar stores throughout the city. The large hotels and clubs also advised guests of his progress by regular bulletins in their main lobbies. At the Hotel Gotham the night clerk had called every guest in the hotel to report Curtiss had left Albany. There was disappointment when it became known that Curtiss had landed at some point within the northern limits of the city because it was thought that the flight was over. When the news was flashed that Curtiss had left 214th Street and was now visible over the Hudson River, a rush was made for all points of vantage.

Warning of Curtiss' approach was signaled by every vessel, yacht, launch, or steam barge over which he flew. By the time the machine was off 150th Street, Riverside Drive was crowded with admiring thousands, while from windows and roofs other thousands watched.

At precisely 11:51 A.M., *Albany Flyer* was abreast of West 42nd Street. Six minutes later he passed the Battery on the tip of Manhattan Island. Then, after circling the Statue of Liberty, he set his aeroplane down on the sandy parade ground at Governors Island. The total time of his 150-mile flight had been 2 hours and 46 minutes. He started from Albany at 7:03 o'clock in the morning and concluded the flight at 12 o'clock sharp, spending 1 hour and 4 minutes resting near Poughkeepsie and 1 hour and 7 minutes at 214th Street while he replenished his oil. The New York Central's fastest train, the *Twentieth Century Limited,* could make the same run, minus the distance from 42nd Street to Governors Island, or 143 miles, in 2 hours and 51 minutes, or 49.6 miles an hour, while Curtiss' average speed was 54.18 miles an hour.

The officers and men of the garrison rushed to the parade grounds to greet him. A short while later, the *Albany Flyer* was wheeled into the hangar built for Curtiss in 1909 during his stay on the island. On hand to congratulate him on his landing was W. J. Hammer, who, as Secretary of the Hudson-Fulton Aviation Committee, had been one of Curtiss' most severe critics for his failure to make the contracted flights the year before.

A short time after the landing, Mrs. Curtiss arrived via automobile from Grand Central Station and a government ferryboat from the Battery. A little later a representative of the New York *World* reached the island to take him in charge. "It will please you to know," he said to the aviator, "that the check for $10,000 in your behalf is being drawn." Curtiss' smile showed that it did please him, and presently, with his wife and friends, he departed for a luncheon at the Astor Hotel.

On the way, Curtiss stopped at City Hall to deliver the first letter sent by an aeroplane. It was the message of greeting James B. McEwan, Mayor of Albany, had asked the aviator to deliver to Mayor Gaynor of New York City. It read:

OFFICE OF THE MAYOR

ALBANY, N.Y.

May 27, 1910.

Hon. William J. Gaynor, Mayor of New York

DEAR SIR:

On the occasion of the first long flight by aeroplane in this country I take this opportunity of sending Your Honor greetings and good wishes.

This great flight, if accomplished, as I hope, will be historic. It is possible, too, that it is but the forerunner of what may in the not too distant future be a commonplace occurrence.

The speed of this new instrument of locomotion seems to fit it admirably for many purposes of service to humanity, especially in the way of rapid communication. So far, however, no letter has yet been carried by this new means and I am glad that these greetings between us should be the first.

I know you will be with me in wishing Mr. Curtiss success in his daring trip and in complimenting *The World* newspaper in fostering the progress of this new art by putting up so large a prize.

Sincerely yours

(*Signed*) JAMES B. MCEWAN, *Mayor*

After the luncheon, the Curtiss party stopped at the *World* office. There they were ushered into the Sunday department, where several officials of the Press Publishing Company and a group of newspapermen and photographers were gathered. After an introductory speech by William Johnson, one of the Sunday editors, J. Angus Shaw, secretary of the company, presented the check.

A banquet was arranged for Curtiss at the Astor Hotel on the night of May 31. Mayor Gaynor presided and read a few of the scores of telegrams of congratulations that poured in from all over the world. Several distinguished guests addressed the gathering, and Curtiss spoke for a period generously esti-mated at "less than five minutes." He told the guests, "I care-fully planned everything about the flight in advance except the possibility of making a speech."

Without doubt, the Albany–New York flight did more to awaken the public interest in aviation than any previous aerial event in the country. It was the first river flight, the first city-to-city flight, and the longest flight in the history of the United States. Under date of May 29, 1910, President Taft wired the New York *World* the following:

> I am intensely interested in what Mr. Curtiss has done. It seems that the wonders of aviation will never cease. I would hesitate to say that the performance of Mr. Curtiss is an epoch, because tomorrow we may hear that some man has flown from New York to St. Louis. Mr. Wright told me at the time the ten mile flight from Fort Meyer was made that the chief difficulty was in flying over unknown territory. Mr. Curtiss seems to have surmounted this, and I am glad he has. His flight will live long in our memories as having been the greatest.
>
> (*Signed*) WILLIAM H. TAFT

An interesting by-product of the flight was the winning for the third time of the *Scientific American* trophy. Having flown one kilometer in 1908 and 30 miles on a triangular course in

1909, he now, by the new terms specified by the *Scientific American,* had succeeded in winning the trophy permanently. But one of the most important contributions of the Albany–New York flight was the change in attitude of the American press. On May 30 *The New York Times* devoted six pages to the flight, which was record coverage for a single news event.

There was also an outburst of editorial comment from newspapers all over the United States, not only long and technical articles, but the kind of brief, snappy paragraphs that make the press of this country such an interesting reflection of public feeling on all extraordinary achievements. For instance, the St. Louis *Times* spoke of the passing of the new aerial menace over West Point where cadets were studying the history of military science along ancient lines, and the Chicago *Inter-Ocean* chuckled over how the achievement "would jar old Hendrik Hudson."

The Newark *News* declared that "the Indian canoe, the *Halfmoon,* the *Clermont,* and the *Curtiss biplane* each represented a human achievement that marked an epoch," while the York *Gazette* compared the flight to the conquest of the North Pole. Other interesting points of view were taken by the press. The Birmingham *News,* for instance, expressed the opinion that the New York *World* was extravagant: "It had paid $10,000 for Curtiss' ticket from Albany to New York, when it might have brought him down by train for $4.65." The Battle Creek *Enquirer* said that Curtiss ought to go into politics, for "a man who can soar as high, stay up as long, travel as far, light as safely, *all on wind,* would have the rest of them tied to the post." The Birmingham *Age-Herald* declared that the way was paved for other and greater flights, even across the Atlantic Ocean, and, indeed, the ocean flight now seemed to the press a not far distant possibility. It was left to the Houston *Post* to break into poetry in the following outburst of local pride:

> The wonder is that Curtiss did
> Not pass New York and onward whizz
> Southwest by south, half south, until
> He got where Houston, Texas, is.

There was even some adverse feeling about the flight, and one of Curtiss' worst fears was realized by the following short article that appeared in a Poughkeepsie newspaper:

> The Rev. William H. Hubbard, pastor of the Mill Street Baptist Church, passed out some sharp criticism at both morning and evening services yesterday because so many of his members were absent from church to see Curtiss fly over Poughkeepsie. He lashed the church folks for neglecting to attend church and railed at Curtiss for *desecrating the Sabbath*. In the morning service, Mr. Hubbard also condemned automobile riding on Sunday, but at the evening one he made an apology because he himself had ridden in one in the afternoon to Mr. Gill's farm to see where Glenn Curtiss landed.

But perhaps the most thoughtful analysis of the flight appeared on the editorial page of *The New York Times:*

> Glenn H. Curtiss, in his aeroplane, flew down the Hudson Valley yesterday morning, landing briefly at Poughkeepsie and at 214th Street in this city. The flying machine, floating above the New Jersey cliffs and the tall buildings of Manhattan, passed Forty-second Street at 11:51 o'clock and after encircling Liberty Island landed on Governors Island at the stroke of 12.
>
> Curtiss' actual time in the air was 2 hours and 46 minutes and his average speed was much greater than that of Paulhan in his recent trip by aeroplane from London to Manchester. Yesterday's flight was seen by excited crowds all along the

line, and it was a most inspiring sight. Man has now conquered the air. As Orville Wright has said aeroplaning is as yet only a sport, though the utility of the new machine in warfare is no longer doubted. Happily there is no war to test that utility and no prospect of one. But this much having been accomplished, the development of the airship practically and commercially and the growth of its usefulness as a carrier are only matters of time. For the present, however, the flight of Curtiss is the uppermost topic in aeronautics. It was a splendid feat, successfully accomplished, with wonderful courage and skill, and it seems to make human flying more of a reality than hitherto it has been.

The following short piece that appeared two weeks later in the late edition of the New York *Evening Mail* undoubtedly was of greater importance to G. H. Curtiss:

NEW YORK, June 15th. The United States Circuit Court of Appeals today has dissolved the injunction granted by Judge Hazel, of Buffalo, to the Wright Brothers, restraining the Herring-Curtiss Company from manufacturing aeroplanes on the ground that they were infringing the patents of the Wrights.

The decision is greeted by aviation experts throughout the world as a severe blow to the group of financiers who are supporting the Wrights' attempt to form a so-called "Air Trust." The Wrights intend to carry the case to the Court of Highest Instance.

The next day, Curtiss was again front-page news. The New York *Herald*'s headline read "Curtiss Conquers Wrights," while the one on the Chicago *Daily News* said "Court Breaks Air-Trust." At least for a while, aviation was free from the yoke of the Wright infringement problem.

Chapter 6

WINGS FOR THE NAVY

THE floodgates of public enthusiasm about aviation were open. Civic leaders everywhere stepped on each other's heels offering cash inducements to airmen. Over $200,000 in prize money was posted within a week of the Albany–New York flight.

The New York Times offered $25,000 for the first flight between New York and Chicago over a 960-mile course in less than seven days. The Chicago *Evening Post* duplicated the offer. Then the New York *World* and the St. Louis *Post-Dispatch* offered $30,000 for a flight over the 1,000-mile distance from New York to St. Louis. The Washington Chamber of Commerce and the Aero Club of Washington offered $25,000 for a 225-mile race between Washington and New York. A $10,000 prize was offered by *The New York Times* and the Philadelphia *Public Ledger* for the first round-trip between the two cities. This was claimed almost immediately by Charley Hamilton, who, on June 13, made the journey in less than the stipulated 24 hours.

In addition to intercity flights, every area in the United States wanted to stage an exhibition air show of some type. Flyers could now participate without fear of the Wrights' injunction. But, of all the early aviators, Curtiss was the one most in demand. Offers came to him from the four corners of the nation, and he accepted as many as he could. For instance, Atlantic City offered $5,000 for a flight over the ocean, and Curtiss claimed it on July 4, by making 10 laps over a 5-mile course before a boardwalk crowd of 35,000. Later that day, he flew down the beach from Atlantic City and landed at the summer home of a friend in time for tea, the first social call ever paid by aeroplane.

After giving several exhibitions at Pittsburgh, Curtiss decided to capitalize on his New York City popularity by organizing an "International Aviation Contest" at Sheepshead Bay Race Track in Brooklyn. The use of the word "International" for this event, which began on August 19, might be questioned since all the contestants were members of the Curtiss "team"—Bud Mars, Charles Willard, Eugene Ely, Jack McCurdy, and the G.H. himself. True, an invitation to participate was sent to the Wright brothers and their newly formed exhibition group, but no reply was ever received.

Prizes were offered for the greatest height; the fastest and slowest lap around a 1⅜ mile course; the greatest distance covered in one flight; the longest time in the air; the quickest start; and the shortest distance covered before the machine left the ground. The most popular event of the meet was the half-mile dash. In the usual aeroplane race, the machines flew separately over a measured course and the one with the fastest time was declared the winner. In the half-mile dash, as in an automobile race, the aeroplanes were strung along the starting line, all tuned up and ready for instant action. Then, at a signal from the starter, all five machines hurled themselves down the course together. The start was at the judges' stand, immediately in front of the grandstand, and the finish was a line laid across the field a half-mile away. In this event, the spectators witnessed for the first time five aeroplanes racing against each other through the air. Curtiss, Willard, and Mars had to give a slight distance handicap as they had the more powerful machines, making this the first aeroplane handicap race in history. Originally scheduled for only three days, the air show went on for eight in order to accommodate the crowds. Actually, only previous commitments on the part of the aviators prevented the contest from continuing longer.

On August 31 Curtiss flew from Euclid Beach, Cleveland, to Cedar Point, near Sandusky, Ohio, a distance of 64¾ miles over the waters of Lake Erie. There was a possible purse of $15,000 awaiting him at the end of this stunt. The Cleveland *Press* guaranteed him $5,000 for the flight, promoters at Euclid Beach offered him $5,000 if he beat the existing speed records, and the managers of Cedar Point another $5,000 if he beat the altitude mark of the day. Curtiss was content with the original purse of $5,000 and did not try for any speed records or altitude marks. The flight was, however, the longest trip over water made up to that date, and remained unchallenged for several years.

Curtiss made the return flight the next day, delayed because of prevailing high winds and inclement weather. The return flight took one hour and 42 minutes compared with 78 minutes the day before. On landing at Euclid Beach, he told a *Press* reporter that the return trip was the most difficult he had ever made. He went on: "It was a battle with the air every mile of the way from Cedar Point. At one point, particularly, off the cliffs just before reaching Cleveland, I thought my trip had ended. I was flying 500 feet high and suddenly dropped a sheer 100 feet. Instinctively I shut my engine partly off. Then I righted my aeroplane and the flight continued. This mishap, which came very near being fatal, was caused by a whirl of wind going the same way I was. If I run into other flights like this, I may stop flying."

But Curtiss did not give up flying, and he honored his commitment to enter the meet staged by the Harvard Aeronautical Society at Squantum Field, near Boston. He did not, however, fare too well in competition with Ralph Johnstone, Walter Brookins, and Claude Grahame-White. Johnstone set the meet's endurance record with a flight of 3 hours, 5 minutes, and Brookins took the altitude prize with a climb of 4,732 feet. Both flew Wright biplanes. Flying a Blériot, Grahame-White of England captured the speed race, with Curtiss second. The Englishman also won the big prize in the race around Boston Light, pocketing the Boston *Globe*'s $10,000 award.

The gate receipts at this meet were enormous, and there were many distinguished guests in the audiences, among them President Taft, who earnestly assured Curtiss that only his advisers and weight prevented him from accepting an invitation to go aloft.

New York's Belmont Park had been selected as the site of the International Aviation Meet in October, although there had been furious bidding from other cities, including Oakland, Washington, Des Moines, Los Angeles, St. Louis, and Chicago. Americans generally expected Curtiss to defend the Gordon Bennett Cup. After the Squantum meet, however, he returned to Hammondsport, and a short statement dictated by him was given out by his New York office:

> While I greatly appreciate the consideration given me by the Aero Club of America, in waiving in my behalf the requirement for participation in the elimination trials for the Gordon Bennett Aviation Trophy, I regret that I cannot give immediate notice of my acceptance of the invitation to become the first member of the American Team for the defense of the

International Cup. Until I have conferred with the Committee, regarding the details of the arrangements which have been made for the International Meet at Belmont Park, I cannot reach a definite conclusion. It would, of course, be impossible for me to participate in the meet on any basis different from that which governs the participation of any other contestant, and while I have had assurances, unofficially, that the Aero Club has not entered into any contract which will put the International Meet on any but a sportsman-like basis, I do not wish to enter until I know that this is a fact.

For the International Aviation Meet, Curtiss built a special monoplane. It was the first of the type he made and, while it was faster than any of his other machines, he found it had one serious defect: a tricky response to the controls which, at high speeds, made it rather unsafe. He shipped this aeroplane to New York with four other machines in which Ely, Willard, McCurdy, and Mars would fly in the meet. The monoplane was never flown during the days prior to the opening of the affair. Then the evening before, Curtiss withdrew from the Gordon Bennett race. The Aero Club members, newspapermen, and Curtiss' friends were frantic and begged him to reconsider. Reporters asked him if his refusal to defend the cup he had won the year before was because of a misunderstanding with the Aero Club. He said, "No—all the differences between the Club and me have been cleared up. I am not entering because I don't want to make a monkey of myself." Old friends who remembered Curtiss' motorcycling days knew the reason for his withdrawal. His racing had always been characterized by a calculated daring which weighed the risks, assessed the competition, and *withdrew if the odds were too stiff*. Despite pressure from many sources, he was just one of the thousands of spectators at the Second International Aviation Meet.

Ralph Johnstone shattered the world's record for altitude

by flying to a height of 9,714 feet. Walter Brookins, in a Wright single-seater designed especially for racing, flew at an estimated speed of 70 miles an hour in the speed trials, but crashed during the Gordon Bennett Cup race. The International prize went to England when Claude Grahame-White piloted his Blériot at an average speed of 61 miles an hour.

The highlight of the meet, however, was the $10,000 elapsed-time race between Belmont and the Statue of Liberty, a round trip of 32 miles. Early in the day, Grahame-White completed the circuit in 35 minutes, 21 seconds. Just before the time limit expired, the American aviator John B. Moisant took off in a Blériot aeroplane borrowed from another flyer because his aircraft had been wrecked previously. When he returned a little over a half-hour later, everyone assumed that he had not completed the course. The announcement that Moisant had beaten Grahame-White's time by 43 seconds brought charges of technical violations, and the Belmont meet ended in controversy.

Early in September, the Curtiss Exhibition Company was incorporated "for the purpose of giving flight exhibitions." Jerome Fanciulli was made the general manager of the new operation. With booking offices in New York, he took care of promotion work, arranged dates, engaged flyers, and handled the exhibitions. A short time later, the Curtiss aviation school, which had been organized earlier in the spring, was placed under the jurisdiction of the exhibition company.

The day after the Belmont meet, Curtiss announced to the press that he was giving up exhibition flying, and all future flights of this nature would be done by members of his new firm, under Fanciulli's direction. When asked by reporters for the reason, he tersely replied, "The experiments that I am now involved with take up all my time."

Few newspapers, however, took Curtiss' statement as valid.

Some speculated that it was because the new "breed" of flyers was superior to such "old-timers" as Curtiss. To prove their contention, they pointed out that none of the Rheims participants had won at Belmont. They failed to mention that Captain Feber, Lefebvre, and Delagrange had been killed. (Between the two Gordon Bennett Cup races, thirty-two flyers had lost their lives pioneering aviation.) Seven others, including Blériot and Curtiss, had "retired." Other papers thought that several recent "close calls," such as the Lake Erie flight, were the real reason for Curtiss' giving up exhibition flying. While some accused Mrs. Curtiss of nagging her husband into his decision, a few went so far as to say that America's "best" flyer was "afraid" to fly again.

Although Curtiss never again gave flight exhibitions or entered aviation meets, he did continue to fly. His close associates knew that G.H. wanted to solve the problem of flying from the water and landing on it. Curtiss believed aviation was about to enter a commercial phase. He said:

> Of course, one of the first developments in commercial aviation will be the use of the flying boat and seaplanes for passengers and packages carrying between the largest seaports along the Atlantic coast and in the West Indies. I believe that we shall soon have transatlantic flights. The reason I believe that this will be true and the reason I believe marine flying will be developed quicker than land is because there are no new landing fields needed. In other words, terminal facilities are already provided.
>
> Quiet harbors, rivers and small lakes are ideal landing fields for seaplanes and flying boats. Furthermore, there is no limitation in the width of a plane because there is ample room for even our largest sea boats to maneuver. We know more about weather conditions on the sea, more about tides and more about the general directions of the wind than we do on land.

Mariners have been studying meteorological conditions over the sea for years and the Government already issues wind charts of all oceans and has a well organized service covering weather conditions. Another thing, the relative speed of boats is slow as compared with the speed of railway trains, so that aerial transportation at a speed of from 75 to 100 miles an hour is bound to cut down materially the time required to go from one seaport to another, thereby coming into early favor.

In addition, Curtiss wanted to explore the use of aircraft as a military weapon. Unlike the Wrights, who considered the aeroplane's military value limited to scouting, he thought of the flying machine as a weapon of offense. During the Astor banquet, he told Major General Walter C. Howe, "My aeroplane could have carried 300 to 500 pounds of excess weight composed of an air gun and picric bombs. I could have scattered destruction all along the route between Albany and New York City.

"I think also that I can hit a target within a reasonable radius. Experiments abroad have proved that a missile thrown from a moving airship can strike within twelve feet of a given spot. Think what this means. I could have blown up the bridge at Poughkeepsie, set fire to the homes of the wealthy along the Highlands, destroyed the railroad tracks on both shores, and cleared the river of its shipping.

"An aeroplane flying like mine over the length of the North River could have demoralized its busy commerce. Transatlantic steamers, ferries, battleships, all are equally vulnerable from above. I could have touched them without danger to myself or to my machine. By swooping down low and darting up again at high speed before their cumbersome guns could be brought into play, I could escape unscathed."

On several occasions, Curtiss and Captain Tom Baldwin had given demonstrations designed to attract the attention of military experts. In one such exhibition during the month of June, 1909, Baldwin dropped a number of shell-like objects from his dirigible into a National Guard encampment to show how in time of war bombs could be dropped on an enemy camp from the air. And in August of the following year, at the Curtiss' Sheepshead Bay Meet, Lieutenant T. E. Fickel of the Army first demonstrated the possibilities of sharpshooting from an aeroplane. At the same meet the first wireless messages were sent from an aeroplane by Jack McCurdy and received by a ground station operator.

Even a few newspapers began to see military possibilities for aeroplanes. For instance, at the instigation of the New York *World* and for the benefit of Army and Navy officials, Curtiss gave a series of demonstrations on June 30, 1910, to show the feasibility of dropping bombs from an aeroplane. Lead weights with colored streamers attached served as "bombs" and were dropped from altitudes of 500 to 800 feet onto a raft target anchored in Lake Keuka. While the representatives of the *World* found the accuracy relatively good, the military was unimpressed. Curtiss stated later in *Aeronautics,* "that in order to accurately drop bombs in actual warfare, one man would have to be carried for the purpose of dropping the bombs, since it was impossible for the pilot to make accurate calculations of angle and speed."

The experiments of such experts as Baldwin and Curtiss gave the science fiction writers of 1910 themes for aerial adventure stories. Man who had never flown, experienced battle, or been to sea wrote of blasted cities, helpless armies, and bombed-out navies. Writers predicted that in just a few years flying machines would make armies and navies obsolete. The American public, having changed from complete disbelief to gullible credulity, wanted to know what the Army and Navy were doing about flying machines.

It could not be said that the United States Navy was enthusiastic about the possibilities of aviation or that it was eagerly awaiting an aeroplane it could employ. In 1898 Theodore Roosevelt, Assistant Secretary of the Navy, had recommended careful study of Langley's experiments for possible naval application. The Navy sent Lieutenant George C. Sweet and Naval Constructor William McEntee to the Fort Meyer demonstration of the Wright's Army aeroplane in 1908. They recommended that a similar machine be equipped with floats and pontoons for naval use. Rear Admiral William S. Cowles, Chief of the Bureau of Equipment, submitted a report on aviation prepared by Sweet to the Secretary of the Navy. It outlined the specifications of an aeroplane capable of operating from naval vessels on scouting and observation missions, discussed the tactical advantages of such capability, and recommended that a *number* of aircraft be purchased and "placed in the hands of the personnel of the Navy to further develop special features adapted to naval uses." Not unexpectedly, his memorandum fluttered down into the round file.

After the second set of military trials in August, 1909, the U.S. Army had finally bought its first aeroplane, a Wright Model A, the first aeroplane to be purchased and owned by a government. On August 16, 1909, Admiral Cowles made another impassioned plea for authority to purchase "two heavier-than-air flying machines." A few days later his request was disapproved by the Acting Secretary of the Navy with the comment: "The Department does not consider that the development of an aeroplane has progressed sufficiently at this time for use in the Navy."

In September, 1909, Commander F. L. Chapin, U.S. Naval Attaché at Paris, reported his observations at the Rheims Aviation Meet, expressing the opinion that "the aeroplane would have a present usefulness in naval warfare and that the limits of the field will be extended in the near future," and in elaborating upon that theme noted two means by which air machines could be operated from naval vessels that were to be proven true. The first was the use of the Wright launching device (a catapult) to launch aeroplanes from the cleared quarterdeck of battleships, and the second was the construction of a floor (a flight deck) over the deckhouses of auxiliary ships to provide the clear space required for take-off and landing.

Navy officials were becoming a bit embarrassed by persistent newsmen and enthusiastic civilians who kept asking what the service intended to do about progress. As a result of this pressure, in September, 1910, the Navy Department assigned Captain Washington Irving Chambers—then assistant to an aide for matériel procurement in the Bureau of Equipment—the responsibility for keeping in touch with flying developments.

After attending several air meets, Captain Chambers became sold on the aeroplane. Within a month, his work load was so heavy that he had to have help. Naval Constructor McEntee and Lieutenant N. H. Wright were made his assistants. Both became outspoken supporters for the aeroplane. The "battlewagon" admirals had no use for flimsy man-carrying kites, and so McEntee suggested, and Chambers agreed, really to shake up the braid: "We'll fly an aeroplane from a battleship!"

Chambers had a very limited knowledge of the field of aeronautics, so he proceeded to read everything he or the naval librarian could find on the subject, including the article that appeared in *The New York Times* on May 31, 1910, quoting Curtiss as saying: "Some day soon aeroplanes will start from the decks of battleships and from the water, and I am not sure but what they could be launched from a battleship going at top speed even now. I also believe that a dozen aeroplanes, very similar to the machines of today, could annihilate a fleet of battleships of one thousand times their value, not to mention the havoc which might be wrought to a fortress or seaport city near which a ship could launch these flying machines. I am confident that it is only a matter of a short time when our Government will spend the large sums of money now being expended in the construction of battleships for that more up-to-date means, the aeroplane."

Rather than going to Curtiss, Captain Chambers approached the Wright brothers with the proposal that they fly one of their planes from the deck of a ship. They flatly refused the offer, saying such a scheme was too dangerous. During the Belmont Air Meet, however, Chambers discussed the matter in great detail with Curtiss and found him willing to test the idea. He agreed to provide, without charge to the Navy, one of his exhibition flyers and aeroplanes. Chambers, on the other hand, would have to provide the ship and the launching platform.

After the New York *World* published the story of the Chambers-Curtiss proposal, the Hamburg-American Steamship Company came forward with the "sporting offer" of the after-deck of their S.S. *Pennsylvania* for the experiment. A large platform was erected at a right angle to the ship on its stern. It sloped downward and was wide enough to allow an aeroplane space to gather headway for its flight. The plan was to take Jack McCurdy on the outward voyage from New York, and 10 miles at sea launch the machine for return to shore.

A mishap at the last moment upset all the plans. In trying out the engine just as the *Pennsylvania* was about to leave its dock at Hoboken, an oil can, carelessly left on one of the wings by a mechanic, was knocked into the whirling propeller. The result was a broken propeller, and since the ship could not delay its sailing schedule long enough for Curtiss to get another, the plane was lifted to the dock and the attempt abandoned.

Other Navy officers became curious as to whether or not such a flight was possible. Arrangements were made to construct an 83-foot launching platform on the bow of the heavy cruiser U.S.S. *Birmingham,* anchored at Hampton Roads, Virginia. The finished wooden ramp sloped at a 5-degree angle from the bridge to the main deck at the bow, and the forward edge was 37 feet above water.

Curtiss asked Eugene Ely, who was flying for him in an air show near Baltimore, if he would make the flight from the battleship. Although Ely was willing, his aeroplane had been just damaged during a storm and, in addition, the engine needed repairs. Curtiss immediately dispatched from Hammondsport one of his best mechanics with the necessary parts and a new engine. Ely's plane was quickly repaired at Hampton Roads Naval Base and put aboard the *Birmingham.* Because of a prior commitment Curtiss couldn't be present for the momentous event.

On November 14, in the mists off Old Point Comfort, the cruiser lay at anchor with the Curtiss biplane sitting on the platform ready for flight. Everyone aboard was waiting for good weather so that the test could get under way. But after waiting impatiently for several hours, Ely determined to risk a start, even though a strong wind coming offshore carried a heavy mist that made it almost impossible to see more than half a mile. Ely decided to take off before the fog closed in altogether. Two small launches and their crews were lowered over the side of *Birmingham* to act as possible rescue vessels. After the engine was started, Ely signaled the sailors to remove the blocks holding the wheel and give him a push. The aeroplane moved down the short runway under full power and dropped off the planking. Because it had gathered insufficient speed before it left the deck, it dropped so low observers thought the wheels must have touched the water. Fortunately, the aeroplane lifted quickly, and Ely flew straight to shore, where he landed on the beach at Willoughby Spit, two miles away.

This first flight from ship to shore resulted in a blaze of publicity. While most naval officials were seriously impressed, few were ready to accept Ely's short junket as convincing evidence that aeroplanes could yet be essential naval equipment. If the Navy brass wasn't sold, Curtiss and Chambers were.

While Captain Chambers battled the Navy Department bureaucrats, Curtiss tried another idea to break down military resistance. The first Army air squadron had become a reality in 1909, when Wilbur Wright gave flying instruction to three Army officers at College Park, Maryland, the first government air field. While two other officers learned to fly in the ensuing two years, there was no organized training program such as existed in European countries, where large numbers were being instructed to fly. Because there were no funds available for the purpose in the United States, on November 29, 1910, Curtiss sent to Secretary of War Jacob M. Dickinson and Secretary of the Navy George Von Lengerke Meyer an offer to teach flying without charge to one or more officers of their respective departments, as a means of assisting "in the developing the adaptability of the aeroplane to military purposes."

On December 23 Lieutenant Theodore Gordon Ellyson, a husky redhead who had graduated from the Naval Academy in the Class of 1905 and had had two commands in the submarine service, was ordered to the Glenn H. Curtiss Aviation Camp at North Island, California. After his training there and at Hammondsport, Ellyson became the Navy's first pilot.

The North Island camp had been established during the first week of December, 1910. While in Los Angeles early that year, Curtiss noted the advantage of Southern California's climate for year-round flying, something that was impossible at Hammondsport. In addition, Curtiss never cared for the cold winters around Lake Keuka. Thus the moving of a portion of his aircraft operation to North Island, an isolated island near San Diego, permitted him to continue his experimenting under conditions he considered ideal. It also allowed operation of his flying school the year around—in summer at Hammondsport, in winter at North Island.

The land mass of North Island, about 4 miles long and a mile or so wide, was flat as a pancake and covered with sagebrush. Spanish Bight, a strip of sheltered water, lay on one side of the island. At low tide, a stretch of narrow sand connected it with Coronado Island, but it was completely cut off from the mainland. This inaccessibility to the curious made it an ideal location for a flying camp. Curtiss leased the land from the Spreckels Company for under $100 a year.

Colonization of North Island moved forward rapidly. A machine shop was established by Damon Merrill, shop foreman of the camp. Then a workshop and two hangars were erected with the help of members of the San Diego Aero Club. Actually these buildings were wooden frames with canvas and tar paper covers that blew off with maddening regularity. A tent hangar for the hydro-aero equipment was set up on the beach. The only original structure on the island was a little cottage that served as living quarters for a few men, though most of them roomed in San Diego and shuttled back and forth daily by motorboat. Curtiss and his wife stayed for a while at the Coronado Beach Hotel, then they rented a house in Coronado.

While the camp was being completed and two aeroplanes assembled, Curtiss went to an air meet at San Francisco in which several of his exhibition pilots were taking part. There he met Rear Admiral Edward Barry, commander of the Pacific Fleet. The Admiral, who was a good friend of Captain Chambers, knew of Curtiss' desire to complete the experiment begun at Norfolk—to land an aeroplane on a ship and then take off.

The battleship U.S.S. *Pennsylvania* was made available and ordered to nearby Mare Island to be outfitted. This ship had nearly four times the tonnage and was 100 feet longer than the *Birmingham*. The platform was like that built on the *Birmingham*, but landing on it necessitated the development of a device of some sort to stop the aeroplane quickly.

The platform, built over the quarterdeck, was about 125 feet long by 30 feet wide, with a slope toward the stern of some 12 feet. Twenty-two cables were stretched taut across the runway, 12 inches above and at about 3-foot intervals. They were held in place at each end by sailor's sea bags containing 50 pounds of sand. Three hooks were hung under the standard Curtiss biplane to snag the cables. To protect the pilot, tarpaulins were stretched along either side and at the upper end of the runway.

Fortunately, Eugene Ely was flying in the air meet, and he volunteered to make the flight. Bad weather set in, but the air meet was automatically continued since the promoters had signed the aviators for ten flying days. One stormy day, as Curtiss visited the *Pennsylvania,* a reporter asked him what he thought the result of the flight would be. "This is the first time an aviator has attempted to land on a battleship," he answered. "Ely will alight on the *Pennsylvania*. I'm willing to guarantee that much. The only question is, can he do it without damaging his machine?"

Curtiss was deeply concerned. In spite of the elaborate precautions which he had supervised, it would require extreme precision to land safely on the narrow platform and avoid disaster. With the bad weather persisting, Curtiss was called back to San Diego on January 16 to clear up some difficulties that arose at North Island. The next day the weather improved.

At 10:53 on the morning of January 18, Ely took off from the Presidio parade grounds of Camp Selfridge, headquarters of the 30th Infantry, where the air meet was being held. The air was clear and fairly calm. He flew over land for a short distance and then headed for the warship anchored in the bay some 13 miles away. The *Pennsylvania* with its platform of new lumber aft was readily distinguishable from the air. A fleet of small boat launches stood by to rescue the aviator if he missed the runway. Ely circled the battleship and headed for the stern. Officers and enlisted men of the fleet watched him. They saw him dip a little more sharply than for a regular landing. At 40 mph, he skipped over the first eleven arresting cables on the *Pennsylvania*'s "flight deck," caught the twelfth, and was dragged to a smooth stop at 11:01, after a 30-foot landing run. The sand bags and taut lines worked. This landing-cable feature became the basis of today's very elaborate plane-snubbing system used by all naval carriers.

It was a truly skillful piece of flying. The harbor vessels tooted, the ship sirens shrieked, and the din continued during the forty-five minutes Ely was lunching with the officers of the Pacific Squadron. During the meal, Captain Charles F. Pond, the battleship's skipper, said, "I desire to place myself on record as positively assured of the importance of the aeroplane in future naval warfare. As a matter of fact, this feat which we are witnessing may revolutionize naval warfare even more than the first battle of the *Merrimac* and *Monitor*."

The machine was turned around and the ropes across the platform pulled away. The aviator shook hands with Admiral Barry and Captain Pond and, at 11:58, took off, dropped almost to the water again, rose, and flew back over the admiring crowds at the air meet and landed at Camp Selfridge.

Despite newspaper demands for immediate recognition of aviation as an important branch of its service, the Navy refused to be forced into precipitate action, advancing what seemed at the time like a plausible reason. They explained that a battleship would be handicapped by a platform like that built on the *Pennsylvania,* that it was impractical, that the gun turrets would remain a constant hazard.

Secretary of the Navy Meyer, in effect, suggested a compromise when he wrote Curtiss:

> Before you can convince us that the aeroplane is a weapon in which the Navy Department could officially interest itself, you will have to show us that you can land your plane, not on an interfering platform on a fighting ship, but on the sea alongside. When you have invented an aeroplane that can be picked up by a boat crane and dropped over the side to the water, so that the flyer can go off on an errand and later return to the water alongside, get picked up by the crane and brought back to the deck . . . well, then I shall be ready to say that the Navy Department is convinced.

The logic of Secretary Meyer's position was sound. Whereas an expert like Eugene Ely could make a perfect landing in a small space, disaster might easily overtake less skillful flyers. In his letter to Dr. Bell on August 19, 1908, Curtiss had stated that the scheme of starting a flying machine from and landing on the water had been on his mind for some time. Actually, the idea was not new. Hugo Matullath of New York had suggested it in patent applications in 1899. The Frenchman, Henri Fabre, had done it on March 28, 1910, in Mede Bay, near Marseille. He had made a flight of about 1,500 feet, but never rising more than a few feet off the water. His monoplane was equipped with three hollow flexibly mounted floats, one forward and two aft under the wings. After several other short hops, on May 18, he made a very successful water take-off and flew more than 2 miles at an altitude of 75 feet. Unfortunately, he landed at too steep an angle, and the hydroplane was wrecked.

While Fabre had used three floats, Curtiss, remembering his experience with two on the *Loon,* decided that a single main supporting surface would offer greater ease of take-off. Some sort of device at the wing tips would keep the machine from tipping while at rest. If Curtiss had paid more attention to the A.E.A.'s hydroplane type of boat hull on which Casey Baldwin had been working just before the dissolution of the Association, his task of shaping a pontoon would have been much simpler. Although a few hydroplanes had been built and proven in 1911, their design was not generally accepted. Under American Power Boat Association rules, for instance, all championship motorboats used displacement hulls, the theory being that the longer, narrower, and more sharply pointed they were, the faster they could be driven through water. Curtiss' experiments had convinced him, however, that the use of displacement-hull-type floats would not do. It was possible to accelerate to a good speed using long, narrow floats, but aircraft so equipped showed little inclination to leave the water and become airborne.

Many different floats had been built previously at Hammondsport during efforts to take off from the water in a standard Curtiss land-type biplane. At San Diego, Curtiss, Ellyson, George E. A. Hallett, Hugh A. Robinson, Charles C. Witmer, and a couple of mechanics under the direction of Damon Merrill worked together throughout the latter part of January, 1911, trying this scheme and that. It was essentially a question of finding the right curvature so that the water would not wrap itself around the pontoon and create a suction, of trying out pontoons until they found the right design.

At least fifty combinations of float shape, size, location, and angle of incidence were tried. Then on January 25 a new arrangement was tried. A small pontoon, about 6 feet wide, 1 foot from front to rear, and 6 inches at the deepest part, was placed where the front wheel had been. A short, wide pontoon, 6 feet wide, 7 feet from front to rear, and 10 inches thick at the deepest part, with a flat bottom that was angled downward from the front approximately 10 degrees, took the place of the rear wheels. When this rig was put in the water, it needed flotation on the wing tips to keep the machine from tipping over in the wind, so inflated motorcycle tubes were added to the ash "shingles," which acted as planing surfaces on the wing tips while the craft was taxiing on the water.

When the engine was started, the thrust of the propeller, which was about 4 feet above the water, pushed the nose under the water. A wood planing surface was then added at the nose. With this combination, Curtiss could taxi slowly, but water boiled over the top of the rear pontoon and the aeroplane could not get up any speed.

On the front of the rear pontoon they next built a "snout" of wood and canvas, which prevented the water from flowing over it and the added planing surface. With this combination, Curtiss could taxi a little faster; but as he opened the throttle, the nose pontoon was again pushed under water. They then extended a wide planing surface on bamboo poles about 6 feet ahead of the front pontoon. When Curtiss tested this unwieldy rig, it actually moved along rapidly on the surface of the water. He did not let it get into the air, but taxied around a little at high speed and finally skidded sidewise, in a turn, and wrecked part of the pontoon on a mud flat.

The next day, after repairs, Curtiss rode the machine across San Diego Bay. The craft felt increasingly lighter and was fairly skipping along. With the controls, he tilted it up in the front just as he had a hundred times before. But this time it rose from the surface of the water, flew for a minute and a half and landed. After that he made several short flights a few feet above the water in this weird contraption.

Once he had learned how to make a water take-off Curtiss proceeded to simplify the float arrangement. On January 31 a single float replaced the original conglomeration, thereby establishing a basic aircraft float configuration. The new design was a flat-bottomed, scow-shaped float, 12 feet long, 2 feet wide, and 1 foot deep. Made of thin spruce by the Baker Machine Company of Point Loma, the bow was curved upward and the stern downward. The float was placed under the aeroplane so that the weight was slightly to the rear of the float's center, causing it to slant upward in the necessary angle for hydroplaning on the surface of the water. Small cylindrical pontoons were attached to the ends of the lower wings in place of the wing skids.

After making a few final adjustments, Curtiss sent the machine across the water and in a few minutes took off and flew a half-mile. It was the most fun he had ever had. He took off a second time, flew several hundred feet high and over two miles out over the bay. The naval repair ship, the U.S.S. *Iris,* caught sight of him as he went flying by, and blasted her siren; other craft blew their whistles, until it seemed as if all San Diego knew of the achievement. Satisfied that the take-off problem had been solved, Curtiss landed within a few yards of the shore, near the hangar.

On February 17, after many test flights involving a great deal of experimenting, Curtiss was ready to demonstrate that this craft could satisfy naval requirements. He sent word to Captain Pond of the U.S.S. *Pennsylvania,* which was in San Diego Harbor, that he would like to fly over and be hoisted aboard whenever it was convenient. The Captain replied immediately, "Come on over right now." No special arrangement was necessary for this test. All that would be needed to get the aeroplane and its operator on board would be one of the big hoisting cranes used for handling the ship's launches.

Lieutenant Ellyson and Charles Witmer, one of the civilian air students at North Island, rode out to the battleship in a launch, while Curtiss gave the aeroplane a final check. After making sure the launch was alongside the *Pennsylvania,* he took off from Spanish Bight shortly before noon. In three or four minutes Curtiss landed alongside the warship, just off the starboard quarter. There was a strong tide running, and when he shut off the propeller, the machine drifted until a line thrown from the ship was made fast to one of the wings by Ellyson aboard the launch. The aeroplane was drawn close to the battleship, where a boat crane was lowered and Curtiss hooked it in a wire sling previously attached to the top wings. He then climbed on top of the aeroplane and slipped his leg through the big hook of the crane, not caring to trust too much weight to the untested sling.

In five minutes from the time Curtiss landed on the water alongside the ship, the hydro-aeroplane (seaplane) reposed on the superstructure deck of the *Pennsylvania*. After ten minutes, Curtiss climbed back into his craft and was lowered over the side by the big boat crane. The propeller was cranked by Ellyson aboard the launch and, after a few bounces, the aerocraft skimmed off the water and flew back to the shallow surf a few yards from the hangar on the beach. The entire time from the moment Curtiss left North Island for the *Pennsylvania* to the moment he landed on the water near the hangar was less than half an hour, and yet within that brief space naval aviation was born.

The San Diego *Union*'s account gives an idea of the general editorial reaction to the landing and take-off alongside a battle-ship:

> It was just like any other day's work for Curtiss. He set about it with the same assurance with which he flew the now famous *June Bug* at Hammondsport, N.Y., and put a crimp in the plans of the Wright brothers for cornering the aviation business in the United States.
>
> The entire program required less than half an hour to carry out. There was no hitch and not the least difficulty was experienced in hoisting the plane on board or lowering it over the side. The officers were enthusiastic over the ease with which the landing was accomplished.
>
> "We know now," Captain Pond said, "that a machine can rise from the water, fly alongside and be picked up, then go over the side and sail away. Or the process may be reversed as necessity requires."
>
> Secretary of the Navy Meyer has been shown. Another page in aerial history has been written full by the hand that already has penned so many chapters. But that is nothing to the unassuming, almost bashful king of the birdmen. He had set about doing an ordinary day's work and inwardly hoped the boss of the Navy Department would be satisfied.

A skeptical Navy was finally interested. Both land- and float-equipped planes could be used in conjunction with its precious battleships. No time should be lost, argued Chambers; enough had been squandered already. Naval officers worked closely with Curtiss in his over-water flying experiments.

In March, 1911, the Wright Company made a formal offer to Secretary Meyer to train one pilot provided that the Navy would purchase one of their aeroplanes. Then, because of severe criticism by the Navy Department and some Congress-men, in light of Curtiss' free training arrangement, the Wright Company quickly revised the offer, making it unconditional.

The Navy Department promptly ordered Lieutenant John Rodgers to Dayton, Ohio. Two months later, Lieutenant (j.g.) John H. Towers was sent to the Glenn Curtiss flying school at Hammondsport and Ensign Victor D. Herbster went to Dayton. During the next month, Ellyson was designated Naval Aviator No. 1, while Rodgers became No. 2, Towers No. 3, and Herbster No. 4.

The United States Army also accepted Curtiss' offer of free instruction, and Lieutenant John C. Walker of the 8th Infantry was detailed to North Island. Lieutenant Paul N. Beck of the Signal Corps and Lieutenant G. E. M. Kelly of the 30th Infantry, during the spring, were the next Army detail to the Curtiss aviation camp. Their names had been selected from a list of thirty applicants.

Within a week after the flight to the *Pennsylvania,* on February 23, Curtiss made a successful flight in what has been called the world's first amphibian. In this new aero-craft, he took off on pontoons from the inlet adjacent to North Island, and came down at Coronado Beach on wheels. Actually, all Curtiss had done, following a Hugh Robinson suggestion, was to fit his hydro-aeroplane with tricycle landing gear, with a simple lever arrangement which permitted lowering the wheels for landing or take-off on ground, and raising them for operation from water. (This was the first use of a retractable landing gear.) Adding wheels to a hydro-aeroplane was no great feat for Curtiss. He had already combined flotation gear and wheels to good advantage in *Albany Flyer.*

The Associated Press dispatch of February 23 from San Diego reported the flight of the new hydro-aeroplane as follows:

"Well, what shall we name the boat?" That was the point which most worried Glenn H. Curtiss, the daring American

aviator, when he today landed at the Coronado Hotel in his—
well, the name is yet to be coined.

He asked the question in all seriousness, and the detail of
a name appeared to him of more moment than the fact that
for the first time in the history of the world three elements
had been mastered by using but one machine.

He rose from the water in San Diego bay, flew to the sand-
spit connecting Coronado and North Island, came down to
get a new grip on the tricky, fish-tailed, 25 mile-an-hour wind,
then shot up from land and alighted on the beach near the
hotel just south of the pier.

After luncheon he replaced his rubber boots, tucked a fresh
newspaper between his waistcoat and coat, climbed into his
"what-you-may-call-it" and starting from the ground alighted
on the water at the North Island hangar.

The marvelous machine in which he thus accomplished the
safe navigation of three elements—land, water and air—is a
standard biplane equipped with a pontoon about three feet
wide by twelve feet in length, placed immediately between the
aviator and engine, with its long axis at right angles to the
planes. At the extremes of the lower plane are two small triangular copper tanks, whose function is to prevent the planes
from cutting too deeply in the water. These complete the
water factor.

Of all the names suggested, hydro-terra-aeroplane seems
most euphonious. For lack of a better title it has been tenta-
tively accepted.

From an army and naval standpoint this machine is a distinct advance over any previous type. Today's experiment is
the first since his arrival at San Diego in which Mr. Curtiss
has sought for improvement from the Army standpoint. His
previous work here has been of more importance to the Navy.
This machine is of particular importance to the coast artillery,
the work of which branch is closely allied to the Navy in time
of war.

The new "amphibious" aeroplane was officially called the *Triad* because of its three spheres—land, air, and water. This new craft had another difference. The first water machine was like all Curtiss biplanes, a pusher (with the propeller in back of the engine). In the second hydro-aeroplane, the engine was reversed, with the single propeller in front, making it a so-called tractor. But Curtiss found that the propeller blast interfered with his vision, and quickly returned to the previous propeller arrangement.

In Washington, Captain Chambers prepared requisitions for the purchase of two Curtiss biplanes and one Wright Model A land plane. One of the Curtiss flying machines was to be equipped as a *Triad;* with provisions for carrying a passenger alongside the pilot; and with controls that could be operated by either the pilot or the passenger. When completed, this machine became the Navy's first aeroplane, the A-1. Although these requisitions lacked the signature of the Chief of the Bureau of Navigation necessary to direct the general storekeeper to enter into a contract with the Curtiss Aeroplane Company, they did indicate Chambers' decision as to which aeroplanes the Navy should purchase, although Navy records show that the purchase requisition called for "an experimental machine," not an aeroplane. May 8 has come to be considered the date upon which the Navy ordered its first aeroplane and has been officially proclaimed to be the birthday of naval aviation.

The naval contract had added significance to Curtiss. It was the first major transaction of his new organization, the Curtiss Aeroplane Company. This new firm, as well as the Curtiss Motor Company, was formed as a result of the bankruptcy reorganization procedure of the Herring-Curtiss Company early in 1911.

The Navy's first aeroplane was completed at the Curtiss plant on July 1, and at 6:15 P.M. on that day G.H. demonstrated A-1 by taking off from and alighting on Lake Keuka— a flight of 5 minutes' duration and to an altitude of 25 feet. Three other flights were made the same evening, one by Curtiss with Lieutenant Ellyson as a passenger, and two by Ellyson alone. The following day, Ellyson qualified for his aviation pilot's license. To celebrate the event, the next day he flew the A-1 from Penn Yan to Hammondsport (22 miles) on the first night flight by a naval aviator, landing successfully on the water in the second attempt without the aid of lights.

When Captain Chambers received the A-1 at Hammondsport on July 6, he saw a small pusher-type biplane, which sat upon a fabric-covered, flat-bottomed mahogany float. Two cylindrical floats extended below each wing to prevent tipping on the water. "Overhanding" interplane ailerons extending beyond the equal-span wings (span 28 feet, 8 inches; chord and gap, 5 feet; total lifting area, 286 square feet) gave an over-all span of 37 feet.

Within a few days of its delivery with a 50-hp Curtiss engine, the A-1 was found underpowered and the newer Curtiss Model "M" 75-hp engine was substituted. This reliable power plant remained in the A-1 until the craft was scrapped. The A-1 flew at 60 mph with a maximum rpm of 1,250; throttled to 1,050, it cruised at 45 to 50 mph. Engine controls were crude but adequate. The two seats, control column, and a bar for a foot rest were fastened on the forward diagonal struts that connected the main float and the lower wing. The throttle or "accelerator" was pivoted upon the foot-rest bar accessible to the pilot's left foot; it worked like the gas pedal on an auto. The ignition switch consisted of an electrical wire extending from the magneto to the control wheel; a circuit breaker was attached to the wheel rim where the pilot's left thumb rested—hence the term "cutting the switch."

The A-1 used the conventional Curtiss flight control. Directional control was accomplished by turning the wheel which moved a small, all-movable vertical fin or rudder—"The result was something like steering a car." The pitch of the plane was controlled by the steering column, whose forward and backward motion operated the elevators. Banking was also a neat trick: a shoulder yoke moved the ailerons when the flyer moved his body from side to side. Thus if he saw the water coming up too fast on one side, by instinctively pulling away he would move the ailerons, thus righting the aircraft.

Ellyson and Curtiss perfected a "dual" control system for the aircraft in May, 1911. By mounting the control wheel on a throw-over arm, control could be shifted between pilots while in flight. The throttle and ignition switch was reserved for the pilot in the left-hand seat. A dual throttle and switch had to be added for the man who flew from the right-hand position.

Typical of Curtiss' flying machines, the A-1 was known for its light, sturdy, well-built construction. Curtiss had estimated all-up weight at 1,400 pounds—it came in at 1,575. The aeroplane itself weighed only 500 pounds. The floats added 128; the engine, prop and sundry items, another 300. Water for the radiator weighed 50 pounds, gas 180, and oil 40. After miscellaneous equipment totaling 27 pounds, 350 pounds were allowed for the two pilots. Two 175-pound men could fly with ease in the 75-hp A-1.

But the A-1's life wasn't all beer and skittles. Lieutenant Ellyson reported as follows: "No records were kept between July 21 and August 30 because the engine failed in so many respects that it had to be rebuilt. All breakage to engine and machine while experimenting or practicing, were repaired or replaced by the Curtiss Company without charge to the government. The Navy paid $5,000 for the A-1, including an extra set of landing wheels."

The first crash of the A-1 occurred on August 30. Ellyson logged this as follows: "Spark lead on magneto broke, engine stopped and land machine landed in Lake Keuka. Lt. Ellyson and Lt. Towers carried under water with the machine, but swam up through plane without injury. Machine capsized, breaking front control and three panels. Renewed magneto. Gasoline tank was removed to clean and by mistake the strainer was left out when reinstalled. Lead filings choked carburetor."

In September, 1911, A-1 was taken by train to the Greenburg Point Aviation Camp. Funds for this experimental and training camp were included in the Navy's 1911-12 appropriation of $25,000 for "experimental work in the development of aviation for naval purposes." Captain Chambers had selected an unused piece of government land at Greenburg Point, near Annapolis, for the purpose.

Under date of October 10, Ellyson reported troubles on the first trip with Towers, who was under instruction:

Started on flight to Old Point Comfort, Virginia, at 12:30 P.M., landed and ran on beach 30 miles below Annapolis on West Shore eight miles below Chesapeake Beach. Safety wire on after end of gasoline tank broken and one bolt out of after hangar on same. Underway at 1:00 P.M. Lt. Towers driving from right seat. At 1:20 P.M. landed on water off Cedar Point, and ran on beach. Bracket on carburetor adjuster broken. Underway at 1:30 P.M. Lt. Ellyson driving. Landed at 2:05 P.M. at Smith's Point, Virginia, owing to #3, #4, #7, and #8 crank bearings burnt out. Total distance 79 miles in 85 minutes. Disassembled the machine and placed it aboard the U.S.S. *Bailey,* which had been summoned by wireless, and the aeroplane was returned to Annapolis.

On October 25 the next attempt succeeded, with the A-1 making the 147 miles to Buckroe Beach, adjacent to Old Point, nonstop in 2 hours, 27 minutes—this despite a leaking radiator hose connection which Towers had to hold in place for more than an hour of flight. Not long after, Lieutenant Towers, in A-2, made a duration flight of 6 hours, 10 minutes, 35 seconds—a world's record for a hydro-aeroplane and an American record regardless of type.

The A-1 stayed at Greenburg Point Aviation Camp until January 2, 1912, at which time it was shipped by rail back to San Diego. It was housed in a tent on Curtiss' North Island base.

In spite of many troubles, flight and maintenance training in the A-1 continued at North Island until April 23. During part of this time, Ellyson was stationed with four other enlisted men at the naval radio station at Point Loma, overlooking San Diego Bay and North Island, and each flight became a free show for all hands. The A-1 went back to Annapolis at the end of May, 1911.

On October 10 Ellyson as "operator" and "Lt. B. L. Smith" as "passenger" took an eight-minute hop. This was the last flight of the A-1. On the page following the entry logging this flight there is typed: "Machine wrecked last flight." Under this is written in ink: "Expended except motor. Not rebuilt." The log closed with 54 hours' and 47 minutes' flight time. At the bottom of the page we find the signature "T. G. Ellyson by J. H. T."

Early experiments with A-1 yielded many useful facts and ideas. One was the shipboard launching device or catapult designed by Ellyson and Curtiss. Two heavy posts were driven into the ground near the lake shore to form an inverted V, the apex of which was 16 feet above the ground. A 250-foot length of ¾-inch steel cable secured at the top of the V, extended downward at a 10 percent incline to a submerged piling. A metal-lined groove was cut in the keel of the pontoon to fit the cable. The V was braced and a small platform built around it near the top. After the machine had been placed on the cable and backed up to the highest point, the pilot would, if all went well, take off from the cable after the plane had gathered sufficient momentum. Two light parallel cables, on which the wingtips rested, were intended to keep the hydro-aeroplane from tipping sideways before it attained flying speed. As it began to move, two men, each holding a wing line, would run alongside to help balance the craft as long as they could keep up with it.

After several trial runs of the aeroplane down the cable, the experimenters were ready, on September 7, to test the device under power. Two men stood by grasping the wing lines, another on the platform ready to spin the propeller. Ellyson, the pilot, wrote Captain Chambers of the first run:

> The engine was started and run at full speed and then I gave the signal to release the machine. . . . I held the machine on the wire as long as possible as I wanted to be sure that I had enough headway to rise and not run the risk of the machine's partly rising and then falling. . . . Everything happened so quickly and went off so smoothly that I hardly knew what happened except that I did have to use the ailerons, and that the machine was sensitive to their action.

While the Hammondsport launching rig worked well, it was obvious that it was impractical for service use. Captain Chambers and Naval Constructor Holden C. Richardson designed and constructed a compressed-air catapult at the Naval Gun Factory under the direction of Lieutenant St. Clair Smith. On

July 31, 1912, it was tested. But the aero-craft, not being secured to the catapult, reared when the plunger of the compressor was at the mid-stroke point whereupon the craft was caught in a cross wind and thrown into the water. The pilot was not injured, but by November 12 Richardson's improvements made possible successful take-offs of the Triads. So far as Curtiss was concerned, the catapult was the most important flying device since the addition of wheels to land planes.

There was an "unavoidable delay" in the delivery of A-2. In some respects the new hydroplane was to be similar to A-1; in others it was to be different. Since no complete set of plans of the earlier machine had been made, the workmen were supposed to remember how it had been built. The white walls of the design shop were covered with sketches made by Kleckler and Curtiss for their benefit, until a new employee, having been told to clean up the shop, whitewashed over all the sketches. This little episode delayed completion of the A-2 by about a week, for nobody, not even Curtiss, could reproduce the sketches. The A-1 was in Maryland, and most of the changes had to be worked out all over again.

A-2 was finally delivered in August of 1911 and enjoyed a long and useful life. It was afterward converted into the E-1, or Experimental Machine No. 1 and used as the "Owl"—*O*ver *W*ater and *L*and—machine (another name for Triad) in tests at Hammondsport. Many notable flights were made by the A-2/E-1 throughout 1911-13. The Wright plane, when delivered, was given the designation "B-1." (The "B" indicated a second manufacturer.)

Other A's were built, and soon Hammondsport became the "unofficial" headquarters of naval aviation. For a while, the town even had an official U.S. Navy Camp, consisting of a tent hangar and a group naval officers and Navy mechanics, located on Lake Keuka. With full access to the Curtiss factory, the mechanics had an excellent opportunity to learn about engine and aeroplane assembly. The officers learned about aero design from Curtiss, while he had their assistance in solving knotty problems.

Chapter 7

MAKING AVIATION A PAYING AFFAIR

WHILE the Navy was experimenting with hydro-aeroplanes, Curtiss tackled the job of building a boat that would fly off the water. The first hull with a pair of wings attached was modeled somewhat after the shape of the hydro pontoon. From the front it resembled an ordinary flat-bottom boat. The engine was in the hull in front of the pilot's seat. It had two chain-driven tractor propellers. It was shipped to North Island from Hammondsport, and Curtiss motored patiently all over San Diego Bay in it, but with never a "real" take-off.

On January 10, 1912, he managed one brief departure from the water, but he was not able to do it again. Obviously the flat-bottom hydro-pontoon was not the answer. That spring, the flying boat was shipped to Hammondsport for major changes. The engine was moved back between the wings to drive a single pusher propeller.

The results of further experimentation on Lake Keuka were the same: the flying boat refused to become unstuck from the water and fly. Then, early in the summer, Curtiss and Naval Constructor Holden Richardson, who was also interested in the possibility of flying boats, went out on the lake in a power boat to study, at close hand, the interaction of the flying boat hull and the water. After following the machine around for nearly three hours, they returned and Curtiss told Henry Kleckler to attach a couple of wedge-shaped blocks to the bottom of the hull to form a step. "Perhaps in this way, the suction on the after part of the hull can be broken up."

Whether the idea of the step was Richardson's or Curtiss' is not too important. The wedges were screwed onto the bottom of the hull, and the first flying boat in the world left the water readily. The little step on the bottom had done the trick.

The rest of the process, most of which was a matter of streamlining, was clear sailing. The bullet-shaped hull, resembling that of a flying fish, which evolved that year, as well as the general structural principles, have survived in flying boats to the present.

Most of the design bugs in early aircraft were "flown out" rather than worked out in an engineering fashion. And many of the new design features were "flown in." For instance, while testing a hydro one day, Curtiss noticed that after take-off the craft acted sluggishly and maneuvered like a lame duck. He decided to land to see what the problem was. But instead of going into its normal landing glide, the machine went into a dive. Frantically he pulled back on the control, with no effect. The aeroplane dove right down into the lake.

Curtiss was thrown clear, and a motorboat which started to his rescue met him swimming calmly ashore. He told them to check on the hydro while he swam in. He had already guessed the trouble. The pontoon had sprung a leak while skimming over the lake, and it was half full of water, which had rushed forward when he started his landing glide.

Without even changing his dripping clothes he drove to the factory and told Kleckler to change the pontoon specifications:

"By dividing all floats into several compartments, we can keep this fool trick from happening again."

There was, of course, some "scientific" testing, too. For instance, the 1908 wind tunnel designed by Lieutenant Self-ridge was replaced by an outdoor type employing a flying boat. The wing sections to be tested were balanced on braces a few feet above the top wing of the flying boat, and checked by means of a system of springs, levels, and indicators, Curtiss and his associates obtained performance curves. Observations were made while the flying boat was moving over the water and in flight. A man was obliged to stand on a light scaffolding erected over the aviator's head and hang on precariously while he took the readings.

Having perfected the flying boat, Curtiss launched the new sport of aerial yachting. Here, according to the sales patter, was a "flying machine in which it is practically impossible for the operator to suffer injury in case of accident. Even in the worst kind of accident, the most that can happen to the operator is an exhilarating plunge into fresh or salt water, as the case may be, with the beneficial effects of a good swim if so desired."

By September, 1912, Curtiss had begun production of his two-seat "aero-yacht," advertising it regularly in several flying magazines and sports publications. "ON the Water, OVER the Country Faster than 60 miles an Hour!" ran the caption on one. "For speed and pleasure, it puts motor boating out of the running. It's a revelation to the red-blooded sportsman."

There was, however, no immediate rush of orders for flying boats, although orders for hydro-aeroplanes had begun to come in from abroad. Louis Paulhan became the first Curtiss Company foreign agent; an order for a two-seated hydro and a request for a demonstrator came from the Russian Aerial

League. In February, 1912, Hugh Robinson, a former Curtiss student who became his chief European salesman, made the first water flights in Europe while demonstrating the hydro at Nice before official representatives of several European governments. That August, Curtiss himself went abroad to close contracts for hydros for England, Germany, Italy, France, Russia, and Japan. Twenty hydros had been shipped previously to foreign naval bases. Private business did not begin until early in 1913.

In January, 1913, Curtiss went to San Diego, intending to stay until May. But when he heard that Harold F. McCormick of the International Harvester Corporation was interested in the flying boat and might come to Hammondsport for a demonstration, he realized that this might be the break that would launch his boat's sporting career. Curtiss returned East immediately, calling on McCormick in Chicago on the way. McCormick followed him to Hammondsport, liked the flying boat, and ordered a two-passenger one for commuting between his home at Lake Forest and his office in Chicago. Charley Witmer was engaged as his pilot.

Once Witmer started flying McCormick daily along the Lake Front and dropping him at the Chicago Yacht Club basin, only a few yards from Michigan Avenue, it occurred to other sportsmen that here was something which had the flavor of a water sport with the zest of flying thrown in. Logan A. (Jack) Vilas of Chicago led the procession of would-be sportsmen-pilots to Hammondsport. Marshall E. Reid of Philadelphia was the second customer, and then William Thaw III of Pittsburgh and W. Stevenson MacGordon of New York drove gaily up to the Curtiss factory looking for a brace of water aircraft. G. M. Heckscher of New York ordered a flying boat and sent William "Buzz" King to Hammondsport to learn to fly it for him. There were orders for aero-yachts from William

B. Scripps, Detroit publisher; from George L. Peck, vice president of the Pennsylvania Railroad; and from George U. von Utassy, J. B. R. Verplanck, and Harry Harkness of New York. With customers like these buying hydro-aeroplanes at $5,000 and standard two-passenger flying boats at $7,000, the Curtiss Aeroplane Company began to feel a little easing of its financial strain.

By 1913 the Curtiss Company was producing ten distinct types of overwater machines, ranging from a single-passenger monoplane, through several styles of two- and three-passenger machines, to pleasure cruisers for four and five passengers. The most popular, however, was the Curtiss Model F, which was designed primarily as a sportsman's craft. It was of the pusher type, had a maximum speed of 65 miles per hour, a minimum speed of 45 miles an hour in the air, and would climb at the rate of 1,500 feet in 10 minutes. Its over-all length was 28 feet, and it had an upper wing span of 45 feet, 2 inches and a lower wing span of 35 feet, with a cord of 5 feet, 2 inches. It was built to carry two passengers abreast.

The fastest and smallest of the flying boats was the one Curtiss designed especially for Raymond V. Morris of New Haven, Connecticut. It was the first monoplane flying boat ever flown in the United States, and its supporting surfaces were less than one-third the area of the average biplane. The wing was of a new design, resembling that of a giant bird. Slanting back at an angle of 7 degrees from the center, it measured 34 feet from tip to tip and was fitted with ailerons. Weighing almost 1,200 pounds when fully loaded, the aeroplane's wing loading was but 10 pounds per square foot.

The Morris craft's hull was cigar-shaped and was 22 feet long with a beam of 30 inches and a depth of 3 feet. Its construction was completely new: two layers of very thin mahogany wrapped diagonally around a basket-like framework of ash. The mahogany planking was separated by a layer of "sea island" cotton set in marine glue. Only the top of the aviator's head projected through the single small opening in the deck. This airboat was flown at speeds of over 100 miles an hour!

The popularity of flying boats in 1913 was phenomenal, according to the press. Aviation and "science" magazines carried reports of a thousand men buying boats that year. Curtiss knew the number was exaggerated. He had sold only forty-four machines to sportsmen in 1913, and he was the only *major* producer. Nevertheless, boom days for private over-water business had definitely arrived, and he had more reason than ever before to be optimistic.

As a consequence of his naval and marine aviation work, Glenn Curtiss received the Robert J. Collier Trophy for his hydro-aeroplane of 1911, and for his flying boat of 1912. This aviation award was given in honor of Robert J. Collier, publisher of *Collier's Weekly* and member of the original Wright Company board of directors. Curtiss also received the Aero Club's Gold Medal in 1911 and 1912, and the Langley Gold Medal of the Smithsonian Institution in 1913 for his marine aviation pioneering. The latter medal, which was fashioned from a pound of pure gold, was presented to Curtiss by Dr. Bell—the first time the two former associates had met face to face since February, 1909. Actually, Dr. Bell departed from his usual practice and read his speech verbatim to avoid any argument as to what he did or did not say. His speech was warm and cordial toward his "friend," and was interpreted as a complete vindication of the claim that Curtiss originated the conception of the hydro-aeroplane. This served to dispel the opinion of some "authorities" that the original idea of constructing *Loon* came from Casey Baldwin or Jack McCurdy —or even Dr. Bell.

June 8, 1911, saw Curtiss awarded pilot's license No. 1, United States of America, from the Aero Club of America, under authority of the Féderation Aéronautique Internationale (F.A.I.). Actually, the matter of license priority caused some debate. A number of people felt that the Wright brothers, because they were known to have flown five years before 1908, should be awarded licenses No. 1 and No. 2. But the Aero Club contest committee ruled that Curtiss' was the first officially observed and recognized flight in America and that he was properly entitled to the honor. License No. 2 went to Lieutenant Frank P. Lahm (Army Pilot No. 1); No. 3, to Louis Paulhan; No. 4, to Orville Wright; and No. 5, to Wilbur Wright. The 1911 F.A.I. license test required the would-be pilot to take off and make five consecutive figure eights around two pylons set a thousand feet apart, and to make an accurate landing, stopping the machine within 50 feet of a given mark. This test had to be completed twice and, either during the flying of the figure eights or during a separate flight, the plane had to reach an altitude of 500 feet.

Beginning in 1912, another important step forward in aviation was undertaken. While Curtiss was in Europe, his superintendent of engine production, John H. McNamara, tried several techniques to get more power from the 80-horsepower Model O type. While testing a slight change in valve action, he noted that the engine was producing at normal speeds some 90 to 95 horsepower. He kept this information to himself until Curtiss returned and then, after considerable hesitation, demonstrated that the modified Model O, on a brake test, was capable of producing more than 105 horsepower.

At first, Curtiss thought there must be some error in the calculations. But a careful rechecking showed that the change in the valve action made the Model O more powerful. The new engine type was originally designated Model O+, until someone mistakenly changed the plus sign to an "X" and made it read OX.

When the OX was produced as a "stock" Curtiss engine, it was rated at 90 horsepower at 1400 rpm. The bore was 4 inches, with a stroke of 5 inches. The cast-iron cylinders, which were arranged in two banks at a 90-degree angle, had Monel-metal water jackets, and the overhead valves were operated by two concentric push rods. The inner rod operated the exhaust valve through large rockers, and the outer rod, worked by a powerful spring and an aluminum rocker arm, pulled the inlet valve open at the proper time. The crankshaft had five bearings, and the connecting rods were mounted side by side. The weight of the engine, with propeller hub but without oil or water, was only 375 pounds—a dead weight of 4.17 pounds per horsepower.

Late in 1913, a new, large, V-type engine—Model V—was developed. This power plant had 8 cylinders and was rated at 160 horsepower at 1400 rpm. A later model, the V-2, also with 8 cylinders, gave 220 horsepower. This engine, with a bore of 5 inches and a stroke of 7 inches, had cylinders of drawn steel, with a steel water jacket top and a Monel-metal cylindrical jacket, both of which were brazed to the cylinder barrel. A 12-cylinder model, the V-3, was originally rated at 250 horsepower, but actually gave about 300 horsepower at 1500 rpm. The V-2 engine was the most used of the V series.

Curtiss engines were still being used by motorcycle and dirigible builders, and he wanted to enter the auto engine field. Once, when he had installed an aeroplane motor in his big 6-cylinder Keaton automobile, it worked so well he announced he would lay a bet that he could travel to Bath and back on one gallon of gasoline. The distance was 16 miles, and 10 miles to a gallon was good average mileage at the time. J. B. R.

Verplanck, sportsman-pilot, put up a suit of clothes and a hat, so certain was he of the preposterousness of Curtiss' wager. The newspaper correspondents, students, and others followed his example. The tank was drained, two gallons put into it, and Curtiss and an observer started off on their journey to Bath.

When they returned, there was great excitement. While the crowd looked on, four quarts were drained out of the tank. Curtiss glanced up to ask whether anybody wanted to bet him he wouldn't get another quart and found more takers. One more quart was drawn out. "All right," said Curtiss, "how about another pint?" The few diehards who responded, "Sure I'll see you," whistled in amazement when another pint, with a few drops over, was extracted from the tank. According to exact calculation, he must have made 24½ miles to the gallon. G.H. spent the next several years trying to wear out all the shirts, collars, ties, and other clothes he had won.

In the early fall of 1912, Henry Ford visited Hammondsport to discuss the possible use of the Curtiss lightweight aeroplane engine in his Model T automobiles. He had several different types sent to Detroit for test, but the engines were too expensive for low-cost cars. Curtiss tried to interest the automobile manufacturer in purchasing a flying boat. Although he failed to make a sale, he and Ford became good friends.

The flying school portion of the Curtiss Aeroplane Company was busy in 1911 and 1912 with both military and civilian students. There were two regular training camps—the summer school at Hammondsport and the winter school at North Island, San Diego. The former was open from the fifteenth of April until the fifteenth of November, and the latter from November 15 to April 15. These were supplemented during the cold months each year by another school in Florida. The Curtiss Training School booklet describes the course as follows:

There is no rushing through the training, no turning out of aviators with a meager knowledge of aeroplanes hastily acquired. The pupil is not put through in a week or two as is the case with many so-called aviation schools, but is given a knowledge of the theory of aviation and a practical training in the care of an aeroplane. Mr. Curtiss believes that every pupil in aviation should have a thorough practical instruction before he is allowed to attempt a flight. He must know the Curtiss machine, its construction, and its motor before he is allowed to make any extensive flight.

The student will be taught to run the machine over the field on the ground in order to accustom himself to the control. Afterwards he will be allowed to make short "jumps" with a machine that will not rise higher than a few feet from the ground. When he has learned to make landings from this height, he will be put on a more powerful machine and allowed to make straight flights the length of the training field. After this, comes the important part of his training, and that is, to make circles and landings from a great height, successfully. The pupil must know what to do should the engine stop high in the air, and with this idea in mind, he is taught how to glide safely and to learn how to land properly. All this is taught to the Curtiss pupils by a practical and competent aviator, and under the supervision of Mr. Curtiss himself.

The early aeroplane was fairly easy to control, but learning to fly was a different story. There were no instruments to guide the fledgling pilot or even the experienced flyer. The early aviator generally relied upon the rush of air against his face or the flutter of his shirt sleeve to assure him that he was going at the desired speed. The pilot usually estimated the revolutions per minute by listening to the engine. The first primitive instruments were introduced late in 1912, but they were not, in the beginning, overly dependable.

In the first three years of the Curtiss school, represented

among the pupils were the following nationalities: English, French, Scots, Irish, Germans, Russians, Spaniards, Mexicans, Greeks, Chinese, Japanese, Cubans, and one Hindu. The latter, Mohan Singh, had come from far-off India to enroll in the school. This tall, gaunt, young Oriental, who seldom smiled, never ate meat, and never drank anything but water, was one of the most agreeable souls imaginable. He passed his Féderation Aéronautique Internationale (F.A.I.) test at North Island, but Singh wanted to learn how to fly a flying boat so he could purchase one to take to his homeland.

There were also several women students at the school from time to time. The first was Blanche Stuart Scott. She was a very good student and later became the first woman professional pilot in America. Others included Julia Clark, who became an exhibition flyer; Lillian Platt Atwater, who flew with her husband in China and Japan; Ruth Law Oliver, who became a star attraction at fairs and aviation meets; and Katherine Stinson, who was the first woman to carry mail by aeroplane under the direct authority of the Post Office Department.

Several other graduates of the school stayed on in Curtiss' employ as members of his exhibition team. In 1911, 80 percent of the successful aviation exhibitions and contests conducted in the United States were directed by the Curtiss Exhibition Company, with 541 flying dates in 210 cities and towns. From December, 1910, to December, 1912, its gross receipts were over $1,000,000. But overhead expenses were so high that only a small net profit was realized. However, the organization's primary function was to keep Curtiss aeroplanes and engines before the public, and in this the results were rewarding.

Former students, including Cromwell Dixon, Beckwith Havens, James J. Ward, Hugh Robinson, Charley Witmer,

Robert C. St. Henry, Charles Walsh, and Lincoln Beachey, had become popular exhibition flyers. Beachey dazzled the country on June 28, 1911, by flying over Niagara Falls, down the gorge and under the suspension bridge. A one-time dirigible aeronaut with Captain Baldwin, Beachey had joined the Curtiss team in 1910. He promptly wrecked two aeroplanes, but went on to become, in the opinion of his boss, "the greatest aviator of all." On the ground Link Beachey appeared as sedate as a deacon and was always neatly attired, with a celluloid collar and a jeweled stickpin. In the air he was a wild man. A Frenchman made the first loop-the-loop by accident, but Beachey made it a standard part of his repertoire of flying tricks.

The Wright Company had difficulty recruiting good flyers because of their policy of never letting their aviators keep any of the prizes they won. The company flyers were paid a base salary of $20 a week, and $50 a day when they flew. A good flyer, who didn't have any crack-ups, could earn $5,000 or $6,000 a year. On the other hand, the Curtiss Company aviators were allowed to keep 50 percent of all the prizes they won, plus a small salary. Some of the better-known flyers had even more lucrative arrangements. For example, Becky Havens— who began his aviation career as Curtiss' first aeroplane salesman and became the Midwest's most popular flyer—worked at first for 25 percent of the gross contract price, later for 50 percent. As the contracts ranged from a minimum of $500 to a maximum of $2,000 a day, Havens soon amassed a nice bank account.

To the adventurous young flyers, the "big money" talk was very alluring. As a result, many Curtiss graduates joined exhibition teams. It would not be fair, however, to imply that all the students at the Curtiss flight schools became devil-may-care barnstorming aviators. Lawrence B. Sperry, for instance, took up flying primarily to assist in the work of his father,

Dr. Elmer A. Sperry, the inventor of the gyro-compass and gyro-stabilizers for ships. Curtiss and the elder Sperry became acquainted through Captain Chambers, and both were convinced that a gyroscope might be harnessed to the controls of an aeroplane. To foster Sperry's work, Curtiss suggested that young Lawrence, better known as "Gyro," enter the flight school at Hammondsport.

During the summer of 1913, Lawrence quickly qualified for an F.A.I. pilot license, in a Curtiss flying boat. Both he and Dr. Sperry worked for months in the Curtiss shop trying to perfect a gyro unit that would originate signals to operate the elevators and ailerons like a human pilot. Then Lawrence spent the winter at North Island, experimenting with the gyro-stabilizer unit. By the spring of 1914 the forerunner of the modern autopilot was ready for public demonstration. Lawrence went to France, taking with him a Curtiss biplane equipped with the gyro-stabilizer. The French War Department had offered a 50,000-franc prize for the best flight safety device. There were some fifty-three entrants.

On June 18 Lawrence Sperry lifted the Curtiss off the waters of the Seine near Paris. At an altitude of about 600 feet the pilot could be seen to rise from his seat, while the mechanic climbed out on one of the wings, well to the side of the craft's center of gravity. The shift of weight produced no effect: the craft flew on, level and true. The mechanic then climbed to the tail of the ship, with similar results. The gyro mechanism was holding the craft level against radically unstabilizing movements, plainly without human control. The demonstration was convincing and won Lawrence the prize. The modern autopilot was born, hardly a decade after the first powered flight. Later in the year, the Robert J. Collier Trophy was awarded to Dr. Sperry for his and Lawrence's work on gyroscopic control.

Most of the male students stayed at the Aviators' Home, as Mrs. Lulu Mott's boarding house on Sheather Street was affectionately called. Her arrangements were simple—pay five dollars a week and eat all you can. For night entertainment, they went dancing at Mrs. Young's pavilion down the lake or to the movies over the firehouse and they visited the bowling alley installed by Jim Smellie next door to his drugstore. If the students became a little unruly, the Curtiss instructors acted as police, judge, and jury, with the usual sentence being two days' suspension from flying. Luckily, the sentence seldom had to be imposed.

During 1912 Curtiss found little time to devote to either his schools or the exhibition company. He was too engrossed with improving the flying boat and furthering the practical aspects of aviation. For instance, he claimed that sportsmen would find the aeroplane, especially the hydro, an admirable vehicle for hunting. Hubert Latham, while in California for an air meet, demonstrated that it was possible to shoot wild ducks from a Curtiss hydro-aeroplane. Later he flew into the Rocky Mountains in an attempt to shoot a grizzly bear. His last undertaking was to take his aeroplane with him to the Congo for use in hunting big game. Ironically, after having braved the dangers of flight since 1908, he was gored to death by a wounded and infuriated wild buffalo in July, 1912.

Another demonstration designed to arouse public interest in flying was the first recorded doctor-to-patient flight. Dr. Philias Alden was flown by Hugh Robinson from Hammondsport to the home of an injured child in nearby Bath. The physician could have reached his patient's bedside by automobile in less time than it took to get to the field and make the flight, but the story was given wide press coverage and won public acclaim. Fortunately, the boy's condition was not serious.

Curtiss had always maintained, "When we've got the aeroplane perfected, we won't have to press its claims on the Post
Office. It will become the long-distance postman automatically."

Air mail was first actually handled at Allahabad in India
in 1911. A mail route via aeroplane was on trial between
London and Windsor. In the fall of that year Postmaster General Hitchcock was at Nassau Boulevard Airfield, Long Island,
where Curtiss was training some students. On September 23,
Lieutenant Dewitt Milling had just established a new American altitude record, when a tall, youngish-looking man in a
blue serge suit and a gray cap, with the visor at the back of his
head, climbed into a Curtiss aeroplane driven by Captain Paul
Beck of the United States Army. The rest of the story is told
by Frank O'Malley in the New York *Sun:*

> "The Honorable Frank H. Hitchcock, Postmaster-General
> of the United States," the megaphone man announced "will
> now fly to Mineola with Captain Beck to deliver the mail.
> Postmaster Hitchcock will carry the mailbag on his knees and
> drop the bag at Mineola in a circle in which will be the post-
> master of Mineola."
>
> Mr. Hitchcock was far out on the field with Attorney-
> General Wickersham and Captain Beck. Postoffice Inspector
> Doyle handed the postmaster-general a mail bag containing
> 1,440 postcards and 162 letters and Captain Beck and Mr.
> Hitchcock flew off in a northerly direction.
>
> The Curtiss machine circled three-quarters of the field and
> then climbed rapidly until it was 300 or 400 feet above the
> south end of the track. Earl L. Ovington who had also got
> under way with a second bag of mail in his monoplane, shot
> up in the same acre of sky occupied by Captain Beck and
> Mr. Hitchcock and shot eastward as a track finder for Cap-
> tain Beck.
>
> The field could see the two machines almost all the time

in the cross-country flight. Over a big white circle at Mineola, Ovington from his monoplane and Mr. Hitchcock from Captain Beck's machine plumped the two pouches and hit the circle in each case.

"Air routes," said Mr. Hitchcock, "are all right for practical mail-carrying. The vehicles will continue toward perfection. I would like to see the postoffice department do something definite in this direction for the good effect it will have in stimulating the development of the machine."

In ten days 43,000 pieces of mail were carried. Postmaster General Hitchcock then asked Congress for an appropriation of $50,000 for further experiments. The Post Office Department budget carried that item every year until 1916. Curtiss planes and Curtiss flyers had a major share in the development of the air post of those years. These Curtiss men, among others, were licensed in 1911 and 1912 for the carrying of mail: Milling, Ovington, Henry (Hap) Arnold, Hugh Robinson, Charley Walsh, Becky Havens, Charley Witmer, Eugene Godat, and Link Beachey. To be of value, Curtiss felt that air mail must be carried a considerable distance; and on October 9, 1911, Robinson, in a Curtiss hydroplane, carried a load of first-class mail 375 miles, from Winona, Minnesota, to Rock Island, Illinois, with stops at Prairie du Chien, Wisconsin, and Clinton, Iowa. Though this flight made an excellent impression, Congress failed to approve the recommendation by the Post Office Department of an appropriation for air mail experiments.

Actually, little financial aid was to be expected from official governmental sources by American aeroplane inventors and manufacturers. Congress had appropriated $125,000 for U.S. Army aeronautics in February, 1911, and decided to establish aviation training stations at San Diego, College Park, Maryland, and Omaha, Nebraska. In March of that year, the first

Curtiss military aeroplane was accepted by the Army and sent to the Texas-Mexican border for use by the U.S. Army encamped there. It was the second plane purchased for use in the Army flying school, and was officially designated Signal Corps Aeroplane No. 2. Actually, it was a Curtiss Model D, two-place pusher, powered by a 50-horsepower E-4 engine. It had a wing span of 38 feet, was 26 feet in length, and weighed 1,387 pounds—the heaviest aeroplane in the U.S. Army.

But even the slight governmental interest in aeronautics shown in 1910 and 1911 started to taper off. The Navy could see no way in which to expend so large a sum as $25,000 during 1911-12, and a surplus was reported returned to the Treasury. The lack of interest in aviation, however, was primarily confined to the United States. Other governments were spending comparatively huge sums, as can be seen by the amounts appropriated by the leading nations of the world during 1912:

France	$7,400,000	Italy	$2,100,000
Russia	5,000,000	Great Britain	2,000,000
Germany	2,250,000	Japan	600,000
United States	140,000		

(Army: $115,000; Navy: $25,000)

Actually, the United States stood fourteenth in the list, below not only Spain, but Greece and Bulgaria. An estimate, as of March, 1913, of the total governmental expenditures for aeronautical work during the preceding five years approximated $100 million. This itemized report credited Germany with 400 aeroplanes and 30 dirigibles, acquired and maintained at an expense of $28 million; France had the same number of aeroplanes and 25 dirigibles, at an expenditure of $22 million. England, with 100 aeroplanes and 6 dirigibles, had spent $3 million, whereas the United States had spent a mere $435,000. Its total military equipment consisted of 28 aeroplanes (14 of which could be called obsolete) and one dirigible.

U.S. Army and Navy officials had so little money to spend they were forced to demand an unusually high return on their investment, and specifications for military aeroplanes were very stiff. Those issued by the Navy Department for hydro-aeroplanes in 1912, for instance, stipulated as a full load, two passengers with a combined weight of 350 pounds, plus wireless gear and other necessary instruments. While a maximum speed of at least 55 miles an hour was stipulated under most conditions, the required 4-hour nonstop flight with full load could be made at an acceptable minimum of 50 miles an hour. Under still-air conditions, the aeroplane had to take off from the water with a run of less than 1,000 feet. It also had to be seaworthy, when the engine was dead, in 20-mile-an-hour wind velocity. In addition, the aeroplane had to be so constructed that it could be hoisted intact aboard ship, and be capable of quick disassembly. The later Curtiss A models of Triads, of course, met all the Navy's rigid specifications. The Model C flyboat, which was similar to the Model F but larger, was also acceptable.

As a matter of expediency and economy, the Army decided to limit its purchase to two types of aircraft. The first, to be known as the Scout series, was to be a two-seater with dual controls, capable of a minimum of 45 miles an hour and a maximum of not more than 60. When fully loaded, including instruments and wireless equipment, the Scout had to be able to climb to at least 2,000 feet in 10 minutes, with a flight duration of at least 3 hours. The second type of machine, called the Speed Scout series, was to be a single-seater which would be employed for strategical reconnaissance. Its speed was to be not less than 65 miles an hour, with a climbing capability of 600 feet per minute and a range of approximately 100 miles.

During February, 1913, the Army issued a completely new set of specifications for its Scout series. The speed requirements were lowered to a range of 38 to 55 miles an hour, while endurance was increased to 4 hours with a minimum range of 180 miles. Take-off and landing, using harrowed fields or fields covered with high grass, had to be within 300 feet. Another specification required that the fuselage be protected with chrome sheet steel, 0.075 inch thick. Special preference was to be given aeroplanes equipped with an efficient stabilizing device, an engine with a self-starter operable by the pilot, an effective muffler with a cutout, and a geared "tractor" propeller.

The latter stipulation was the one that gave Curtiss most concern. He had attempted on several occasions to build tractor-type aeroplanes, but with little luck. All his successful designs had been of the pusher variety. However, Curtiss had the foresight to realize that the open pusher designs were on the way out and that the tractor type, with the engine mounted in the nose of an enclosed fuselage, was the coming aircraft.

With an eye on the 1913 Army specifications for the Scout, Curtiss developed his Model G. This two-seater, employing a side-by-side arrangement, used a 3-blade, geared tractor propeller, and had a top speed of 53 miles an hour. The fuselage, with a length of 24 feet, was fully covered, and the biplane wings had a span of 37 feet, 4 inches, with a chord width of 61 inches. The wings were made as a single unit, out from the center section, and had a slight rearward dihedral or angle. Interplane ailerons were still employed. Landing gear was close-coupled tricycle; normally the aft fuselage re-mained clear of the ground, but a tail skid was fitted as pro-tection from hard landings.

The Model G, however, was not a notable success and only two were built. Curtiss, recognizing his inability to design a tractor aircraft, decided that the easiest way to obtain Army business would be to employ an aeronautic designer who was already thoroughly experienced in this type of aeroplane. He hired B. Douglas Thomas, an Englishman who had worked for Avro and Sopwith, Britain's two leading aeroplane build-ers, who had been notably successful in tractor designs. Thomas started to work on the new Curtiss tractor, designated Model J, while still in England and completed it shortly after moving to Hammondsport.

The Model J was a tandem two-seater with dual controls. Its upper wing measured 43 feet, 10 inches, while the lower spanned 32 feet. The chord for both was 5 feet. Powered by an OX-5 engine, the Model J's speed range was 40 to 75 miles an hour, and its initial rate of climb was 400 feet per minute. Duration of flight time was about 4 hours.

For the first time a Curtiss aeroplane had the radiator, en-gine, and cockpits set in line in an enclosed fuselage. Actually, this machine pretty well standardized the aerodynamic and structural pattern for all subsequent American tractor bi-planes. The control system was of the standard Curtiss type. That is, the ailerons were operated by a shoulder yoke, with the aviator leaning in the direction he wanted the aeroplane to bank while he operated the rudder with the steering wheel. This system did not use rudder pedals. The Army accepted the basic design of Model J near the end of the year.

In 1913, while the Curtiss factory was busy making Army scout-type aircraft, Navy hydroplanes, and flying boats, the over-all Curtiss organization had been growing in technical

A standard Curtiss biplane of 1910 vintage coming in for a landing near Stony Brook farm.

Alexander Pfitzner sitting at the controls of one of the first successful American monoplanes.

Though it crashed six times (one of them is shown here), Pfitzner's aeroplane made a successful flight on January 12, 1910.

The photograph at the top was taken before the Albany–New York flight. Left to right: Curtiss at the controls of *Albany Flyer*, Mrs. Curtiss, Augustus Post, and a proud young local flying fan. This photo was taken on May 28, 1910.

Curtiss starting off on his "bomb"-dropping test on June 30, 1910. The aerocraft was *Albany Flyer*.

However, like all his previous attempts to take off from the waters of Lake Keuka during the summer and fall of 1910, it failed.

Mrs. Glenn Curtiss awaits her husband's return from his hydro-aeroplane tests at San Diego. (Official U.S. Navy photo.)

Curtiss ready to board a standard biplane equipped with a single canoe-like pontoon.

Flotation arrangement on the *Albany Flyer* with one of Curtiss' mechanics at the controls.

Eugene Ely about to land on a specially constructed platform on the stern of the U.S.S. *Pennsylvania*. (Official U.S. Navy photo.)

Curtiss demonstrates *Triad*'s ability to taxi ashore during its first trial on February 23, 1911.

Having turned the aeroplane around, Ely takes off, returning to a field ashore. This first shore-to-ship and ship-to-shore flight took place on January 18, 1911. (Official U.S. Navy photo.)

Getting ready to make the first attempt to launch a hydro-aeroplane into the air from a cable launcher on September 7, 1911, at Hammondsport. (Official U.S. Navy photo.)

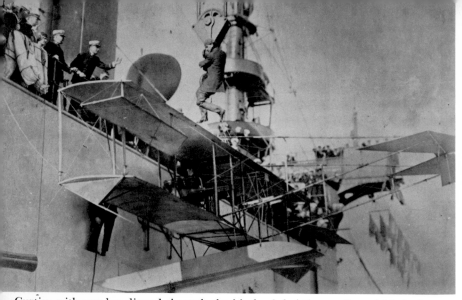

Curtiss, with one leg slipped through the big hook hoisting craft, and his hydro-aeroplane are being taken aboard the U.S.S. *Pennsylvania* on February 17, 1911. The completion of this flight convinced naval officials that aeroplanes were practical for their use. (Official U.S. Navy photo.)

Curtiss shows the control system of *Old Red Boat* to Henry Ford, during the latter's visit to Hammondsport in 1912. The craft was so named because of its red hull.

All the major types of aeroplanes of the time were present at the Chicago Aviation Meet, August 12 to 21, 1911. On the ground (left to right): the Farman, Blériot, and Wright aeroplanes. The Curtiss type is in flight.

The famous Model F flying boat, which was responsible for the start of the U.S. Coast Guard aviation branch.

Charles Manly is seated at the controls of the Langley machine, with Curtiss and Dr. Albert Zahm in the foreground.

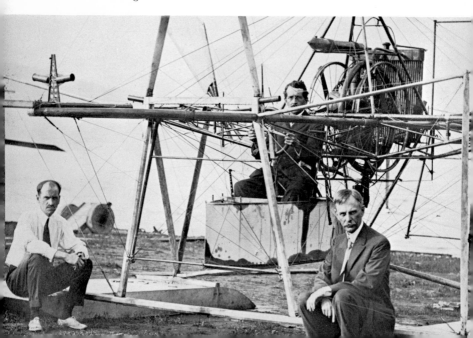

Assembly work on the Langley machine was done in the public view.

Professor Langley's machine with a Curtiss motor flying over Lake Keuka. It was flown with W. E. (Gink) Doherty at the controls.

Miss Kathrine Masson holding a bottle of Great Western Champagne prior to the christening of *America*. Lt. Porte is wearing the striped vest, while George Hallett is in overalls.

America in flight over Lake Keuka.

Experimental work being done on *America*.

Two views of World War I's most famous aeroplane—the JN-4 or *Jenny*.

Possibly the most famous aircraft engine ever built—OX-5—which was used to power most of the *Jennies* of World War I.

The Model L Triplane was designed by Curtiss and Douglas Thomas, but it proved never to be very successful.

The Model N-9 hydro-aeroplane was used to train Allied Naval Aviators in World War I. These aeroplanes were also used by Marine aviators for patrol duty in the Azores during World War I.

The NC-4 taxies triumphantly into Lisbon harbor on May 27, 1919, upon completion of its famous flight—the first aerial crossing of the Atlantic. (Official U.S. Navy photo.)

The largest aeroplane manufactured by the Curtiss Engineering Corporation in Garden City during World War I was this huge bomber. Unfortunately, it never flew properly and was disbanded.

The huge Model H-12 flying boat being built in the Curtiss Buffalo plant. This was one of the largest aeroplanes flown successfully in World War I.

Sperry automatic pilot on a Curtiss plane at Hammondsport in 1912. This was the world's first gyroscopic automatic pilot to fly an airplane.

A typical Curtiss hydroplane used by the United States Navy. (Official U.S. Navy Photo.)

Curtiss NC-3 flying boat at Trepassey Bay, N.F. (Official U.S. Navy Photo.)

strength as well as in other ways. In addition to Doug Thomas, Dr. Albert F. Zahm, who was secretary of the Langley Aerodynamical Laboratory of the Smithsonian Institution, had been engaged to head up company research, and Alfred Verville, an American engineer, had also joined the organization. With the addition of scientific and engineering personnel, many of the old trial-and-error procedures of the Curtiss plant were replaced with precision testing methods.

The Curtiss' flying school was operated at full capacity in 1913, and no new enrollments could be accepted for the summer of 1914 because of the lack of training space. To overcome the latter, Curtiss decided to transfer the school operations from Hammondsport to Newport News, Virginia. He also removed the schools from the jurisdiction of the Curtiss Exhibition Company. Actually the exhibition branch was the only weak link in the Curtiss organization. The exhibition business fell off badly in 1913. The year was not a good one for the exhibition flyer. Not only daredevil air circus performers, but such well-known aviators as Ralph Johnstone, Cromwell Dixon, Gene Ely, John Moisant, Cal Rodgers, Lieutenant G. E. M. Kelley, and Tod Shriver crashed to their death.

"These accidents are dreadful," Curtiss once told a reporter. "Every time a flyer dies in a crash, we not only lose a precious life, but public confidence as well. How can we ever sell the idea that flight can be a safe means of travel?"

The dangers of flying, great as they were, were enormously exaggerated in the "ballyhoo" used to draw in crowds and make flyers supermen people would flock to see. Eventually, such publicity boomeranged, and the public began to lose interest in aeroplanes. In spite of difficulties with the Exhibition Company, the outlook for the future seemed bright, and in the fall of 1913 Curtiss and his wife sailed on the S.S. *Imperator* with young Glenn, Jr., born in June of 1912, for a business-vacation trip through Europe with the intention of staying most of the winter. But, while he was there, his bright future suddenly turned dark.

Early in January, 1914, Judge Monroe Wheeler, general counsel of the Curtiss companies, had a serious disagreement with Jerry Fanciulli over monies spent on exhibition ballyhoo, and Fanciulli resigned. The New York office of the Curtiss Exhibition Company was closed, and the organization was left without a sales or promotion manager. For the time being this portion of Curtiss' enterprises virtually came to an end. Then, on January 13, Judges Cox, Lacombe, and Ward of the United States Circuit Court of Appeals confirmed the opinion of Judge Hazel, who had ruled, back in 1910, that the aileron constituted a patent infringement because it was used in conjunction with the rudder "sometimes," and "a machine that infringes part of the time is an infringement, although it may at other times be so operated as not to infringe." This decision upheld the very broad interpretation placed upon the Wright claims.

On February 21 the higher court granted a permanent injunction restraining Curtiss from the manufacture and sale of planes equipped with ailerons. The Wright Company announced that it would license the manufacture of aeroplanes under their patents for a payment of $1,000 a machine, plus a further royalty of 20 percent of the cost of all parts sold, including engines and propellers.

Curtiss' own associates, including Judge Wheeler, were considerably troubled when notified of the court's actions. They reasoned that unless a more suitable royalty arrangement than that demanded by the Wright Company and authorized by the court, could be settled upon, it would almost be impossible to continue manufacturing aeroplanes without incurring heavy losses. While the injunction specifically applied only to the United States and aeroplanes of Curtiss and Farman design, it actually meant an end of the manufacture of all aileron-equipped craft except those licensed by the Wright Company in most of the civilized countries of the world. Of the major countries, only Germany and Canada had refused to validate the Wright patents.

It was also the overwhelming opinion of the press and the aero trade magazines that the Wall Street "air-trust" had won the battle of the courts and that Curtiss' only apparent hope of continuing in the aeroplane business was to make a settlement with the embattled Wright forces. Curtiss, however, disagreed vehemently. On January 16 he cabled from the French Riviera that he would take the case to the Supreme Court of the United States and informed his associates emphatically that none of the activities of the Curtiss companies "would be affected by the decision."

As Curtiss saw it, there could be no question that his firm would continue building aeroplanes. He had obtained orders for thirty machines while abroad and, on the announcement of the court decision, he received several offers to move his factory to Europe. One of these, made by the Imperial German Government, proved to be most interesting. It promised to build, at no cost to Curtiss, a complete aero factory complex and guaranteed to purchase over 2 million dollars' worth of aeroplanes yearly. In addition, Curtiss would have the full support of the country's technical facilities.

The stipulations that concerned Curtiss were those stating that he give up completely the building of aeroplanes in the United States and that he start production in Germany on or before July 1, 1914. All his previous dealings with the Imperial German Government had proved most satisfactory, and he asked for more time to consider the proposal fully. In the meantime, he thought of possible ways of continuing to manufacture planes in the United States. For instance, since the injunction applied only to aircraft employing the aileron or similar balancing devices, perhaps he could build aeroplane bodies or fuselages and engines at Hammondsport and form a subsidiary company to produce the ailerons in Canada or Germany. Buyers of the aeroplanes would then purchase their own ailerons and attach them according to instructions from the manufacturer. Such a devious way around the problem was not in Curtiss' immediate plans. He believed sincerely the aileron method of lateral control—on which the United States Patent Office had granted a patent to the Aerial Experiment Association in December, 1911—differed completely from the Wright wing-warping system. He knew his cause was just, and he was determined not to be driven out of his native country unless it was the only way to save his company.

On returning to the States in late January, 1914, Curtiss found a letter from his recently made friend, Henry Ford. In it Ford stated that during the most difficult period of his Selden patent litigation suit, when it appeared he might never be permitted to make another automobile, one man had "saved the day for him." He advised Curtiss immediately to seek out this man—W. Benton Crisp, a New York patent attorney and former judge.

Curtiss followed this advice, and after a two-day conference in Detroit between Ford, Crisp, Wheeler, and Curtiss, a course of action was laid out. Judge Crisp became chief counsel of the Curtiss Aeroplane Company for the duration of the infringement suit. Judge Wheeler remained as general counsel of the other Curtiss holdings, and agreed to assist Crisp in the legal actions that would be necessary in the Wright case. "In addition," Ford told the group, "my entire legal staff is at your disposal. Patents should be used to protect the inventor, not to hold back progress!"

As a start, all evidence unknown or unavailable when the patent suit first started was exhumed. Then, after a careful study of the materials on hand, rather than appealing the case to the United States Supreme Court, Judge Crisp decided Curtiss should take action to force the Wright Company into starting a new infringement suit so that he could take a counteraction. In this manner he could introduce a great deal more evidence to prove that the Wright and Curtiss systems of control were different. In the meantime, Judge Crisp obtained a stay on the granting of a permanent injunction against the Curtiss Aeroplane Company. Moreover, in those days the Supreme Court seldom heard appeals of patents cases. It generally tended to go along with the action of the lower courts.

Curtiss' only problem was what he could do to provoke the Wright Company into a new suit. The obvious answer was to change his aileron system without changing the basic principle. But how could this be done? Doug Thomas had the answer. Instead of moving one aileron up and the other down, as Curtiss had been doing, and instead of moving the aileron on the lower side down in accordance with the specifications of the Wright patent, Thomas suggested that they move the aileron on the high side up and provide an interlock which would prevent simultaneous movement of the aileron on the low side. The idea was tried on the Curtiss Model J and, after several tests, 10-by-2-foot turn-up ailerons were fitted to the upper wing surface as the standard method of lateral control. The Army agreed to this basic change in design.

The new aileron system was a success in another way, too. The Wright Company promptly brought suit against this new design, and an answer was duly filed by Judge Crisp. In June the Wright organization announced its willingness to grant licenses upon the payment of a fee of $1,000 for each plane to cover the calendar year. In addition, it asked a further payment of $25 for each day that a machine was "operated, used or exhibited for or in prospect of profit, price, or reward." The new "liberalized license policy" was promptly rejected by the Curtiss people, and the new infringement suit started its way through the courts. Meanwhile, the factory at Hammondsport continued to turn out aeroplanes.

In July several New York newspapers carried a story in their financial sections that a merger between the Wright and Curtiss concerns was imminent. The accounts went on to state that this was a face-saving move by both parties; under the arrangement Curtiss would be permitted to manufacture aeroplanes as a totally independent subsidiary, while the Wright Company could control the destiny of the aviation industry in the United States. While both sides issued denials of the reports, the frenzy on Wall Street was heightened by two meetings between Judge Crisp and counsel for the Wright Company. Nothing occurred, however, and the rumors soon died out. But the legal battle went on.

During a conference with Judge Crisp and Curtiss, Dr. Zahm, who had been one of the technical expert witnesses for the Curtiss Aeroplane Company in the original Wright patent suit, suggested that it would be interesting to determine whether or not the essential features of Professor Langley's aerodynamic theory, as applied in the 1903 model, were correct. After the ill-fated trials of 1903, the craft was returned to the shop, where it was left by the War Department in Langley's possession for further experimentation. Since 1908, Zahm knew that the Smithsonian Institution had considered the possibility of making trial tests of the Langley machine. Judge Crisp "jumped" at the suggestion as an excellent means of obtaining valuable data for use in the new patent suit. It would give them an opportunity to study the Langley aerodrome, whose method of control could not possibly be considered an infringement of the Wright wing-warping method.

In March, 1914, Dr. Zahm went to Washington and discussed the matter in detail with Dr. Charles D. Walcott, Secretary of the Smithsonian Institution. As a result of these talks, the Langley machine arrived in Hammondsport in early April. The Smithsonian Institution agreed to pay Curtiss $2,000 for the task of refitting the machine and making the necessary flight tests. It had originally cost nearly $50,000 to build the machine. John P. Tarbox, Curtiss' patent attorney, who was also an engineer, was in charge of the project. Charles Manly, who was at that time manufacturing hydraulic trucks, agreed to supervise the reconditioning of the engine and its installation. Dr. Zahm acted as the Smithsonian Institution's official observer.

Later in March, Curtiss informed the German Government that he was going to continue, for the present at least, to manufacture aeroplanes in the United States and that he was reluctantly declining their "generous" offer of January 19. The Curtiss Company, however, did purchase land in Toronto, Canada, just in case things didn't go as planned. As mentioned previously, Canada had also refused to validate the Wrights' patents.

The Langley machine was refitted in a little courtyard at the factory between the office and the aeroplane assembly room. While the space was walled in and roofed, and Curtiss enforced his policy that only authorized personnel could enter, there was no "real" secrecy connected with the project. Newspapermen visiting in Hammondsport were advised of progress. Actually, when several of them stated that they would like to see the Langley machine being built, Curtiss ordered the project to be taken and completed outdoors.

It was to the advantage of everyone connected with the project to restore the machine to its exact condition at the time the attempts to launch it were first made in 1903. The framework, controls, and wings were repaired, although more than half of the original ribs of the wings, which had suffered most in the launching accident, were still intact. Curtiss could not afford to replace the broken ribs of hollowed-out wood; they were merely duplicated in spruce, which made them heavier and less efficient than the originals. The original light oiled-silk wing and propeller covers were torn and rotted. These were replaced with doped cotton fabric. Meticulous care was taken during the reassembly process to make certain that none of the aerodynamic principles were altered.

The engine was merely cleaned, but immersion in salt water and eleven years of rust had impaired it to such an extent that it was impossible to obtain more than three-quarters of the horsepower it had originally possessed. A new set of dry cells was added, and the casual reader of some of the stories that were later written might be led to believe there was something unfair about the Langley trials because Curtiss did not use the eleven-year-old set of dry batteries that operated the spark when the machine was dumped into the Potomac River in 1903.

Since the new trials were not to catapult the aerodrome, three pontoons, two forward and one aft, were added so that it could take off from the surface of the lake. The two forward pontoons were placed in such a position under the forward wing that the angle of the guy wires leading from the wings would be unchanged. It was, of course, necessary to remove the long post to which the lift wires had been attached when the machine was launched from the catapult. The weight of the pontoons, as well as the necessary interbracing, added some 350 pounds to the aerodrome.

On May 28 the Langley machine was taken out to Lake Keuka and Curtiss assumed the controls. While several witnesses watched, the venerable aerodrome moved along with the engine running evenly, and as it gained speed, the pontoons broke loose from the water. It rose a few feet above the surface of the lake, flew on a level for a short distance, and landed evenly on the water. Then five days later, on June 2, while Dr. Walcott, Manly, Dr. Zahm, newspapermen, Army and Navy officers, flying students, and local citizens looked on, the Langley aerodrome was launched, with Curtiss again at the controls. A series of "short hops" of less than five seconds and under 100 feet was made.

Later in the year, the Smithsonian Institution consented to the substitution of a Curtiss 80-horsepower engine for the original engine, and a number of longer flights were made. The following March, Curtiss removed the pontoons and attached skids, with which he made several short flights from the ice with the original engine. Then the machine was modified somewhat in keeping with the advanced aeronautical knowledge of 1915, and many officially observed flights were made by William E. Doherty and Walter Johnson. The longest of these was a 10-mile flight which lasted almost 30 minutes and was made in a strong head wind. That fall the Langley machine was restored to its original condition and returned to the Smithsonian Institution in Washington, where it is now.

The reconditioning and flying of the aerodrome have been cited by some as prima facie evidence that, except for malfunctions of the launching gear, Dr. Langley's aeroplane would certainly have made successful flights in 1903. With equal conviction, they have been described by others as a fake operation, perpetrated by men who stood to gain financially. The

Smithsonian Institution's effort to demonstrate once and for all the scientific value of its former secretary's aeronautical experiments gave rise to a situation which one aeronautic writer of the time correctly characterized as "involving temptation for one side to exaggerate and distort favorably Langley's work, and for the other side to belittle and deny it."

Chapter 8

THE BUILDING OF *AMERICA*

L ORD NORTHCLIFFE, the eminent British journalist, proprie-
tor of the *Daily Mail* and owner of a hundred other
English periodicals, had for his motto a statement of Pascal's,
"To foresee is to rule." Certain it is that he was forehanded.
Always an interested spectator at aeronautic events, and realizing that aeronautic progress was certain to have its effect upon
the economic and social condition of the world, he soon became one of its most ardent champions. So, when Rodman
Wanamaker, son of John Wanamaker, the great Philadelphia
merchant, announced his plan of financing an enterprise whose
object was to cross the Atlantic Ocean in an aeroplane, Northcliffe, through the Royal Aero Club of the United Kingdom,
offered a prize of ten thousand pounds to stimulate public
interest in this international event. The conditions of the
London *Daily Mail* competition were as follows:

> The proprietors of the *Daily Mail* have offered the sum
> of ten thousand pounds ($50,000) to be awarded to the avia-
> tor who shall first cross the Atlantic in an aeroplane in flight
> from any point in the United States, Canada or Newfoundland
> to any point in Great Britain or Ireland in seventy-two con-

secutive hours (the flight may be made either way across the Atlantic).

Qualifications of competitors—The competition is open to persons of any nationality holding an aviator's certificate issued by the International Aeronautical Federation and duly entered on the competitors' register of the Royal Aero Club.

Entries—The entry, which must be accompanied by the entrance fee of one hundred pounds ($500), must be sent to the secretary of the Royal Aero Club, 166 Piccadilly, London, W., at least fourteen days before the entrant makes his first attempt.

The starting place—Competitors must advise the Royal Aero Club of the starting place selected, and should indicate as nearly as possible the proposed landing place. All starts must be made under the supervision of an official appointed by the Royal Aero Club.

Identification of aircraft—Only one aircraft may be used for each attempt. It may be repaired enroute. It will be so marked before starting that it can be identified on reaching the other side.

Stoppages—Any intermediate stoppages may only be made on the water.

Start and finish—The start may be made from land or water, but in the latter case, the competitor must cross the coast line in flight. The time will be taken from the moment of leaving the land or crossing the coast line. The finish may be made on land or water. The time will be taken at the moment of crossing the coast line in flight or touching land. If the pilot has any time to leave the aircraft and board a ship, he may resume his flight from approximately the same point at which he went on board.

The placing of the trip in the hands and under the control of the Royal Aero Club of the United Kingdom, which worked in conjunction with the Aero Club of America in New York,

provided the official background that made Rodman Wanamaker's suggested flight an item of world interest. Wanamaker
believed that aeronautics, instead of developing exclusively
into an arm of military science, could be put to novel use as
a force for peace. In announcing his undertaking, he said:
"This year we are celebrating a hundred years' peace between
Great Britain and the United States, and it would be a fitting
climax in this celebration if these two countries could link
themselves more closely together by this international flight
across the ocean, demonstrating to the world that the time for
the disarmament of nations is at hand, if for no other reason
than because aeronautics have reached a stage where even the
greatest dreadnought battleships may become futile in their
power."

In early December, 1913, after conferring with his friend,
Captain Ernest Bass of Great Britain, Rodman Wanamaker
contracted secretly with Curtiss to build a large flying boat at
a cost of $25,000. As Wanamaker later explained, "Glenn H.
Curtiss knows more about flying boats than anyone else in
the world." Bass had attended several of Curtiss' English
demonstrations and was greatly impressed by the American's
flying boat. He had recommended Curtiss to Wanamaker.

Ever since his first water flight, Curtiss had continued to
think about the aerial conquest of the Atlantic. On his return
to Hammondsport, in late January, 1914, design work, under
the direction of Doug Thomas, was started on the Wanamaker
project. The Navy Department sent two advisers, Lieutenant
John Towers and Lieutenant (j.g.) Pat Bellinger, to the Curtiss factory, and William D. Gash was Rodman Wanamaker's
personnel representative on the project. June of 1914 was to
be the target date for the flight. Parts for two additional aero-
boats of the same design would be built as back-up craft should
anything go wrong with the original aeroplane.

By February, 1914, the plans for the undertaking had "leaked" to the press. There was fascination in the idea of attempting the flight Walter Wellman had attempted in his dirigible, *America,* in 1910 from Atlantic City. It was what John Wise of Philadelphia had proposed doing as early as 1843 in an unpowered balloon. On the whole, most newspapers, both at home and abroad, were favorable to the project, but most doubted that a flight of nearly 2,000 miles could be made. Several long, nonstop flights over land had been made by a number of aviators, the longest being that by Victor Stoeffler, 1,296 miles from Berlin to Posen in 1913. While Galbraith P. Rodgers had made a cross-country flight of 3,220 miles in 1911, it had involved sixty-nine stops. The over-water distance record, of 392 miles, was held by Lieutenant Towers.

The announcement was made more intriguing by the flat comment by Orville Wright in a Cincinnati newspaper interview on February 11 that the feat was impossible. Many newspapers interpreted this story in terms of the renewal of the infringement battle. The Springfield (Mass.) *Union,* for instance, had an editorial under the headline, "Flying Across the Atlantic":

Again we are confronted by the old problem "Who shall decide when doctors disagree." Orville Wright declares it is foolhardy for an aviator to attempt to cross the Atlantic with the comparatively weak engines now in use in aeroplanes, and with the present lack of staying powers characteristic of such light craft. He thinks it is most unwise to undertake a Trans-Atlantic flight when efforts to cover the same distance by land have failed. On the other hand, Glenn H. Curtiss has begun the construction of the curious new flying machine which he proposes to make the trip between continents, with funds provided by Rodman Wanamaker. Mr. Curtiss declares

this machine will have both a special motor and the extra staying powers needed to attain the feat.

Possibly Mr. Curtiss and his associates know what they
are about, but the opinion of Mr. Wright seems to an ordinary
mind to be well weighed with common sense. If the proposed
new flier seems theoretically equal to a Trans-Atlantic journey, it is quite the point of prudence to test it out on a land
expedition of similar length before incurring the great hazard
of a voyage across the ocean.

This last sentence is interesting, because it shows that the
common belief at that time was that it was safer to fly over
land than over water. Curtiss, on the other hand, realized that
the ocean offered a much better landing field than did the
land, and he had frequently chosen water as the more desirable
surface over which to fly. In one of the early articles on the
subject in the New York press, he pointed out that steamships
in sight along the route would be useful in inspiring aeroplane
pilots with confidence, and in the event of the abandonment
of the flight because of motor failure, such boats might be of
great assistance. He was also keenly alert to the advantage of
ship searchlights if night flying became necessary, and of the
smoke issuing from ships' funnels as navigational help during
the day. Curtiss once told reporters, "The Atlantic Ocean, one
of these days, will be no more difficult to cross by air than a
fish pond."

Immediately after the announcement of the *Daily Mail*'s
prize of $50,000, other aeroplane enthusiasts began to con-
sider entering the competition. Three French aviators, Pourpe,
les Moulinais, and Garros, declared their intention of attempting the flight in late summer or September. Enea Bossi, of
Italy, also announced he would make the flight. The Wright
Company, having just won the most recent round in the in-

fringement suit, insisted that Curtiss would have to either take out a license or stop manufacturing the Wanamaker craft. Curtiss resolved to go on with the most ambitious project he had ever tackled regardless of any action the Wright Company might take. He thought the choice of Canada as the starting point of the transatlantic flight would be wise, since Canada was one of the two major "civilized" countries in which Wright patents were not recognized.

The Wright Company issued a further warning in the form of a circular letter sent to all aero clubs, aviators, and exhibition companies:

> We are sending you this information in order that you may protect yourselves against making contracts for exhibition aeroplane flying, or other purposes, with persons using infringing machines without a license. This company intends to enforce its right against all manufacturers and users of unlicensed machines, and we therefore wish to advise you that it would be unwise to engage or deal with anyone not using a licensed machine, and who cannot show proper authority and license from us. We shall hold all persons using or engaging others to use infringing machines strictly accountable for all damages and profits accruing therefrom.

This letter, signed by Alfred S. Brown, secretary of the Wright Company, caused much discussion in the Aero Club of America, and it appeared that Wanamaker's proposed ocean flight was in great jeopardy. Whereas on the earlier infringement matter, the press had been more or less divided, now it was almost 100 percent behind Curtiss. There was agitation in Congress to legislate against the Wright Company's attempt to control the aviation industry in the United States. The Justice Department was said to be studying means of putting an end to the "air trust." Even several members of the Wright Company's board of directors made public statements that they were opposed to the "official" company policy in this matter, and one resigned in protest. In spite of the strong public sentiment against the company, none was directed against Orville Wright himself. (Wilbur had died on May 30, 1912, of typhoid fever.) Orville had not played an important part in the company's affairs, either in policy or in technical design, since 1910. Many newspapers considered him divorced from the firm and regarded him as the senior spokesman of aviation in America.

Banking on the public sentiment on their side, the Aero Club of America wired the required $500 entrance fee to the Royal Aero Club of the United Kingdom binding the entry of the Rodman Wanamaker Trans-Atlantic Flyer in the following cable:

> File entry Rodman Wanamaker Trans-Atlantic Flight biplane. Approximate breadth of craft eight feet, approximate length of aeroplane eighty feet. Two hundred horsepower motor. Approximate capacity of fuel tanks four hundred gallons. Aviator's name later. Glenn H. Curtiss constructor. Have cabled one hundred pound entrance fee. Entrance form mailed.

After a "peace" conference in which personal differences between Curtiss and Cortlandt Bishop were set aside, the latter was appointed chairman of an Aero Club Committee to cooperate with Wanamaker and Curtiss in completing plans for the transatlantic flight.

Since the birth of his son, Curtiss had done only a limited amount of flying—mainly over Lake Keuka. In 1912 he had promised his wife that he would do no more land aeroplane flying. Frankly, Lena Curtiss did not want him to do *any* flying and often reminded him of her feelings.

Wanamaker used all his ability to persuade Curtiss to be the chief aviator of the Atlantic flight, but Curtiss refused and said that a Navy man should be the man-in-charge. His choice was Lieutenant Towers, head of the Naval Aviation School at Pensacola, temporarily assigned to Hammondsport as a naval adviser to the project. The request by Wanamaker for the services of Towers, however, was turned down by the Navy Department. While the Lieutenant could remain as an adviser for the time being, neither he nor any other of the Navy's experienced flyers could be spared for the flight because the threat of trouble with Mexico had for the first time made aviation an important branch of the war service. Wanamaker suggested that they hire a British pilot as chief aviator. His reason was his hope that a successful transatlantic flight would have a profound moral effect on the two countries in the sense that it would build a greater rapport between the two nations.

In this vein, Wanamaker cabled Sumner R. Hollander, his representative in England, requesting him and Captain Bass to suggest a suitable candidate for the job. Hollander replied that the best man available was Lieutenant John Cyril Porte. Porte had entered the British Navy in 1898 and joined the submarine branch, where he made a fine record, and was retired in 1911 after being invalided. A year later he studied flying in the Deperdussin School in France and became military demonstrator of the Deperdussin machines. At the age of twenty-seven he achieved the reputation of being one of the finest pilots in England. Porte realized, however, that the strain of piloting a flying boat across the Atlantic would be very great, and it was therefore decided to give him a co-pilot or two. Lanny Callan, a former Curtiss student and flight instructor, and George Hallett, a well-known California airman who worked with Curtiss during the first hydro flights in San Diego in 1911, were selected. Curtiss continued to wish a

U.S. naval pilot could go along on the transatlantic flight, but the Navy Department persisted in its refusal. Thus Hallett, because of his mechanical ability, was recommended by Curtiss as the second pilot. Porte agreed with the selection.

In mid-April, the Navy's earlier fears of conflict with Mexico were justified. On the eighteenth of the month, Lieutenant Towers and Lieutenant (j.g.) Bellinger were ordered to return immediately to Pensacola. Two days later, an aviation detachment of three pilots, twelve enlisted men, and three aircraft, under the command of Towers, sailed from Pensacola on board the U.S.S. *Birmingham* to join Atlantic Fleet forces operating off Tampico in the Mexican crisis. The following day, a second aviation group of one pilot, three student pilots, and two aircraft, commanded by Bellinger, embarked aboard the U.S.S. *Mississippi* and sailed for Mexican waters to assist in military operations at Veracruz. The combat record of the latter detachment was as follows:

April 25—On the first flight by the USS *Mississippi* aviation unit at Veracruz, Bellinger piloted the Curtiss AB-3 flying boat to observe the city and make preliminary search for mines in the harbor. (To avoid confusion with submarines, the original Navy designations of aircraft were changed to a system, using two letters and a number, in which the first letter indicated class, the second indicated type within class, and the number followed the order in which aircraft within class and type were acquired. Four classes were set up: A for heavier-than-air craft, D for dirigibles, B for balloons and K for kites. Within the A class, the letters L, H, B, X and C represented [respectively] land machines, hydro-aeroplanes, boats, combination land and water machines, and convertibles. Thus the third hydro-aeroplane, the A-3, became AH-3, and the first flying boat, the C-1, became AB-1.)

April 28—Lt. (j.g.) Bellinger and Ens. W. D. La Mont

made a flight in the AB-3 flying boat to photograph the harbor at Veracruz.

May 2—The Curtiss AH-3 hydroplane, piloted by Bellinger with La Mont as observer, flew the first mission in direct support of ground troops as the Marines, encamped near Tejar, reported being under attack and requested the aviation unit at Veracruz to locate the attackers.

May 6—The Curtiss AH-3 hydroplane, piloted by Bellinger with Lt. (j.g.) R. C. Saufley as observer, was hit by rifle fire while on a reconnaissance flight over enemy positions in the vicinity of Veracruz—the first marks of combat on a Navy plane.

May 19—As the need for scouting services diminished at Veracruz, the aviation detachment resumed routine flight instruction while awaiting orders to return to Pensacola.

While Curtiss planes were in combat for the first time, construction of the airboat at Hammondsport went forward rapidly behind closed doors, and progress reports were issued on a nearly daily basis. The Wanamaker Trans-Atlantic Expedition, having all the elements of conflict, adventure, government support, patent litigation, and record-making, found a ready place on the front pages and editorial columns of the world's press. Most Eastern newspapers had full-time representatives there, and when three London news reporters arrived, the town became an international news center.

The reporters failed to realize that Curtiss was a man far more interested in what he was trying to accomplish than in what other people thought or said about him. Once two of them entered his office and tried a little blackmail by suggesting that if he didn't give them a "little break," they would make the name of Curtiss a stench in the nostrils of the public. Curtiss got up from the chair behind his desk and pointed to the door, saying "Out!" Both reporters left Hammondsport that night and were replaced within the week by two new men.

While Curtiss, at times, wasn't overly popular with the men of the fourth estate, Lieutenant Porte was disliked even more. Being a typical military man, he was accustomed to keeping his mouth shut and minding his own business. Although the reporters knew the tall, gaunt Englishman was under a New York *World* contract for his exclusive story of the expedition, they often harassed him with their searching questions. But his conception of tactful handling of the press was rather exasperating. Once, for instance, he said very seriously: "I gave that to the *World* today, so you can read all about it tomorrow."

The initial flight route—from Labrador to the southern point of Greenland, thence to Iceland, and finally to the British Isles—was to cover a distance of approximately 2,100 miles. When prominent explorers were called upon for expert advice, the route was eventually abandoned as impracticable. It was then thought that the straight route of 1,900 miles from St. John's, Newfoundland, to the western point of Ireland would be more navigable. Meanwhile, to make things more interesting, Mrs. Victoria Woodhull Martin, of the Woman's Aerial League of Great Britain, contributed a trophy valued at $5,000, plus $5,000 prize money. The seventy-two-hour condition was not attached to this prize.

On June 17 an announcement was made to the press in New York that an entirely new route had been selected. Instead of the direct flight to Ireland, Porte decided to attempt the crossing in three laps—the first, a stretch of 1,198 miles from St. John's to the Azores; the second, 963 miles from the Azores to Vigo, Spain; and the third, 523 miles from Vigo, Spain, to Ireland. His estimates were 20 hours for the first lap, 16 hours for the second lap, 9 hours for the third lap, and 10 hours for stopovers—a total of 55 hours.

One advantage of the new route was that it would bring the flyers directly over the steamship lanes. When the aviators left Newfoundland and turned southeast toward the Azores, they would cross diagonally every steamship course between this country and Europe. Throughout the first two legs of the flight they would be following the lanes of steamers plying between American ports and Spain and Southern Europe. In case of accident the chances of being picked up by a passing steamer would be increased at least 100 percent. From Cape Finisterre to Queenstown they would not be far from the coast of Europe and in frequently navigated waters. The plan of patrolling the course by steam yachts or cutters had been abandoned, because Lieutenant Porte hoped to be aided in getting his bearings by the sixty or eighty vessels that would be crossing the Atlantic on the south European track while his machine was in flight.

The change in plans still left the flyers eligible for the prize offered by Lord Northcliffe. They would not be allowed to beach the flying boat at the Azores, because the rules provided that stops could be made only on the water. Whether Porte or Hallett would leave the craft to go ashore at the Azores was an open question. The rules said nothing about whether an aviator might go ashore at any intermediate point; they merely stipulated that if he left the aircraft to board a ship he must resume his flight from the same point.

Lanny Callan was sent to Newfoundland and then to the Azores to establish a gasoline supply. Sumner Hollander made arrangements for the airboat to alight and take aboard oil at Vigo. Porte said he hadn't given much consideration to the problem of keeping a food supply on board. The flyer would probably be stocked with light supplies at St. John's, Flores, and Vigo. The Lieutenant said he thought hard-boiled eggs would be the staple of the diet of the airboat's crew.

On the nineteenth it was announced that the official name of the Transatlantic flyer would be *America,* the same name Wellman had given to his dirigible in 1910. It was announced on the same day that the craft would be launched on June 22. But the most important news of the day in Hammondsport was the dispatch which quoted Orville Wright as saying that the Wright Company would take no legal steps to interfere with any attempted transatlantic flight.

"I have not enough expectation," Orville said to an interviewer, "that the craft will ever land near enough to any country where our patents are validated—that is anywhere in Europe—to make it worthwhile for the Wright Company to bother stopping the flight."

America was ready for flight on the twenty-first, and it was set on its cradle for the launching on the next day. The V-bottom, single-step hull, built in the form of a giant whale, was 38 feet long, and with a beam of 4 feet and a depth of 6½ feet. It had a squatty, blunt bow and a long, tapering streamlined afterpart. Because of the continuous vibration from the engines running at high speed for many hours, special hull construction was employed. Instead of having a solid hull of wood, like the other Curtiss flying boats, *America* was constructed of a light white cedar frame covered with a tight skin of varnished Japanese silk, which responded like a drum to the pounding of the engines overhead.

Although the hull was less than half an inch thick, it supported more than nine times its own weight. The hull's weight was only 550 pounds, but it was designed to carry the required 5,000 pounds of machinery, fuel, and passengers. The hull was divided into four compartments, with four watertight tanks or compartments in the tail. The pilothouse proper was in the center of the hull and was covered over by a hood containing celluloid windows. A space left for sleeping quarters should they be needed was stocked with a mattress, life-preserver, and necessary equipment for the voyage.

The control mechanism, which was arranged in front of the pilot's feet, consisted of two wheels connected with each other, so that either of the pilots could handle the ship independently of the other. The shoulder-yoke method of control, which Curtiss had employed for his earlier machines, was discarded for this one, because it required more effort to move the controlling surfaces, and a steering wheel form of control was chosen instead. A pull of the wheel toward the pilot elevated the plane, a push in the other direction depressed it. Another wheel controlled the rudder. The lateral control was operated by a foot bar. If the right wing rose, pressure with the right foot altered the angle of the rudder and the balancing wing sections to depress it. If the left wing rose, the left foot was used.

Although the original plans provided for a single 200-horsepower engine, it was replaced by two 100-horsepower engines of the OX type so that if one failed the other could still support the flying boat. They occupied positions between the wings, on either side of the hull proper about 8 feet behind the cockpit and 4 feet above the hull. Each was equipped with an 8-foot, two-bladed propeller, directly connected to the motor, and was planned to run at a maximum speed of 1,800 revolutions per minute.

The wings were mounted above the hull, the lower ones passing through a joint just amidship, but cut away to make provision for the pilot's cockpit. The lower wing was 46 feet from tip to tip, while the upper was 72 feet. The cord, or width, of each was 7 feet. In order to repair the engines in flight, Hallett would have to climb through a network of wires while the airboat was going about 60 miles an hour. He wore a lineman's belt, by which he could hook himself to the struts when he had to have both hands free.

Cabin dials registered the speed of the aeroplane, the wind velocity and direction, the revolutions of the propeller, and the rate of gasoline consumption. The compass had been especially built so as not to be influenced by the steel on the airboat. But Lieutenant Porte did not mean to rely solely on the compass to guide him. He intended to carry a sextant to make nautical observations of his position, to determine how far the wind had driven him off his course. *America* also carried Lawrence Sperry's latest device for measuring the distances it drifted. His third method of correcting course was the simple one of flying low and watching for ocean steamships over the southern track, which were expected to fly signals showing their approximate distance to the north or south of the aeroplane's course.

Instead of alighting in the ocean near Flores, Porte had decided to attempt his first descent at the Bay of Horta, on the Island of Fayal. A long breakwater in the bay insured smooth water. Porte believed that he might be helped in finding Fayal by a mountain, 7,613 feet high, which rises near Fayal from the Island of Pico. It was said that Lanny Callan would also try to aid Porte in finding Fayal by building a huge bonfire upon an eminence in case *America* should near the Azores at night. Although a wireless apparatus had been offered to Curtiss, he decided that on account of its weight, carrier pigeons would afford a better method of keeping in touch with land, and also preclude the possible danger of sparks setting fire to the boat while in flight.

At 5 P.M. on June 22, *America* was ready to take to the water. A large American flag and a small American banner were raised over the cabin of the machine. Earlier in the day,

Hammondsport had been carefully searched for a Union Jack to float beside the American flag as a reminder that Wanamaker's principal purpose in attempting the crossing was to bring the two countries closer together in the cause of international peace. But no Union Jack could be found, so in its stead a banner was selected whose large red background gave it some resemblance to the English flag and paid an indirect compliment to Great Britain.

A hush fell over the gathering as Katherine Masson, a pretty, dark-eyed girl of sixteen, mounted the launching platform before the nose of the airboat. Katherine had won the privilege of christening the aircraft when she drew the winning straw in a contest against her two cousins, Gladys and Emily Champlin. Lieutenant Porte handed her a package of curious appearance, which turned out to be nothing more than a bottle of Great Western champagne between two horseshoes wrapped with broad bands of white ribbon. This was the arrangement hit upon for smashing the bottle without injury to the airboat's fragile bow of cedar strips and varnished silk. The bottle was slung on a wire from a bamboo scaffold over the airboat.

As the Lieutenant was instructing Katherine as to what she was to do, they were interrupted by a clamor from the inner circle of the crowd. There were cries of "Look this way!" "Smile!" "Hold the bottle up!" "Stand back, Lieutenant!" "Stand forward, Lieutenant!" and many other peremptory commands from the photographers. Three moving picture machines and dozens of cameras were leveled at the platform. Other small cameras from homes around Lake Keuka were snapping from the tops of the Curtiss hangars, from a row of twenty autos, and from points in the rear of the crowd. Miss Masson and Lieutenant Porte changed positions frequently for about five minutes in response to calls for special poses. Many of the watchers began to grow restive and shout for the business of the day to proceed. Porte jumped down from the platform and Katherine took up her position to throw the bottle, when a tall, red-haired man rushed forward, shouting, "What about the speech? Isn't there a speech?"

Katherine paused for a moment, bottle in hand, looked toward the crowd, and began to recite a poem composed for the occasion by Dr. Zahm:

> Majestic courser of the sea and air,
> Within this ample hold
> Two navigators bold
> The Atlantic main abridging are to bear
> Glad greeting from the New World to the Old,
> Peace herald of the century,
> "America" I christen thee.

As she recited " 'America' I christen thee," Katherine threw the bottle of champagne. It struck low, clanged against the side of the bow, and hung in midair. Porte tightened the wire and Miss Masson threw the bottle a second time, but it again remained intact. The Lieutenant jumped on the platform and threw the bottle himself. It struck the bow and bounced away in perfect condition. On Porte's second throw the champagne bottle slipped out of the horseshoes and rolled safely along the ground. The crowd began to laugh and shout advice.

Porte, becoming somewhat vexed at the bottle's hold on life, grasped it by the neck and slapped it against the side of the boat. It escaped from his hands and fell to the ground unscathed. He jumped down from the platform and grabbed the bottle in both hands. As he advanced on *America,* Curtiss, evidently fearing that the airboat would suffer, stopped him. After a consultation, the bottle was trussed up against the bow of *America* with stout wire. Then Porte swung a hammer and broke it.

It was an hour and a half after the christening before *America* was fully equipped. Then Porte and Hallett took their places in the cabin, while the employees of the Curtiss factory reeled the airboat from its cradle into the shallow water of Lake Keuka.

Forty men then pushed the craft into the water. A crowd of five hundred who witnessed the ceremonies cheered at the tops of their voices. It rode high on the water with perfect balance. Because of the late hour, no attempt was made to start the engines or make a trial run. On that day it was decided to assemble one of *America*'s sister ships and send it to New York City for exhibition. Curtiss had reorganized this portion of his business and had taken personal control of its operation. The schools were again made part of the Curtiss Exhibition Company.

The next day *America* made its first flight, and on the next evening it made two mysterious night flights over Lake Keuka. A nasty south wind buffeted the airboat with tremendous force as it made its second trial flight. But steady and true it flew like a swallow through the night and circled Bluff Point with all the ease of a huge bird. *America* had experienced just a taste of what it must encounter when it began its flight against the winds, the waves and the cross currents of the ocean, but it weathered its trials like a gull, traveling at the enormous speed of 60 miles an hour. The second flight was made in complete darkness. After these tests Gash, Wanamaker's personal representative, immediately cabled his boss in Europe that *America* was certain to be the first flying boat to cross the ocean.

Other people also thought *America* would make it. The betting at Lloyd's of London against the success of the flight had dropped from odds of 47 to 1 to 5 to 1. A number of employees at the Curtiss factory stood a chance of winning

$94,000 if *America*'s trip was successful. In February, when the odds were 47 to 1, they had raised a pool of $2,000 and bet it at Lloyd's on the success of the flight.

On the twenty-fifth, *America* made a short flight in order to try out the propellers under a different method of operation. While Curtiss was happy with their operation, he ordered new hydroplaning devices to be added because the ocean flyer needed more lifting power.

With these in place the *America* left the waters of Lake Keuka on June 27 and flew with seven persons, including the two pilots, and 220 pounds of ballast. When Porte stepped ashore, he said, "We lifted twice as much weight as any airboat ever did before. I guess that's pretty good."

Curtiss also was highly pleased with *America*'s performance. "It can fly easily with the load it must take when it leaves Newfoundland," he said. "*America* made a splendid showing with its new hydroplaning boards. It does not yet 'plane' or skim along the surface as perfectly as we want it to do, but that can easily be remedied, we hope."

America broke the record for flying boats when it took to the air with seven passengers. The total weight of the load, in addition to the machine itself, was approximately 1,498 pounds. The weight of the airboat itself was about 2,850 pounds, so that the two 100-horsepower engines drove a total weight of 4,248 pounds.

"We figure that the total weight *America* will have to carry is about 1,900 pounds," said Curtiss. "After we have demonstrated that it can carry this much we will go on adding to the load in further trials until we have found its maximum."

On June 28 a severe thunder shower accompanied by hail and a tornado destroyed almost 50 percent of the grape crop in the Lake Keuka section and threatened to smash *America*. Hailstones broke six windows in the Curtiss aeroplane factory.

One of them picked up on the factory floor measured 2 inches in diameter.

This was the second storm within a week that had threatened to put an end to the transatlantic flight plans. Curtiss had no hangar large enough for the *America,* and it stood in a cow pasture on the lake shore exposed to the full sweep of the storm. Strong ropes were thrown over the wings and made fast to stakes in the ground, but the first blast from the tornado lifted the huge seaplane a few feet above its cradle and dropped it back with a crash that nearly smashed the hull. Curtiss and a dozen of his men grabbed the ropes that had loosened the stakes and held them during the rest of the storm.

After the test on the twenty-ninth, Curtiss stated that *America* would not be shipped to Newfoundland until at least July 11, which meant that the flight to Europe couldn't begin about the middle of July as had been planned. It would take four or five days to make the trip from New York to Newfoundland by steamer, and the assembling of the machine and further trials would delay the overseas flight until at least July 23 or 24.

During a conference between Porte, Curtiss, and Dr. Zahm later that day, it was decided that the best time to leave Newfoundland would be at one or two o'clock in the morning, as this would enable the aviator to reach the Azores about eight o'clock at night, or before dark. In addition, Lieutenant Porte wrote in his *World* column that if *America* was not in perfect trim by mid-July he would possibly postpone the flight until mid-August, so as to have the benefit of the full moon while flying over the ocean.

While Porte took a few days' rest in the Adirondacks, Curtiss experimented with various hydroplane arrangements, but he still couldn't hit on the right combination to give proper lift. He added a third engine above the center section, thus

creating the greatest load—some 6,203 pounds—that had ever
been taken into the air. But this wasn't the answer either, because of the increased fuel consumption and wind resistance
added by the third engine.

Several hull changes were tested before it was decided, on
July 8, to broaden the hull beam by a special boat-type structure suggested by Naval Constructor Richardson, one of the
naval advisers on the project. One newspaperman described
America with its new fins as "a huge flying catfish." Further
work on the finned hull beam proved so successful that on
July 15 it took off and handled perfectly with the full transatlantic load of over 5,000 pounds. After two more days of
tests, Porte was thoroughly convinced that *America* was ready
for its flight under the terms of the contract, and the final
delivery papers were signed.

America and its sister ship were crated and shipped from
Hammondsport to St. John's. Porte, Hallett, and several Curtiss
men left immediately for Newfoundland, while Callan sailed
from Boston for the Azores to handle the refueling and repair
operations there. He also planned to join Porte and Hallett
as a relief pilot for the remaining portion of the flight to
Europe.

On his arrival at St. John's, Lieutenant Porte selected
Trepassey Bay as the take-off site and ordered the crates
shipped there from St. John's. He told the press, "We'll set
operations at Trepassey on August 1 and flight should be ready
between the tenth and twelfth of the month. Mr. Curtiss will be
here to make the final check before take-off."

Finally all seemed ready, and the world waited in interested
anticipation for news of the start. But as Bobby Burns has so
well said, "The best laid schemes o' mice and men gang aft
a-gley."

On August 3 Germany declared war on France, and next

day Great Britain was at war with Germany. Transatlantic flying was off for the duration. Lieutenant Porte immediately offered himself for duty in the Royal Navy and was promptly accepted. Before the end of 1914 the "peace herald of the century" and its sister ship were purchased by the British Navy for war duty, and made their crossing of the Atlantic ignominiously hidden under tarpaulins on the deck of a freighter.

But the labor of building *America* was not wasted. Porte, on his return to service, exerted a great influence upon the military flying boat design and construction programs of his country. Only a few weeks elapsed before the British Government had dispatched officers to Hammondsport, and a contract for fifty duplications of *America* was signed with Curtiss. This craft carried the designation H-4, and was used by the British Navy for service over the English Channel as a submarine chaser.

Chapter 9

THE WAR THAT ENDED A WAR

WITH the declaration of war in 1914, almost overnight aviation became an industry, one that drew to it some of the finest industrial brains in the world. In a short period of time the kitelike contraptions of the Wrights, Blériot, Farman, Voisin, Curtiss, Latham, Paulhan, and their contemporaries gave way to trimmer, fabric-covered designs, greatly streamlined and with greatly improved performance. Prior to the war there was a limited market for American aircraft. But now European countries, who had formerly been hesitant about dealing with firms not licensed under the Wright patents, would buy aeroplanes regardless of the infringement problems.

During the early days of the war, the European aviators flew over the front lines as scouts, observing the opposing forces, their numbers, and troop movements. When they encountered an enemy machine, they fought it out with shotguns. It soon became apparent, however, that the aeroplane might become a mighty battle auxiliary, not only as the eyes of an army or fleet, but as a combat weapon for harassing the ground forces at the front, destroying munitions behind the lines, and raiding enemy territory.

While Curtiss had advocated the use of the aeroplane as

a powerful offensive weapon as early as 1910, Germany was the first country to employ them in any number. Some of the German aeroplanes dropped explosives, while others escorted them to ward off attacks, until the Allied military leaders admitted aerocraft had become a powerful offensive weapon, and, further, that the aeroplane was the best weapon with which to combat an enemy in the air. They then began developing their own aerial strength, and in 1915 placed orders with some of the American companies.

At the time, however, the American aviation industry was in bad shape. Manufacturing facilities essential to the production of large quantities of military aerocraft were unavailable. The tremendous demand for aeroplanes erupted with paralyzing suddenness. Actually, when the war broke out in Europe, the Curtiss Aeroplane Company was the only major American firm producing aerocraft in any numbers. While the Burgess Company was building a limited quantity of hydro-aeroplanes, the Wright Company was completely revamping their designs, and production was at a standstill. Soon after the war began, some nine new concerns entered the aerocraft-manufacturing field.

Although military orders were plentiful, the uncertainty of the patent situation made it essential that business be conducted on a cash-and-carry basis. Curtiss sold three flying boats to Italy, but before they could be delivered, the cash had to be forthcoming. A Curtiss agent and Italy's representatives combed Italian villages for American dollars until the staggering sum of $9,000 had been collected in worn-out, one-dollar bills. This served as part payment for the three boats. The balance was probably made up with spaghetti.

Many odd deals were consummated before the United States actually entered the war. A number of Curtiss aeroplanes were sold to neutral nations, including Spain. Unknown to the sellers, these were intended for unfriendly warring coun-tries. A Russian contract was procured by Curtiss' London representative, Lyman Seely, and later an order totaling $750,-000 was received from England for Curtiss flying boats. The receipt of so large an order created a problem in itself, for to fill it required a large cash outlay which the company just did not have.

Curtiss felt that the only way by which he could finance such a contract was to ask the English for an advance of $75,000. When he cabled this request, for reasons of economy, he omitted the word "dollars" after his figure, and British au-thorities took it for granted that he meant pounds. Thus they sent him £75,000 (over $365,000), and this slight misunder-standing started the Curtiss ball rolling. The gross amount of that first British order was something like $14 million—the largest single order received to date by an American aircraft firm.

At the beginning of the war, the English had been interested in obtaining two types of aircraft—one a suitable training machine and the other a good-sized flying boat which could be used for reconnaissance work over the British Channel. Dur-ing the summer of 1914 other Curtiss designs were being de-veloped while the Model J was under construction, including another Army Scout class biplane, the Model N (the K and M were contemporary flying boats, but the L, a triplane trac-tor, while already designed, did not appear until 1916). After manufacturing a few Model N's, Curtiss, with Doug Thomas' help, combined the best features of Models J and N into a single model and acknowledged the union by naming the new plane the JN-1. Even at that early date aeroplanes had come to be regarded, like boats, as having feminine personalities and were often given unofficial feminine names. The aviators soon and quite logically converted the initials *JN* into the name

Jenny, which turned out to be one of the most popular aeroplane names of all time.

At first the British airmen looked askance at the JN. The price of the machine, complete with engine, was said to be less than British builders were charging their government for machines without engines. The wooden parts of their aeroplanes had a highly polished piano finish, whereas the Curtiss machines were merely varnished. At first the British said: "Just like the Model T Ford automobile." But sooner or later generals of many armies left their Rolls-Royces stuck in mud holes and were glad to use the good old Ford to get about in, and after little more than a year the JH, with its Curtiss motor, had become a most respected plane, because of its general durability, in the British aeronautical training services. Actually, it was selected as the international primary training machine.

The typical model JN (the JN4-B was probably the best-known) had a maximum horizontal speed of 75 miles an hour and a minimum of 45, and would climb 3,500 feet, fully loaded, in 10 minutes. Powered with an 8-cylinder, V-type Curtiss OX-5 motor, which developed 90 to 100 horsepower at 1,400 rpm, it consumed slightly more than ½ pound of gasoline per-horsepower per-hour. It was comparatively light and, for its useful load-carrying capacity, was very compact. With an upper wing span of 43 feet 7⅜ inches, and lower of 33 feet 11¼ inches, plus an over-all length of 27 feet 4 inches, it weighed only 1,430 pounds empty but would carry a load of 490 pounds. (This figure was based on the following estimate: fuel [21 U.S. gallons], 130 pounds; oil, 30 pounds; and the pilot and observer, 165 pounds each.) It was equipped with a dual control and carried two passengers tandem, each in a separate cockpit. While the first two series of Jennies retained the shoulder-yoke aileron control system, the JN-4 used the "Deperdussin" type of control where the wheel operated the ailerons and the rudder was controlled by the aviator's feet through a rudder bar. This system had been adopted on the JN-3, which had been built in quantity for the British Royal Flying Corps (R.F.C.) and the Royal Naval Air Service (R.N.A.S.). The Canadian-made version of the JN-4 was commonly called the *Canuck,* and varied in having ailerons on both upper and lower wings, plus a rounded rudder.

The Curtiss JN twin-motored tractor, an Army Scout type, had high maximum speed and fast climbing ability combined with slow landing speed and great weight-carrying capacity. Although it weighed but 2,110 pounds empty, it had a load-carrying capacity of 1,040 pounds. Two "OXX" 8-cylinder engines, one located to the left and the other to the right of the fuselage, gave this battle plane an available 200 horsepower. It had a maximum horizontal flight speed of 85 miles an hour, a minimum of 48 miles per hour, and a climbing speed, under normal conditions, of 4,000 feet in 10 minutes. The front cockpit was placed in the nose of the fuselage, giving the observer or gunner seated therein an unobstructed range of vision and an extensive field of fire. Only a few, however, ever saw combat service.

Another Curtiss land military tractor popular with the British was the Model R-4, which was originally designed as an Army fast Scout type. Larger than the JN, it had a wing spread slightly in excess of 48 feet and an area of sufficient size to carry a total of 1,020 pounds' useful load, of which 625 pounds were fuel. It was powered with a Curtiss V-2 engine, which developed 200 horsepower at 1,400 rpm. Its maximum horizontal speed was 90 miles an hour and its minimum was 48. It climbed 4,000 feet in 10 minutes.

The Curtiss Company also was very active in the naval aircraft field, especially for the British Navy. When *America* was put into naval service, it was redesigned in many particulars. The hull was changed, the nose of the boat altered, the cockpit rebuilt, the wings and tail surfaces made more efficient, the cables strengthened, the struts streamlined and reinforced, the engine bases altered for easy access by mechanics, and many other minor changes introduced. John Porte, who realized the value of a thin-skinned hull, did the work in England, which resulted in an order being placed for a new type of boat having a special tail, the lower part of which was of wood, the upper part made of a frail framework covered with linen.

While *America* never saw much active naval service, it served as the model for the H-4 series of flying patrol boats. They were a basically sound aeroplane which often astonished aviation experts with their range of operation and ability to remain in the air 10 hours or more.

In the fall of 1916 the bigger, more powerful H-12 replaced the H-4 on the Curtiss assembly lines. Powered by either the 275-horsepower or 375-horsepower Rolls-Royce Eagle, the H-12 could fly for 6 hours carrying a 4-man crew, 4 machine-guns, and 400 pounds of bombs at a top speed of 85 miles an hour. While this flying boat design had an outstanding good war record, it was replaced by the slightly larger H-16 just before the end of the conflict.

Another Curtiss flying boat that made its debut just before the end of the war was the HS type, which was produced for both the British and United States navies. This patrol-bomber had an over-all length of 39 feet, a height of 14 feet 7 inches, and a wing span of 74 feet 1 inch. Having a gross weight of 6,432 pounds, its cruising speed was 70 miles an hour and its range was 400 miles. The HS was powered by the "United States (Liberty) Motor," a 12-cylinder water-cooled, 400-horsepower engine, which the Army engineers developed under the direction of Howard E. Coffin.

The popular Curtiss sportsman's Model F flying boat, after several slight revisions, was used as a short-range naval reconnaissance aircraft. Incidentally, during the spring of 1916, Curtiss "loaned" the U.S. Coast Guard a "used" airboat of this type to determine the feasibility of the employment of an aeroplane in the service's search-and-rescue operations. Lieutenants Elmer F. Stone and Norman B. Hall carried on the tests with the help of several Curtiss flyers. On August 29, 1916, after their favorable report, President Woodrow Wilson signed a memorandum establishing the Aerial Coast Patrol. A short while later, the first Curtiss Model F flying boats were ordered by this service and the saga of Coast Guard aviation began.

The vast majority of the pilots of both British and United States navies earned their wings during the war in the N-9. This aeroplane was the first naval aircraft to be developed primarily from wind tunnel data, thus marking a coming of age of scientific research and engineering in the field of aeronautical design.

In the summer of 1916 the U.S. Navy's one air base, Naval Aeronautics Station, Pensacola, was still using pusher hydroplanes, not greatly changed from the AH craft of 1911. The aviators, convinced by a series of fatal crashes that the pushers were unsafe, condemned those on hand. Flying at the training school practically came to a halt. Attempts to purchase tractor training aeroplanes from the emerging aviation industry were disappointing, indicating that it was necessary to design a new aircraft. But the only concern capable of such work at that time, the Curtiss Aeroplane Company, was too "swamped" with orders from Europe and the U.S. Army to give the Navy's request the needed time to study.

In the fall of 1914 the Navy had assigned Naval Constructor Jerome C. Hunsaker to the Massachusetts Institute of

Technology to develop the nation's first course in aeronautical engineering. As part of his research, he made complete wind tunnel studies of the Curtiss JN-2 military tractor which was so popular with Army authorities. Just about the time that the Navy's pushers were condemned, he was ordered back to the Navy Department in Washington.

There Hunsaker continued his study and calculated that with certain modifications the JN could be converted into a naval training aeroplane. Those, of course, included installing a pontoon and increasing the wing span to compensate for the added weight. These changes alone, however, would destroy the aircraft's stability. He proposed, therefore, to add a specified amount to the tail area and install skid fins on the upper wings.

The Chief of the Bureau of Construction and Repair, Rear Admiral David W. Taylor, gambling on Hunsaker's scientific research and engineering judgment, sent him to the Curtiss plant to persuade G.H. to make these necessary changes to the JN in exchange for an order for thirty aircraft—for the Navy an order of unprecedented size. The contract was issued in August, 1916, and in October the first N-9 aircraft was completed and sent to Newport News for demonstrations. Results were obviously successful as production under this contract was completed in December, 1916.

In the early part of 1915 the Curtiss Aeroplane Company had a backlog of $20 million in Allied contracts. No single man among the original executives of the Curtiss plant had suspected the volume possibilities of aeroplane orders which now came in from Great Britain, Italy, and Russia. The complete routine of life had to be readjusted to meet the altered conditions.

Hammondsport, the birthplace of the Curtiss companies,

was too small for such ambitious expansion. Factory facilities were inadequate, and there were not enough people or houses to take care of the immediate emergency. There was also a great deal of "local" opposition to the expansion of the Curtiss factory. Many of the long-time citizens of Hammondsport were afraid that their town would become another city like Rochester, or even New York. The vineyardists could see their lands being used for buildings rather than grapes, which would mean the end of the wine industry in the area. This meant the vintners, who were the region's leading citizens, were also dead set against giving additional lands to Curtiss. So he and his associates began to canvass the situation thoroughly, and finally, as a result of their survey, decided to locate in Buffalo because it offered definite advantages as a supply and shipping port. Thus one fall night in 1915, a special train moved the Curtiss Aeroplane Company bodily, including the key employees' families and their household goods, to Buffalo. The next morning the men were ready for work in their new quarters.

A floor of the E. R. Thomas Motor Car Company's factory on Niagara Street in Buffalo had been leased, and K. B. Mac-Donald, former factory manager of this organization, was selected as general manager. He proved invaluable to the Curtiss organization, which was not geared to an undertaking of the scope it now faced. In a short time, the entire Thomas factory was engaged in the building of Curtiss aeroplanes. The Curtiss Motor Company remained in Hammondsport and shipped aircraft engines to Buffalo by rail.

But still the orders came, and the need for more space persisted. So on March 10, 1915, plans were drawn for the erection of a new factory, known as the Churchill Street plant, next door to the Cutler Desk Company. By May 10 this plant was turning out its first aircraft. After the new plant was in operation, it, too, proved too small, and the Cutler Company building soon became part of it.

Perhaps the most interesting craft which Curtiss built at the Churchill Street plant was a large triplane flying boat, officially known as the Model T, made for the British Government. Actually, the factory wasn't high enough to allow the complete assembly of the wings, but by making the plane in sections which were later fitted together, the workmen were able to line up the struts, test the wires, adjust the tail surfaces, provide for proper motor mountings, and do everything necessary to insure the proper setting up of the complete craft. After the job was done it was found that it could not be accepted by the railroads for shipment. Furthermore, the plane's construction had to be secret and the time of its transportation unknown. Therefore a special canal boat was built, the structure taken apart, and loaded in such a way that it had the external appearance of a load of lumber. In this condition it was towed to New York by way of the Erie Canal and the Hudson River. Even then, on account of its large size, it was necessary to lower the water in the canal in two places, in order to allow it to pass under the bridges.

The Experimental Engineering Department was located in an old building on the Niagara River at the foot of Austin Street. This building had, at one time, been the power station of an electric lighting concern, supplying light and power to that section of the city. It had been vacant for years and was in disrepair and little suited to the purpose for which it was employed. In it, however, Curtiss had segregated a number of his best men, and behind locked doors carried on continuous experimentation. So secret and of such importance was this work that admission was granted only to members of the Army and Navy staff, and to privileged officers of the Curtiss Aeroplane and Motor Corporation. Though careful watch was maintained over all who entered and left the shop, it was no uncommon occurrence for the secret service men to locate and remove enemy spies and workmen. On one occasion a large bomb was discovered in the clothes of a workman, and in several instances struts, wires, and other parts of planes were found to have been sawed nearly through and filled in with sawdust and/or glue.

Four different security organizations were at work, and yet the attempts at destruction continued throughout the whole war period. Fortunately, little damage was done, and most of the faulty material was removed before the machines were shipped, but occasionally parts reached flying fields containing imperfections which were only discovered after careful inspection in the hangars. This led to the development of transparent varnishes, more rigid inspection, a system of identification for all workmen, and the careful government supervision of workmen. Of course, armed guards were stationed at all gates of all factories. A special pass was required for entrance, which showed an employee's department and serial number. This was printed on a photograph taken at the time he entered the plant, and each employee was called upon to show both this pass and the badge he wore.

Curtiss, as president of the company, was always anxious to conform to all rules and wore his badge along with the rest. On one occasion when he left home without it, and the watchman protested that he might be Mr. Curtiss, but he didn't know him, and he didn't "intend to take *no chances,*" he cheerfully agreed to drive back to his house and get his pass.

The vast expansion of the aircraft industry caused inevitable changes in the Curtiss organization. For instance, technically trained engineers were gradually brought in to supervise the men who had grown up with the company. These engineers were conversant with the technical jargon necessary in dealing with men from various countries who came to the factories to check up on every item of material ordered.

A single employee's experience is indicative of the expansion of the engineering department. Paul J. Zimmermann, a graduate engineer with a basic interest in aeronautics, first came to Hammondsport in November, 1914. There were no openings in the engineering department at the time, and he accepted a job in the office at a salary of fifteen dollars a week. A little later he was called in and asked to do some engine design work. On completion of this task, he was promoted to the position of chief draftsman.

When he took over the job, there were approximately 750 tracings on hand. A few drawings were still filed on the wall and had to be copied off. Three years later, there were over fifteen thousand drawings. The department itself grew from six men in 1914 to over two hundred in 1917.

With the transfer of most of the aeroplane-building facilities to Buffalo, the Curtiss Aeroplane and Motor Corporation came into being on January 13, 1916. The new corporation, formed by a New York City syndicate, absorbed the Curtiss Aeroplane Company and the Curtiss Motor Company, with $6 million worth of preferred stock and $750,000 worth of common stock. Curtiss received $4.5 million outright for interest in the two old companies plus 50 percent of the common stock of the new concern. The other stockholders who had been generally employees in the old firms became very prosperous, too.

One small original Curtiss stockholder who held $500 worth of stock had made several desperate efforts to dispose of it for $100. Not finding a customer, he put the stock away, and at the time of the incorporation of the new company, he discovered to his amazement that his original $500 investment was worth $200,000.

A short time after the merger, the new firm acquired the stock of the Burgess Company at Marblehead, Massachusetts, and controlled Curtiss Aeroplane and Motors, Ltd., of Canada and the Curtiss Exhibition Company, which operated the flying fields and schools at Buffalo, Hammondsport, Miami, San Diego, and the Atlantic Coast Aeronautical Station, Newport News. Plants were in operation at Buffalo, Hammondsport, Toronto, and Marblehead. But these facilities were still not adequate. In Buffalo, for instance, the Niagara and Churchill Street plants were taxed to their capacity and were operating on a twenty-four-hour schedule. The old Century Telephone plant was quickly remodeled to take care of the manufacture of aeronautical engines, and the Bradley Street plant, an old incubator factory that produced the wooden parts for aeroplanes, was annexed.

The expansion process also entailed considerable frenzied finance. The increasing inventory, the great difficulty in getting material into the plant on time, the innumerable hold-ups incident to war—all these made the problem of aeroplane manufacture a difficult one. Added to this was the problem of financing large purchases and the meeting of enormous payrolls. In the fall of 1916 Clement M. Keys, a well-known Wall Street broker and personal friend of Curtiss, undertook to unravel this tangled skein. Interesting several New York and Buffalo bankers, he finally refinanced the business. George H. Houston, the chief representative of the banking interests now in control of the Curtiss Aeroplane and Motor Corporation, was placed in charge as general manager.

In less than a year, however, refinancing was again necessary. Curtiss made a trip to Detroit and discussed the situation with Henry Ford. After their long talk, Ford asked for a few days to think over the possibility of his entering the aeroplane field. On Curtiss' return to Buffalo, Keys vetoed the idea completely, saying that he didn't think it wise to get "auto" money, personnel, and techniques involved in their company.

It was known that the automobile industry wanted to get into the aeroplane business. In April, 1917, the Dayton-Wright Company was organized by a group of automobile men who had not previously been connected with aviation. To make a good front and to acquire rights to a desirable name, Orville Wright was retained as consulting engineer. Early in 1916 Wright had sold his interest in the original Wright Company to a syndicate of New York bankers.

Because of the size, experience, and general importance of the Curtiss Company in the aviation industry, it considered the "plum" to be picked by the auto boys, who knew the company was having money problems. Keys obtained some financial aid from local Buffalo banking interests, but he was forced by them to install W. A. Morgan as the new general manager. With Morgan's coming, much of the old organization was eliminated. Even Curtiss himself was removed from actual plant administration and stripped of most of his executive powers. He remained a director of the concern and was "elected" chairman of the board. He also was placed in charge of "the creative work" being carried on by the corporation. While Keys served as a "temporary" president, auto personnel were brought in by the banking interests. John North Willys of Willys-Overland Company became president of the Curtiss organization in June, 1917, two months after the United States had entered the Great War.

The War Department planned to send abroad an army of one million. The strategists thought there should be one aeroplane for every thousand men, with possibly two in reserve—in all about 2,500 machines. The existing companies believed they could produce that number in a relatively short time without further expansion. But then the English, French, and

Italian missions arrived, eager to tell Americans how they might contribute most effectively to Allied aerial strength.

"Twenty-five hundred aeroplanes!" they exclaimed. "That's nothing at all! France and Italy need aircraft badly. England is building her limit, but she is losing as many machines as she builds, month by month. Conditions are such, the importance of aeroplanes has become so great, that we shall need 25,000, perhaps more, from the United States."

That was a big order, and the bulk of the task of filling it fell to the Curtiss Company. Thus the continued pressure from Washington and the greater demands for machines, particularly of the training type, one-seat and two-seat fighters, and large craft for both land and water use, convinced the board of the Curtiss Corporation that it would be wise to secure from the government additional aid to build a still larger plant. Accordingly, on July 28, 1917, Morgan, with help from Washington, began the building of the North Elmwood plant in Buffalo, which with its outlying buildings, yards and transportation facilities occupied seventy-two acres. This plant, a structure of concrete, steel, and glass, which cost $4 million, was completed in ninety days. One of the buildings had thirty-one acres of floor space under a single roof. With the addition of this, the largest single aeroplane manufacturing establishment in the world, the Curtiss organization, which had numbered less than a thousand at the beginning of the war, reached the amazing size of 40,000 employees, 3,500 of whom were women. Among them could be found almost every type of workman, from piano tuner to steel worker.

The gigantic organization which had thus been formed was, of course, unwieldy, and in spite of all attempts on the part of the management, it could not be made to function smoothly. Added to this were problems with labor organizations, occasional sabotage of products, the constant changes necessitated by the war, and the coming of the influenza epidemic in the midst of the busiest year. In January, 1918, W. A. Morgan, broken in health, was obliged to turn over the helm to James A. Kepperley, a lieutenant of Willys, and former legal adviser for the Willys-Overland Company. While the Willys organization was well known as automobile manufacturers, its officials had many new problems in the manufacture of aeroplanes, and although Kepperley possessed level headed executive ability to a marked degree, and started to clean up the loose ends Morgan had left, he too found the task a terrifically hard one. The organization was changing rapidly, and it was not an easy one to control. Housing conditions in Buffalo were growing steadily worse. Men were being drafted, and in many of the departments only the foreman was familiar with the character of the work required. Yet, in spite of all these handicaps, production was maintained.

Unfortunately, on account of the conditions in Washington, and the lack of knowledge of many of those in authority, orders were given and countermanded, contracts were made and canceled, designs were changed, so that at no time was the Curtiss organization given an opportunity to use more than 25 percent of its capacity. It was not until just before the Armistice that the organization and designs were stabilized and left uninterfered with for a sufficient length of time to make quality production possible.

There was much criticism of American production methods and American aircraft, but due to the severe censorship imposed by the government, there could be no constructive exchange of information. Through the long months when conditions at the front were critical, Curtiss, as creative head of the company, worked on designs for aerial torpedoes, flying boats, new fuselages for fighter planes, and better, more efficient wing arrangements. Although he was no longer at the top managerial level, Curtiss was still the "boss" to many of the employees.

Desiring to break the Curtiss image that remained among the old-timers, Morgan, before he retired, suggested to Willys that a special experimental plant, with Curtiss in charge, be set up—*preferably* away from Buffalo. Willys approved the idea, and after careful study, it was concluded that Long Island, with its eighteen landing fields and numerous flying boat harbors, offered the best facilities. A site was selected at Garden City, where model shops, hangars, and the largest wind tunnel in America were erected. The purpose of this new operation, which was called the Curtiss Engineering Corporation, was to produce experimental aircraft, and Curtiss was permitted to bring together a corps of research engineers—mainly old Curtiss Aeroplane Company personnel such as Charles Kirkham, Charles Manly, John Tarbox, Henry Kleckler and Dr. Zahm. Frank H. Russell, former president of the Burgess Company, was made general manager.

At the Garden City plant, Curtiss' achievements included such craft as the L-1 triplane, L-2 hydro, HS-2L flying boat, F-5, HA, and others. Of the designs built there, Curtiss' favorite was the 18-T, which was the prototype for the *Wasp* triplane fighter. This single-engine, two-seater landplane was fitted with two synchronized and two flexible machine guns. It was considered the world's speediest aeroplane, having flown over 165 miles an hour. It was a triumph in streamlining. Not a square inch of the machine, from tail skid to exhaust pipes (they were curved to the flow of the wind), had been omitted from the careful plan of shaping, which cut down air resistance to the minimum. The 309 square feet of supporting surface and the power of the new K-12 Curtiss motor carried the gross weight of 2,900 pounds, fully loaded, to a height of 18,000 feet in 10 minutes.

Working with Dr. Elmer Sperry, Curtiss helped to formulate

the first guided missile for the U.S. Navy. This pilotless aircraft consisted of a specially designed Curtiss airframe, OX-5 engine, and Sperry automatic controls. This "flying bomb" carried better than 1,000 pounds of explosives and its range was over 50 miles at a top speed of 90 miles per hour. Successful test flights were made from a secret field at Copiague, Long Island, and plans were being made to use it against the enemy when the Armistice put an end to this project.

The K-6 and K-12 motors concluded the list of Curtiss' outstanding efforts in engine design. The K-12 was a V-type of aluminum construction, developing 400 horsepower at 2,500 rpm of the crank shaft. It was served by two high-tension, 2-spark 6-cylinder magnetos. It used a centrifugal pump for the water-cooling circulating system, and pressure feed for oil. Its cylinders had a bore of 4½ inches and a stroke of 6. Without oil and water it weighed 728 pounds, a dead weight of 1.94 pounds per horsepower.

The K-6 developed 150 horsepower at 1,700 rpm, had the same general constructural and operating features as the K-12 type, and a weight of 417 pounds—a dead weight of 2.78 pounds per horsepower.

In January, 1918, the various Curtiss plants began to turn out planes at the rate of 112 complete machines per week, and when the Armistice was signed, the promised delivery of fifty a day was close to reality. Before and during the war, Curtiss plants turned out some eleven thousand aeroplanes and flying boats, and fifteen thousand engines.

Of all the planes built by the Curtiss organization, however, the most famous was the Model JN, which was the first American aircraft produced in quantity. It was the training plane on which most of the ten thousand American aviators, plus many beginning British flyers, were trained during the war. And although it looks like an unwieldy mother hen today, it

was once the last word in training ship efficiency. It could
stand up under the terrible punishment of rookie air soldiers.
The JN production reached an estimated total of 6,759, of
which some 6,072 were the JN-4.

After the war the Jenny became synonymous with private
flying and the barnstorming age in the United States. The
War Department made it known that they planned to sell a
large number of the JN-4's as war surplus to the civilian
market. The Curtiss Company immediately criticized the plan,
claiming, "To sell them without guarantee among unknown
buyers would be to reap a harvest of accidents and retard the
development of flying."

Thus, to "protect" aviation, and its own reputation, the
Curtiss organization began dickering with the government to
buy back the Jennies and the stockpile of OX-5 engines. After
considerable negotiations, they were able to repurchase 2,176
used aircraft and 4,608 engines for some two million dollars.
The Jennies were then overhauled at the factory and sold to
the public at a fraction of their original cost. The Jenny became the aeroplane that popularized aviation in the 1920's.

Another contribution made by the Curtiss organization to
the war effort, as well as to aviation, was the fine operation of
its flying schools. A Washington *Post* editorial of February 4,
1916, stated: "The United States is woefully behind all other
nations in the number of trained men able to operate aeroplanes. We have only about 100 trained military aviators as
compared to Germany's 9,000."

Thanks to an arrangement between Curtiss and the U.S.
Army, 1,400 pilots were trained in one year through a plan in
which the students remained civilians until they completed
their flight course. Then they were automatically enlisted in the
Aviation Reserve Corps. Tuition was paid in full by the Government and the student had his choice of any Curtiss school

he wished to attend. In April 1917, the Curtiss School of Aviation at Newport News made a similar arrangement with the U.S. Navy.

"The war to end all wars" did end one major conflict—the aeroplane patent battle. In January, 1917, the Secretary of War and Secretary of the Navy asked the National Advisory Committee for Aeronautics (founded in 1915 by the government to aid the American aviation industry through its research work) to investigate the aeroplane patent situation in the hope of working out a solution that would avoid the payment of excessive royalties by the government. One member of the Advisory Committee stated a fact which had been painfully obvious for quite some time. "The Aeronautical industry," he said, "has too long been throttled by the basic Wright patents and dominated by the many Curtiss ones. We see great restrictions on our military services in the continuation of this situation, which has caused our country to fall from first place to last of all the great nations in the air."

About 130 aeroplane patents had been actually issued. Curtiss held sixty-five of these. Others were pending. Of those already issued, some were basic, without using which no aeroplane could be built. There were others of doubtful value, perhaps half of the total number. But each patent could be the basis of a lawsuit. When a builder turned out a flying machine, he invariably was threatened with court action for infringement of an aeroplane patent. He might even pay royalties to one or two patent owners and still be confronted with claims from several others. Had there been no war, these conditions might have continued, repeating the history of other industries. To help the National Advisory Committee toward a solution, the Congress appropriated, in February of 1917, one million dollars for the purchase, or the acquisition by condemnation, of basic aeroplane patents.

On July 24, as an outcome of the National Advisory Committee's recommendations, the Manufacturers Aircraft Association was organized to effect a cross-licensing agreement under which all manufacturers for the government might have unrestrained use of all aeroplane patents and be free to fulfill government contracts in full accordance with specifications. Two weeks after its organization, the Association, thanks to the work of Judge Crisp, formulated a cross-licensing agreement very similar to that under which automobile manufacturers had been working for some time.

Under the arrangement all the aeroplane builders agreed to cross-license their patents, and each paid to the Association a license fee of $200 for each aeroplane built. This fee was decreased almost immediately to $100 for the duration of the war. After deducting Association operating expenses, the fee money was employed to pay royalties to the owners of all patents that came within the scope of the agreement, starting with the Wright and Curtiss patents and distributing the funds in accordance with the values assigned to each patent. The Curtiss Company received two million dollars for the use of their patents and Wright-Martin Aircraft Corporation about three million. This new concern was formed to take over the Wright Company, the Glenn L. Martin Company, the Simplex Automobile Company, and the General Aeronautic Company of America. John Tarbox, Curtiss' patent attorney, estimated the value of all the sixty-five patents held by the Curtiss organization to be in the neighborhood of $8,750,000. But most important, the cross-licensing agreement put an end to the Wright-Curtiss patent strife. And it blasted the barriers which had for so long dammed the progress of aviation in America.

During the nine years of litigation, Curtiss and the Wright brothers had only one personal contest in the press. After the decision of the court was announced in 1914, the metropolitan newspapers published a long interview with Orville Wright. This time Curtiss was stung to open retort, and he issued a statement to the press:

> In some New York daily papers there have been published during the past weeks certain statements attributed to Mr. Orville Wright, regarding his attitude in the aeroplane patent suit. Mixed in with these direct quotations were interpolated insinuations impugning my good faith in the patent litigation and carrying suggestions easily interpreted as such untruths as I cannot see how Mr. Wright or any other sane man ever made.
>
> The idea that any single line or part of any machine was either copied from the Wright machine, suggested by the Wrights or by their machines is absurd if not malicious. My first public flights, as a member of the Aerial Experiment Association, are a matter of record, and were made mostly before the Wrights exhibited their machine or made their first public flights.
>
> I have never had an item of information from either of the Wrights that helped me in designing or constructing my machines or that I ever consciously used. I believe today, as I always have believed, that the Curtiss control differs fundamentally from that employed by the Wrights, and that its superiority to that of the Wright system is demonstrated by the records of the two machines during the past five years.
>
> That I was unable to satisfactorily demonstrate this intricate technical point to the court I consider a misfortune largely due to the fact that our knowledge of aviation was vastly less when this case went into court several years ago, than it is today. I will continue to fight until the courts will eventually prove that I am correct.

Curtiss did not receive the vindication that he desired from the courts because there was *never* a final adjudication from the United States courts on the question of whether the A.E.A.

aileron did or did not infringe upon the method patented by the Wright brothers. The aviation industry, however, accepted the aileron system, and it is still in use in modern-day "airplane" construction. On the other hand, the wing-warping method of lateral control fell into disuse long before its patent expired in 1923.

Following World War I, Curtiss turned his attention to the last of his great dreams—a transatlantic flight.

Chapter 10

THE TRIUMPH OF THE NC's

A LOOK at the record of the United States Navy air forces during World War I shows a steady increase of men and equipment: flying boats and seaplanes increased from 51 to 1,865; land aeroplanes from 3 to 242; officers from 48 to 6,716; and enlisted men from 239 to 30,693. U.S. naval forces abroad involved 570 of its own aircraft, as well as the use of French and British aeroplanes, and 18,000 officers and men, located at 20 patrol bases in Great Britain, France, and Italy, one in the Azores and two in Canada. Aircraft logged 791,398 nautical miles on patrol and bombing missions, dropped 126,-302 pounds of bombs on German submarine bases and military targets and attacked 25 German submarines and sank or damaged 12 of them. Another 2,455,920 nautical miles were flown on patrol from 12 United States coastal stations.

When the United States became involved in the war, the cry from Europe was for aid in overcoming the German submarine. Ships were being sunk faster than they were being replaced, creating a frantic demand for sub-chasers and far-ranging aeroplanes with which to find submarines. England desperately needed American-built patrol aircraft, but cargo vessels capable of carrying such bulky items were at a premium. The problem of providing sufficient cargo space, out of the rapidly decreasing tonnage available, was most serious. On one occasion, the Navy actually sent an entire shipload of H-12 patrol aeroplanes to England. Though the ship was a large one, the cargo consisted of only twenty-five flying boats with accessories. With Allied troops needing munitions and food, the delivery of such aircraft dropped to a rather low position on the priority list.

With this dilemma in mind, Admiral D. W. Taylor wrote Naval Constructor Jerome Hunsaker: "If we can push ahead on the aeroplane end, it seems to me that the submarine menace can be abated, even if not destroyed from the air. But, the ideal solution would be big flying boats, or the equivalent, that would be able to fly across the Atlantic and take on a U-boat on arrival. This would avoid all of the difficulties of delivery. . . ."

While in Buffalo, Hunsaker discussed the subject with Curtiss. William Gilmore, one of the company's top engineers, then joined the other two and they worked on several sketches of a flying boat that might possibly meet the Navy's needs. On September 9, 1917, Curtiss, with Gilmore and Kleckler, met Navy representatives in Washington, D.C., and decided upon a general course of procedure with regard to large flying craft. The design originally was given the designation of "TH." These letters were chosen from the Curtiss series, whereby designs were indicated in sequence, and had no other significance. But it seemed to Curtiss that a design of such size and of such ambitious intentions should be dignified by a name more meaningful than two arbitrary letters, and he changed the aircraft's name to "D.W.T." These were the initials of Admiral David W. Taylor. He had not, however, consulted Taylor, and after discussion with other men in the Construction Corps, Curtiss decided that the name would fail to find the Admiral's favor. Once more the name was changed. This time the name of NC-1 was selected. In this name, the *N* stands for Navy, the *C* for Curtiss, and the *1* indicates the first of a series of joint Navy-Curtiss designs. The letters NC invited the nickname of "Nancy."

The preliminary design of the first NC contemplated a craft with a 140-foot upper wing span, a 110-foot lower wing span, with an over-all length of 82 feet. It was expected that the whole outfit would weigh about 26,000 pounds, and of this about one-half would be useful load—that is, gasoline and oil, crew of six, equipment, etc. It was estimated that with three motors the boat could carry enough gasoline and oil for the anticipated 15-to-20-hour flight between the nearest points of land on the trip across the ocean. It was found, however, through additional calculation that this figure was perhaps slightly in excess of what the craft would actually do. The naval constructors, Westervelt, Richardson, and Hunsaker, therefore put the problem before Admiral Taylor, and he replied, "Build the smaller design, and we'll go by way of the Azores. With this smaller design, it seemed practicable to make a flight to the Azores, and refueling there, to continue the flight to Portugal, one of our allies. I think we'd better dismiss the whole idea of a Newfoundland-to-Ireland flight, except on the basis of a stop in mid-ocean for refueling from a ship."

More figuring was done, and after another general conference in Washington, it was decided to build a boat with a 126-foot span, the lower wing measuring 94 feet, a wing cord— that is, the depth of the wing, 12 feet; the gap between wings, 13 feet 6 inches at the center, 12 feet at the outer wing struts. The over-all length of the craft was 67 feet 3½ inches; the length of the boat hull was 45 feet 9 inches, and had a beam of 10 feet. The total wing area was 2,380 square feet, the weight empty was 15,870 pounds, while the weight with full load was 28,000 pounds. Its planned power was to be 1,000 horsepower distributed among the three engines.

The new design departed from previous Curtiss models in several important respects. One of the most radical changes was the shortened hull. Previous Curtiss designs, such as the 133-foot Model T and the smaller *America,* had the tail surfaces attached directly to the boat portion of the aircraft. The hull was thus necessarily long, and landing and taxiing put upon it a much greater strain than that borne by the corresponding fuselage of an aeroplane or the hull of a small flying boat. Forced to choose between a hull that would be too heavy or too weak, the NC designers solved the problem by cutting off the rear end of the hull. The "tail surfaces" were then mounted on outriggers from a short, compact hull which, as experience has indisputably proved, achieved an unprecedented strength.

Important changes were also made in the shape of the hull. Naval Constructor Richardson carried on the necessary tests for this in the model basin at the Washington Navy Yard, assisted by Naval Constructor William McEntee. From his own ideas and those of Curtiss, Bill Gilmore developed a hull peculiarly fitted for effective taking off and taxiing and strong enough to put down in ocean waves and stay afloat in the event of a forced landing. The hull was divided into six watertight compartments. The first, in the bow, housed the navigator. The second and third housed the two pilots. In the fourth and fifth were fuel and oil tanks. The sixth was for the radio operator. The other two members of the crew of six—the engineers —when not crawling around the engines, tucked themselves into any available nook not already occupied by supplies or spare gear.

The use of 400-horsepower Liberty motors, an all-aluminum gasoline system, box section beams, and the box tail were other important innovations in the NC boats.

The authorization by the U.S. Navy for the construction of four NC type aircraft was signed by Secretary Daniels in December, 1917. Then the project ran into the quagmire of internal Curtiss Company politics. John Willys decided to supervise personally this important Navy contract, and after his "exile" to the Garden City plant, Curtiss was not kept fully informed on the progress of the NC's.

In April, 1918, Naval Constructor G. Conrad Westervelt complained in a letter to Admiral Taylor that no work was being done on the big flying boats. When the Admiral questioned Curtiss about the delay, he was informed that Curtiss didn't know the reasons and could do little about it since he was "only an employee."

In a matter of a few days, however, the production of the NC's was transferred to the Garden City plant. The reason for this move given by Willys was that the presence of the Curtiss Engineering Corporation on Long Island, its nearness to Rockaway Beach, where there was a naval station, made it possible for the airboats to be constructed at Garden City, trucked over land, and put into the water at Rockaway Beach, without the trouble of packing and entirely disassembling. In reality, little had been done on the project since Curtiss had the original plans drawn up in December because the engineers and officials of the Buffalo plant thought the entire project "silly." True, the orders for the boat hulls had been subcontracted, but none of the major work had been accomplished. So Curtiss took personal charge, at Willys' request, of the building of the NC's. Although other projects were continued, almost everybody in the Garden City plant was involved with the NC's.

On September 11 part of the boat was ready to be moved

overland to Rockaway Beach. And by October 1 the NC-1 was nearly ready for flight.

On October 4 Lieutenant David H. McCullough, a former Curtiss student, was ordered by Naval Constructor Holden Richardson to take the boat out. The three men—Curtiss, McCullough, and Richardson—clambered in, and at a signal from the latter the boat slid down the marine railway into the water. Taxiing out for a position in the wind, it threw a silvery stream across the bay, now small, now great, and its giant hull smashed the waves, until finally with a roar it left the surface and was in the air. A great cheer came from the crowd of naval personnel assembled on the shore, and Richardson with a wave signaled to his co-workers that all was well. After a few brief flights a landing was made, and the boat came back to the hangar no longer a mere mass of wood and steel but a living, throbbing thing—the largest flying boat in the world! Some minor adjustments of weight were necessary, but the boat as designed and built was found to be very efficient, readily controlled, and capable of carrying even more weight than had been anticipated.

On one occasion fifty-one men were taken up for a short flight at Rockaway, and it was on this interesting flight that the first aerial stowaway was found. MM/2c Harry D. Moulton, one of the Rockaway Beach air station sailors, had sneaked in and hidden himself behind the gasoline tank in a narrow passageway. The fifty-one men established a world record, exceeding that just made by a Handley-Page carrying forty passengers.

On November 7, Commander Richardson and Lieutenant McCullough as pilots and several other officers as passengers started on a flight to Washington, D.C. They were compelled to make a landing at Barnegat Inlet where a leaky radiator was repaired, but tied up at the Anacostia Naval Air Station at 5:10 P.M. The next day Admiral Taylor came down and inspected the craft, and at 1:40 P.M. the boat left for Hampton Roads. On the following morning at 11:57 A.M. the boat started up the coast on its return trip to Rockaway Beach, which it reached at 4 P.M. On this trip it was estimated that the gasoline consumption was 83.8 gallons per hour or 1.25 gallons per mile. This flight satisfied many of the critics that a transatlantic flight would be possible with the NC.

The war in the meantime was rapidly entering its final stage, and on November 11, when the Armistice was signed, the NC-1 was at Rockaway, a finished product completed too late to be of value in the Great War.

Curtiss, who had kept the transatlantic idea in mind and frequently talked with Commander John Towers about it, again began to discuss with the navy officials the possibility of a naval transatlantic flight using the NC-1 or one of its sister ships in construction. Admiral Taylor was also anxious to see what the craft could do. So during the holidays he asked Naval Constructor Westervelt to prepare for him some recommendations and a discussion of details on the transatlantic flight. The matter was finally brought to the attention of Secretary Daniels, who immediately shared the enthusiasm of his officers. On February 17, 1919, Admiral Taylor in a letter to Westervelt directed the completion of the NC boats for the specific purpose of the earliest possible transatlantic flight.

The Navy made it clear, however, that NC's would not compete for the London *Daily Mail* prize offered originally in 1914 and still not claimed. The Department even forbade any of the crew members to accept any prize money. The flight across the Atlantic was to be purely for "scientific purposes."

The NC-2 was almost completed when the Armistice was signed, and construction had begun on the NC-3 and the

NC-4. Work on the latter two vessels was hurried. Even with the added effort the NC-4 wasn't launched at Rockaway Beach until April 30, 1919. Actually, the NC-4 was the only one of the four flying boats made *completely* by the Garden City plant. The hulls for the first two came from the boat shop of Lawley & Sons, Neponset, Massachusetts, while NC-3's hull was built by the Herreschoff Manufacturing Company of Bristol, Rhode Island.

The three-motored NC's could have carried sufficient gasoline to make the Azores under favorable conditions. The desire, however, was that they should carry more than an adequate supply. It was realized that the relation of motor power to carrying capacity was favorable to the large number of motors. By adding a fourth motor, designers could increase the NC carrying capacity by four thousand pounds, adding but a little over a thousand pounds in actual weight of the motor, bracing, etc. It was a good trade, and the frames of the NC's were sufficiently strong to allow it. The fourth motor was added.

The original NC-1 had three tractors; i.e., motors whose propellers are before rather than behind the engine. The NC-2 had been fitted for experiment with a pusher in the central nacelle and two tractors. This arrangement was completely and interestingly altered in the NC-2 when a fourth motor was added by incorporating motors in two nacelles, a motor at each end. The front motor was, of necessity, a tractor and the rear one a pusher. The head wind resistance of two extra nacelles was thus eliminated.

The new arrangement proved successful. Another type of disposition—three tractors and one pusher, the central nacelle of the type of the NC-2, two others single-motored and between the wings—also gave satisfaction. The NC-1 and NC-3 had both followed this form of installation. When the NC-2

broke away from its mooring in a storm in late March and
was badly damaged, its salvageable parts were used as spares
and its engines put aboard NC-4.

While the finishing touches were being put on the NC-4,
the Navy Department was perfecting radio apparatus, lights,
and instruments for the flying boats. Commander Towers was
placed in command of the expedition. To a large degree the
course of the expedition was determined by consultation at
Washington. On April 14 Commander Towers received orders
with regard to the chief features of the trip. The course was
laid out in stages—the first from Trepassey Bay, in Newfoundland, to the Azores; the second from the Azores to Lisbon,
Portugal; the third from Lisbon to Plymouth, England. (The
first two legs followed the same course as the proposed *America* flight.) Over this route, twenty-four United States Navy
destroyers were to be stationed in a string from Newfoundland
to the Azores at intervals of approximately 50 nautical miles;
thereafter, fourteen United States and British warships would
stretch to Lisbon and another ten to Plymouth, to act as
"marker buoys" for the flyers. These vessels were prepared to
emit soot-black smoke signals by day and flame at night. Each
ship would indicate wind direction to the NC navigators by
aiming its searchlight into it, and to fire star shells at five-
minute intervals throughout the night. Should an aeroplane
be forced to land, the two vessels nearest to it were under
orders to break station and proceed at full speed to its rescue.

The trip was to be made during the month of May. If possible the flyers were to take advantage of the full moon of
May 14. In any case the start from Rockaway was to be made
as early in May as possible. From Rockaway to Trepassey
was not to be considered a portion of the main voyage, and
no risks were to be taken during this stage.

At *9:30* A.M. Commander Towers joined the other crew members with a smile. "Well, boys, let's go!"

Instantly all was bustle about the launching way. The crowd, carefully limited to Navy men, Curtiss officials, newspaper reporters, and friends and relatives of the crews, saw much work and little ceremony. Captain Noble E. Irwin, Chief of the Bureau of Naval Aviation, distributed four-leaf clovers among the nineteen men who were soon to take to the air. The big boats were drawn into position by tractors and the guiding hands of sailors. The crews, hardly able to realize that the hour of starting had come at last, nervously adjusted goggles and telephones over their heads. The pilots gripped their wheels.

9:57 A.M. With a roar the four engines of NC-3 broke an electric silence. The flying boat shot down the ways and taxied out into Jamaica Bay. The NC-4 and NC-1 followed: at *9:59* all were in the water.

There were a few minutes of maneuvering to warm up the engines. Then, with a tail of foam flashing behind it, the "Three" headed down the long stretch of water, the foam lessening as it went and finally changing to a thin white space between the airboat and the gray water. The others followed. The great airboats then turned eastward and flew into the farthest haze.

Flying in formation, all went well until *1:20* P.M., when Commander Read discovered while they were passing over Manomay Point, Massachusetts, that one of his engines was acting improperly. Lieutenant Breese soon reported that the oil had stopped flowing, and very soon after this the other engine just forward of this one developed trouble so that it was necessary for NC-4 to land on the open sea 100 miles east of Cape Cod. Taxiing slowly all night on its two good engines and startling some fishermen out of ten years' growth as it

In the latter part of April Commander Towers
Rockaway Beach. On May 5 he made the final as
of the crews:

NC-1

Commanding Officer—Lt. Commander P. N. L. Belling
Pilot—Lt. Commander M. A. Mitscher
Pilot—Lt. L. T. Barin
Radio Operator—Lt. (j.g.) H. Sadenwater
Engineer—Chief Machinist's Mate C. I. Kesler
Reserve Pilot Engineer—Machinist R. Christensen

NC-3 (Flagship)

Commanding Officer—Commander J. H. Towers
Pilot—Naval Constructor H. C. Richardson
Pilot—Lt. D. H. McCullough
Radio Operator—Lt. Commander R. A. Lavender
Asst. Navigator—Lt. Commander R. E. Byrd
Engineer—Machinist L. R. Moore
Reserve Pilot Engineer—Lt. (j.g.) B. Rhodes

NC-4

Commanding Officer—Lt. Commander A. C. Read
Pilot—Lt. E. F. Stone (U. S. Coast Guard)
Pilot—Lt. (j.g.) W. Hinton
Radio Operator—Ensign H. C. Rodd
Reserve Pilot Engineer—Lt. J. L. Breese
Engineer—Chief Machinist's Mate E. C. Rhodes

May 8 was a little more hectic than normal at Rockaway
Naval Air Station. For one thing, there had been more than
the normal amount of brass present at the base since the formal commissioning of the NC-1, NC-3, and NC-4 five days
earlier. Second, the crews were ready to fly. They only awaited
reports from Washington of favorable weather along the northern Atlantic coast.

emerged from the night like an incredible sea monster, the flying boat reached the Naval Air Station at Chatham at dawn.

By May 10 the trouble was repaired and the aircraft was ready to resume the flight. Favorable weather at *11:17* A.M. on May 14 found the crew receiving a radio message from Assistant Secretary of the Navy Franklin D. Roosevelt: "What is your position? All keenly interested in your progress. Good luck!" They replied three minutes later: "Thank you for good wishes. NC-4 is 20 miles southwest of Seal Island, making 85 miles per hour."

The NC-3 and NC-1, suffering no major difficulties, had continued on their course and landed at Halifax, Nova Scotia, on the evening of May 8, a distance of 540 nautical miles. The next day they headed for Trepassey Bay, Newfoundland, and arrived in the evening, a distance of 460 nautical miles. Bad weather conditions, however, indicated that they should wait for a more propitious occasion, so on receiving the news that NC-4 could continue, Commander Towers decided to wait. When the NC-4 arrived on May 15, it was immediately overhauled. A new engine and three new propellers were installed. On May 16, 1919, all three craft were ready to start. They had fulfilled almost to the day the suggestion of their April 14 orders that they take advantage of the May 14 moon.

The long, narrow harbor at Trepassey was not favorable for a flying boat to take off. Indeed, Commander Richardson, reconnoitering on the forenoon of the sixteenth, found the waves toward the farther end too high to warrant a start. In the afternoon, however, they subsided and a take-off was planned. The tenders, U.S.S. *Prairie* and *Arvostook,* at once began preparations to start for Lisbon. The NC crews prepared for flight, slipping their air togs over their naval aviation uniforms. Commander Byrd and Lieutenant Rhodes, reserve navigator and pilot engineer respectively, were left at Trepassey.

"Let's go!" shouted Commander Towers.

The engines of the NC-3 began to revolve. The three flying vessels taxied out, maneuvered a few minutes, and then, the NC-3 in the lead, shot forward for flight. They left at *10:06, 10:07,* and *10:09* P.M., the NC-1 bringing up the rear. (All times given in the remaining portion of this chapter are Greenwich Mean Time.)

The story for the three boats during the first night was about the same. The sky was dark, utterly dark save for stars. These, however, were of great assistance to the pilots in keeping the plane level and on its course. The engines were hitting on every cylinder. There were no mufflers fitted, so that the exhaust flame could be seen, and it was most reassuring to see the flame shooting out regularly from each exhaust valve without missing a stroke. The oil pressure, which was normally at 30 to 40 pounds by gauge and which had given trouble at intervals previously, held up perfectly. The water temperature of the four radiators aboard each plane could not be improved. In short, everything about the three big machines seemed to be on their best behavior, and as time went on the crews' confidence increased to such an extent that their entire thoughts were centered on their own individual duties.

The pilots took turns at the controls for stretches of thirty to forty-five minutes; the one off duty sometimes remained in his seat, sometimes squirmed down into the fairly roomy space forward of the seats and aft of the bulkhead on which the chart board was slung. He would occasionally catch a few winks of sleep; the "off" engineer also slept a little. The radioman had no relief—he had to stick to his job; but he found it of such absorbing interest that the thought of sleep never entered his head. The commanding officers, who also served

as navigators, felt not the least inclination to sleep, even had
there been an opportunity.

The destroyers marking the course were checked off on the
chart one after the other. The star shells which they fired from
their antiaircraft guns were always sighted at great distances.
In several cases a shell from one destroyer would be seen when
the planes were passing over the next destroyer to the westward,
fifty miles away. Then after an interval the searchlight could be
seen, and finally, as they approached at a speed of about
eighty-five knots, the ship's deck lights would appear. If the
lights were nearly ahead, a sufficient change in course would
be made to pass directly above, but if too great a change would
be required, the skipper would assume that the destroyer was
in its exact position, estimate his distance from it, and lay a
new course directly for the next one. All the destroyers had
large, illuminated figures on their decks to indicate the number
of their station, but since all of the ships were sighted one
after the other, it was never necessary to verify these numbers.
The searchlights, laid directly into the wind at the surface,
showed that the breeze was still with them at each successive
station.

In this manner the night passed. At 5:45 A.M. came the
first indications of dawn. The engines were still thundering on
with not the least appearance of wishing to stop. Aboard the
NC-4, Ensign Rodd was having the time of his life, picking
up messages from places as far distant as Bar Harbor, Maine;
the last one received was distinct at 1,330 nautical miles. He
talked with Cape Race, Newfoundland, and sent, via the operator there, a message of greeting to his mother in the States.
He reported that NC-1's radio was working very well, but
that NC-3's was weak. Each destroyer broadcast the passing
of the NC's. This message was flashed to the base ship in the
Azores and relayed to the Navy Department at Washington

so that the Department was kept in touch with the progress of the flight at all times.

As the light increased, the crews had coffee from vacuum bottles and sandwiches. A small piece of chocolate completed the first transatlantic air meal. As the morning progressed, it became rather monotonous flying hour after hour over waves that looked exactly alike and never seeing anything except an occasional destroyer. But the monotony was not to last long.

The NC-4, now well out in front of the other two flying boats, passed over destroyer No. 15 at *7:45* A.M. Ten minutes later what seemed to be a considerable area of rain appeared ahead. The aeroplane's course was changed to port for a few minutes to dodge the thickest part, but the crew soon saw that instead of rain, light lumps of fog were forming and blowing along in the same direction they were making. Their former course was resumed, and the aircraft passed through the foggy area at *8:12*. This didn't impress the crew very strongly since they came again into nearly clear air and easily picked up Destroyer 16 a little later. They passed the vessel at *8:30*.

But visibility grew less and less, and NC-4 missed No. 17, although little fog was really encountered until about *9:40*. Then it began to show the crew what real fog was like. At *9:45* the plane entered an impenetrable layer as thick as pea soup. The sun disappeared entirely. As the craft flew on and fog still continued, the crew began to wonder how they were going to come out of all this uncertainty. Was the fog going to last indefinitely? The islands of the Azores were high, and perhaps they might sight one of them over the fog. Pico was more than 7,000 feet; they didn't know then that Pico is always covered with thick clouds except in the clearest sort of weather. The aeroplane still had several hours of gas and the engines were running beautifully, but they could not keep on going forever.

At *10:40* the fog was just under the plane at about 3,000 feet, and thinking that it might have lifted from the water, NC-4 inquired by radio to Destroyer 19 concerning visibility conditions at the surface. The reply came in: "Thick fog." Then No. 20 was called; her reply was "Heavy mist." Then Ensign Rodd tried 21, which was some distance ahead; she came back with "10 miles visibility." At last the crew had something to encourage them. If they kept on going, they should get out of this mess. A light, stinging rain was encountered for a few minutes, but that soon passed, or rather the NC-4 passed through the rain, and the air was again fairly clear. The minutes ticked by. It had been getting thicker to the left of their course, but to the right there was still a streak of blue sky showing between the fog layer and the cloud layer.

Then suddenly, at *11:27* or nearly three hours after passing the last destroyer sighted, while flying at 3,400 feet altitude, they looked down, and on their port side, saw a tide rip through one of the rifts in the fog that had of late become less frequent. The water on the far side was slightly darker than that on the near side. Tide rip waves don't occur far away from land, therefore land must be somewhere nearby. Suddenly, above one of those waves appeared a dim line of rocks. They had found Flores! Delightedly they skirted the coast. "And," says Commander Read, "as we rounded a point a peaceful farmhouse came into view in the midst of cultivated fields on side hills. That scene appeared to us far more beautiful than any other ever will."

The friendly shores of Flores were soon left behind, but the crew could now see for about 10 miles all around. Soon the smoke of Destroyer No. 22 was seen, and the aeroplane passed over the vessel at *12:08*. The crew was feeling quite cocky; they had passed through the fog and were again on their line with visibility now about 12 miles. Chief Rhodes assured Commander Read that there was sufficient gas and oil left to make Ponta Delgada about 250 miles away. Why stop at Horta then? Pilots Stone and Hinton had the same idea; NC-4 flew on, and soon left the destroyer astern. But their jubilation was brief. Dense fog closed in again. They missed Destroyer No. 23. "No Ponta Delgada for us today; any port would look good."

Commander Read figured that keeping their course until *1:18* P.M., then making a right-angle turn, allowing any speed between 70 and 85 knots from Destroyer 22, they should sight land somewhere between the western end of Fayal and the eastern end of Pico with some margin to spare. Before it became necessary to execute this maneuver, however, land was again sighted—this time the northern end of Fayal Island. A region of comparatively clear air to leeward of the island enabled them to see it. Again they breathed more easily. Horta, where one of the Navy's base ships was at anchor, must be just around the aerial corner.

They lost no time in heading for the beach, rounded the island through the very rough air tumbling down from mountains, and headed for a landing. It was too thick ahead to determine whether Horta was there or not, but as soon as the plane had landed and taxied a few minutes, it was evident that they were in the wrong bight. Again the craft took to the air, rounded the next point, and caught sight of the U.S.S. *Columbia* less than a mile away just before the obliterating fog swept in and hid it completely from view. It was only a matter of a few seconds' time to pick the vessel up again and to land close by the stern. The landing was made at *1:23*.

NC-4 was safe in a snug harbor at last, 15 hours and 18 minutes from Trepassey Bay, Newfoundland (a distance of approximately 1,200 nautical miles), or 15 hours and 13 minutes actual flying time, counting out the time on the water after their first landing in the wrong bight. The flying boat's average speed for the entire run was about 79 knots, or 90 statute miles, per hour. The crew needed sleep, but nothing else; the aeroplane was in excellent condition except for the necessity of a few very minor repairs.

Not so fortunate the NC-1 and the NC-3. The "Three," by dawn some distance behind Commander Read and his flying boat, had sighted no destroyers since No. 13.

"We passed," said Naval Constructor Richardson, "through five hours of rain squalls and fog, so thick at times as to make it impossible to see the horizon or the surface of the ocean." After this experience, with 15½ hours of travel behind it, the NC-3 was contemplating a landing 45 miles southeast of Fayal.

The NC-1, last of the three to start, held its original position with reference to the others. "We didn't meet any trouble," said Commander Bellinger, "until we got into the fog at *11:10* A.M. Saturday, when we were near Station 18."

Once in the fog, the NC-1 lost its bearings and decided to alight. It did so at *1:10* P.M. and was then about 100 miles west of Flores. The position of the NC-3 almost two hours earlier has been noted. Both vessels were at the gates of the Azores. Their motors were in perfect condition. They had adequate supplies of fuel for several hours' further flight. Fog alone prevented them from reaching Fayal or even Ponta Delgada.

In landing, however, both aeroplanes found the ocean heavier than they expected. They sustained damage from high waves which made the resumption of flight impossible, even if a take-off on so heavy a sea could have been managed. The NC-1, after taxiing on the surface for five hours, was discovered shortly after *6* P.M. by the S.S. *Ionia,* a Greek merchant vessel. At *6:20* P.M. the *Ionia's* boat took off the crew. An attempt was made to tow the seaplane, but the line broke, and after a time the first Navy-Curtiss flying boat disappeared beneath the waves.

Meanwhile, the 12-foot sea on which the NC-3 came down damaged hull, struts, and control connections. It was apparent that it couldn't take the air again. Its radio system, although allowing it to receive messages, could not effectively send them. Though the crew fixed its position as 45 miles southwest of Horta, the wind forbade an attempt to taxi in the known direction of Fayal.

Night came, and the boat was buffeted by wave and rain. One of the elevators, badly damaged, had to be cut loose. The crew took turns steering, those off duty attempting to sleep. With morning, in the twenty-second hour of surface riding the left wing tip was washed away. One of the crew crawled out on the right wing and clung there, deluged occasionally by waves, to keep the left wing from being submerged. Radio messages were received telling of the rescue of the NC-1 crew, but also disclosing to the NC-3 that those who were searching for it were looking west instead of south of Flores. Rescue, then, was improbable. The NC-3 must save itself. A crew with radiator water to drink and scant supplies of chocolate and salty sandwiches must bring a damaged hull for hundreds of miles over seas running often as high as 30 feet. Could they do it? Could a vessel built primarily for aerial travel make such an ocean voyage?

They were riding the swells with these thoughts when in the morning, across a sea clear of fog, the form of a high mountain, its head hidden in clouds, showed ghostly in the distance. Pico—the 7,000-foot volcanic cone of the highest peak in the Azores—undoubtedly lay before them. Observations, feverishly taken, checked with the testimony of their eyes. They were 45 miles southeast of Fayal.

Should they make directly for the land they saw? The tanks held a two hours' supply of fuel; the idea was feverishly alluring. Sanity, however, whispered the futility of such a course. They couldn't safely ride against the waves and wind. Their only road lay eastward, through another night of tossing, toward Ponta Delgada. They must watch the tangibility of that great mountain die away as they planed off toward an island they couldn't see.

Who can describe those next twenty-five hours? Coasting backward over the great waves, beaten by rain, sleepless and hungry and worn, the five endured more than even they could tell. They were blown southward for a time. They lost a second elevator. The right wing float threatened to come loose. Officers trained to use the most advanced navigating instruments trailed canvas buckets over the edge of the hull to assist in steering their craft. Constantly, however, observations showed an increasingly favorable position. At length they calculated that they could make Ponta Delgada in two hours. Then land appeared—farms, vineyards, roads, and a lighthouse. Finally the U.S.S. *Harding* became visible, racing toward them. But they didn't want help now.

"Stand aside!" they signaled. "We're going in under our own power."

They taxied by the breakwater and into the harbor. Crowds lined its shores. Whistles, sirens, guns, and voices made a bedlam of the afternoon air. Flags waved gaily; photographers in motor launches raced about. "The scene was one never to be forgotten, and our relief from the long tension, our feelings, can't be described," exclaimed Commander Tower, above the noise of the harbor. So ended a 52-hour, 205-mile journey over the open sea. But the gloriously battered NC-3 was unable to continue the voyage to Portugal.

On May 20 at *8:40* A.M., the NC-4 took off from Horta and

arrived at Ponta Delgada 1 hour and 44 minutes later (a distance of 150 nautical miles). Bad weather forced the aeroplane to stay out of the air until May 27. While there was talk among staff officers about shifting the commander's flag to NC-4, Commander Tower, after consulting with Washington, declared, "Read has earned the glory—let him take it the rest of the way."

On May 27 a faint but penetrating hum grew in the sunset over Lisbon. It was an alien sound to the old city beside the Tagus. It seemed to have no location, but to diffuse itself through the sky, growing in volume and intensity. Suddenly with a jet of steam the U.S.S. *Shawmut* and the U.S.S. *Rochester* sent out a shrilling answer.

"There it is!" came a voice, cutting the great spaces like a thin ray of light. Sirens, guns from Forts San Julian and Bugio, cannon of Portuguese warships, and the shouts of innumerable men on land and water echoed from wall to wall of the natural amphitheater. A silhouette became visible against rosy banners of clouds. It gathered definite shape; the noise of its motors became loud and thundering. With a gleam of wings the NC-4, completing the first flight ever made by men across the Atlantic Ocean, dove in a wide spiral toward the river and came to rest upon it as lightly as the vessel of a dream.

There was a moment's pause. Then a voice broke the silence. "Tell the *Shawmut* to direct her searchlights westward into the wind, so as to shine upon the water."

A sword of light swung into the dusk and found the NC-4. It taxied toward the *Rochester*. A motor boat from the *Shawmut*, hovering in wait, took off the crew. They went up the *Rochester*'s gangway, smiling men whose faces were tinged with the gray of a long-sustained and nervous effort. Admiral R. D. Plunkett, U.S. Minister B. W. Birch, and Portuguese officials stood there to receive them.

"A happy nation for a successful flight has no history," telegraphed Walter Duranty of the 1-hour-and-40-minute flight from Ponta Delgada to Lisbon (a distance of about 800 nautical miles). And, indeed, the NC-4 had a comparatively simple time of it. Two thousand pounds lighter than when it left Newfoundland, it succeeded in taking off from heavy swells at Ponta Delgada's harbor mouth. Though off its course sufficiently to lose Destroyer No. 3, it picked it up again and kept it the remainder of the way. Rain and mist were encountered, but didn't interfere seriously with the 93 statute miles per hour which the NC-4 made. The flight was almost a triumphal parade.

There remained only one more accomplishment—the flight to Plymouth, some 775 nautical miles away. Here, on May 31, 1919, a pilot of Massachusetts birth was to set foot on the shores of the harbor from which the Pilgrim fathers took ship for a new world three hundred years before. Here, after a flight of 3,936 nautical, or 4,526 statute, miles, made in a *flying time* of 52 hours and 31 minutes, Commander Read wired this laconic message to Washington:

NC-4 arrived at Plymouth 13:24 (9:24 A.M. New York time) in perfect condition. Joint mission of seaplane division and destroyer force accomplished. Regret loss of NC-1 and damage to NC-3; nevertheless, information of utmost value gained thereby. Has Department any further instructions?

The Atlantic had been crossed by a flying boat. Navy men had done it. Curtiss' dreams had come true. His judgment had once again been vindicated. *America* was the victor!

AN EPILOGUE TO GREATNESS

AFTER the flight of the NC's, Curtiss had little part in the affairs of the Curtiss Aeroplane and Motor Company. While remaining as a director in the firm and serving as its "Chairman of the Board"—a title he held even during his exile—he spent much of his time in Florida. In the spring of 1920, when the war slump came, Clement Keys again reorganized the company and assumed the presidency. The Willys-Overland interests were bought out and most of their officials were removed. Frank Russell, who became general manager under the new arrangement, persuaded Curtiss to assume the position of "Chief of Engineering."

One of his first tasks was to remove some of the "bugs" from the company's three newest models—the *Oriole,* the *Seagull,* and the *Eagle.* The latter, known as an aerial limousine, was built with a power plant of either three K-6 or two K-12 engines and carried eight or ten passengers (including one or two pilots) respectively. The passenger cabin was "luxuriously" finished and offered complete protection from the wind. It traveled at speeds over 100 miles an hour and had a range of up to 750 miles. After Curtiss revamped its various problems, the *Eagle* became the United States' first airliner. In the month of August, 1920, for instance, it flew over 4,400 miles and carried 943 paying passengers.

The *Seagull* was produced for the individual owner who wanted "an NC of his own." Carrying three persons, this miniature of the famous Navy aeroplanes was powered by a K-6 engine and had a maximum speed of 75 miles an hour. After studying the *Seagull's* performance for several weeks, Curtiss noted that the problem was in the hull and suggested several changes that made this craft remain popular throughout the twenties.

Curtiss disliked the *Oriole* design from the beginning and even went so far as to recommend that all production be stopped. But, since the company had spent a considerable sum already to tool up for its production, Russell asked him to give the *Oriole's* difficulties his upmost attention. With the help of several young engineers and designers, he was able to make the three-passenger *Oriole* an aeroplane that would be of practical value to general aviation for many years to come. While working on this craft, Curtiss learned that engineering and science had replaced his method "of flying the bugs out."

Curtiss' next assignment was to start the design work on a new model, the *Robin,* but when winter came to Buffalo, he requested a leave of absence to go to Florida. He never returned to work for "his" company and completely retired from the aviation business in the spring of 1921, although he held his position as a director in the corporation for a number of years.

During a stay in Miami in 1917, he had met James H. Bright, a wealthy cattleman. They formed a friendship from which developed, after Curtiss' retirement, an ambitious real estate venture. Their first major project was a town designed primarily to attract visitors from the North and it was given the Seminole Indian name, Hialeah. In addition to thousands of homes, a large parcel of land was set aside for the Miami Jockey Club to build a luxurious race track. The Miami Kennel Club was organized to feature greyhound dog races. And jai alai, Cuba's national game, was introduced into this country in a beautiful, marble-walled court, or *fronton*.

With Hialeah prospering beyond all belief, the Curtiss-Bright Industries moved across Miami Canal and began their second development. In this, originally called Country Club Estates and later renamed Miami Springs, Curtiss built his home as well as one for his mother, sister, and half-brother, Carl Adams. Many of his old friends from the Curtiss Company and Hammondsport came to retire in this town.

In 1925 Opatishawaukalocka, seven miles north of Hialeah, was started. (Today, because of the length of the name, this city is known by its first and last syllables, Opalocka.) At this project Curtiss constructed several aeroplane hangars, and a canal was dug and designs prepared for a concrete ramp for seaplane use. Unfortunately, the Opalocka development never was completed. But the sums of money Curtiss and Bright made from their land deals were fantastic. In the Hialeah project alone, they multiplied their original investment several times. Even when the Florida "land boom" collapsed in 1926-27, they had made too much money by this time to be seriously affected.

Curtiss once told some friends, "I made more money in five years in Florida than I did in all my days of aviation."

When asked how he could give up the profession he loved, Curtiss simply replied, "Aviation has just passed me by. It's now big business . . . for engineers, financiers and the like—not for a simple bicycle mechanic from Hammondsport."

Although he had returned "home" several times during the years of his Florida retirement, Curtiss went back on July 4,

1928, for a special reason. Twenty years before, the Aerial Experiment Association had announced that one of their members would fly an aerodrome a certain distance on a certain day if the weather was right. And just before sundown the weather had been right.

Hammondsport was inordinately proud of its flying past, and of its citizen who had built aircraft on the side of a hill and flown them between the aisles of other hills. When Curtiss was forced to move the major portion of his company to Buffalo in 1915, the factory facilities in Hammondsport were used to build engines. Charles Kirkham, who machined Curtiss' first successful motor, was chief engineer in charge of motor construction from 1915 to early 1918. During this time, he greatly improved the efficiency of several important types including the OX-5, K-6, and K-12. The latter two were officially named the Kirkham-6 and Kirkham-12 in his honor. Actually, the Hammondsport plant produced about 55 percent of all the engines used on the Jennies.

After the Armistice the engine factory was shut down. All attempt to bring new industry into the idle Curtiss building failed. With the passage of the Eighteenth Amendment the wineries were forced to close, and the population in this one-time hub of the motorcycle, airship, and aviation industries shrank to less than a thousand persons. Old Lazarus Hammond's town slept, except on that day of July 4, 1928.

In the summer of 1929, two of the oldest names in aviation, Curtiss and Wright, were joined in one corporate title with the merger of the Curtiss interests and the Wright Aeronautical Corporation. While the Curtiss-Wright Corporation was successful, efforts to bring together the two men failed. Curtiss sent a letter to Orville Wright on October 14 proposing that they meet sometime in the very near future for a friendly chat. The letter was never answered. It seems that the remaining

Wright brother was not ready yet to loosen his hold on the resentment of years. He could not forget that it was Curtiss who had endeavored to prove the Langley aerodrome capable of flight.

Comparing Curtiss with Wright, one might say that the Wright brothers, to whom belongs the credit for the fundamental developments that made modern flight possible, having made their contribution, then settled back in to take their ease and to enjoy the financial fruits of their initial accomplishment. Little or no advance in aeroplane design or construction came from them after 1910, and as a result the name of Curtiss became synonymous with progress in aviation in the United States from 1908 to 1919. It has often been said that the Wrights and Curtiss were the physicians responsible for the life of aviation in the United States. The brothers from Dayton brought the flying machine into the world, but it was Curtiss who doctored and cared for it through its infancy.

Curtiss' contributions to aviation were numerous. Anyone of them—flying boat, hydro-aeroplane, amphibian aeroplane, dual controls, tricycle landing gear—was important enough to land him in Aviation's Hall of Fame. But his most outstanding achievement was that of keeping American aviation alive —through his flights, aeroplane designs, and court actions— when the Wrights wanted to keep it for themselves. The history of the world could have been different, for instance, if Curtiss had decided to abandon his Wright patent fight and move his concern to Germany. This would have left the United States without a major aircraft-producing company at a time when it was needed most.

Early in May, 1930, Representative Ruth Bryan Owen of Florida, and daughter of the celebrated "Boy Orator of the Platte," William Jennings Bryan, introduced a bill to award Curtiss the Congressional Medal of Honor. The bill read:

Be it enacted by the Senate and House of Representatives of the United States of America in Congress assembled, That the President of the United States be, and is hereby, authorized to present in the name of Congress a medal of honor to Glenn Hammond Curtiss in recognition of his services to the Government of the United States in advancing and developing the science of aeronautics.

Unfortunately, the bill was never enacted because of subsequent events that happened all too rapidly.

On May 30 (rather than May 29, the actual anniversary date), 1930, the Aeronautical Chamber of Commerce arranged to re-enact Curtiss' flight down the Hudson. Many of his early associates joined him in Albany for the celebration, including Augustus Post, official timer; Jacob Ten Eyck, starter of the flight; Stanley Beach, Alan Hawley, and Ernest Jones, witnesses of the *June Bug* flight; Frank Russell, Jerry Fanciulli, and Commander Callan, Curtiss Company employees. Don Seitz, business manager of the New York *World* in 1910, was also present and reported that Curtiss on this occasion was "about as communicative as a cigar store wooden Indian." And he added, "He was always that way, too shy to let anyone know how he really felt about anything." But though neither Seitz nor the vast majority of the assembled gathering suspected it, Curtiss had an excellent time. Only his wife and his closest friends realized it.

At the luncheon in his honor, held at Hotel Ten Eyck, Curtiss spoke a total of three and a half minutes. While this may have been a duration record for him, it caused the program committee some embarrassment since they had allotted ten whole minutes of radio time to the guest of honor. In addition, it was a poor speech and almost as laconic as the one he had given at a dinner by the Los Angeles Press Club during the 1910 International Air Meet, when he arose and said in all sincerity, "I can't talk. I can't even tell a funny story. When I get up to speak, I feel as uneasy as if my motor had stopped and there was nothing below to alight on but church steeples. So, if you'll excuse me, I'll sit down and let somebody else, who can, talk."

In the afternoon, all the anniversary dignitaries drove to the new Albany airport and went aboard chartered airliners for a flight to New York. Captain Frank Courtney, the pilot of the Curtiss *Condor*—a twenty-passenger plane and the latest development of the Curtiss-Wright Company—which was to carry Curtiss and several friends, had accepted the newspaper guarantees that Curtiss would fly the aircraft himself. But the pilot was ignorant on two points. He didn't know that Curtiss had not flown a plane in sixteen years, or that he had never used the standard modern controls.

After the *Condor* took off and had climbed to 2,000 feet, Courtney passed the controls to Curtiss. He seemed to have lost little of his deft touch, nor had age dimmed that keen, penetrating look. Afterward, co-pilot Curtiss said, "Y'know, I didn't know just what to do. The plane seemed to be going all right, so I pulled back on the wheel very gently and saw the nose come up. That was like my old control. I pushed forward a bit and the nose bent down. Fine. Knowing that the wheel also operated the ailerons, I turned it first to the right and then to the left and felt the plane bank as I expected.

"The real trouble I had was with my feet. They were on the rudder bar, which I had never used, and I just did not know what to do with them. By experimenting, I soon found out what happened, and it was not long before I began to feel much more comfortable than I did when I saw Courtney lean out of the window, leaving me practically alone to pilot the largest ship I had ever flown."

As the *Condor* roared smoothly over Storm King Mountain,

Curtiss said to Courtney, "You wouldn't believe this, but the air currents over these mountains darn near cost me my life when I flew through them twenty years ago."

The captain replied with a grin, "It's going to take something a lot more than an old mountain and a couple of air pockets to kill a tough bird like you."

Two months later, Courtney's prophetic words came tragically true. After an apparently successful appendectomy in a Buffalo hospital, a small blood clot ended the life of Glenn Hammond Curtiss on July 23, 1930, at the age of fifty-two.

They brought G.H. home to lie in the Pleasant Valley Cemetery over which he had so often flown. Hammondsport became again, for at least one day, the aviation center of the world. Great men and small gathered there to do honor to G. H. Curtiss. Once again the air was full of wings, as "airplanes" flew singly and in formation above Lake Keuka and the fresh grave near Stony Brook Farm.

Although Glenn Curtiss rests in peace, his accomplishments are daily being magnified in the skies above us. Today, when you turn your eyes toward the heavens and ponder man's probing into the universe, spare a moment to reflect upon the memory of a quiet, determined man from Hammondsport who provided the beginning of many of the present and future aviation miracles. And sometimes, even today, as you pass between the quiet hills of Pleasant Valley, you can almost hear the whir of a tiny engine and a host of muffled voices raised in a distant cheer. "G.H." is once again raising his hopes and ambitions toward the beckoning sky. Perhaps nobody has done more for the progress of aviation than Glenn Hammond Curtiss.

INDEX